# LANDSHAPES

# LANDSHAPES

*Denys Brunsden, Rita Gardner*
*Andrew Goudie & David Jones*

DAVID & CHARLES
Newton Abbot London North Pomfret (Vt)
In Association with
CHANNEL FOUR TELEVISION COMPANY

# PREFACE

This book has been written for the numerous thoughtful and observant poeple with a love of scenery who would like to know more about the forces that have shaped the ground that underlies the varied and beautiful landscapes of the British Isles. This is a fascinating area of study but also an extremely challenging one. There is such a bewildering variety of rocks that have been shaped, such huge spans of time to achieve the shaping, and such variation in shaping forces from quiet chemical rotting to huge grinding glaciers. The result is a veritable kaleidoscope of ground shapes – some young, some old, some created when the climate was hot but mostly when it was extremely cold. Indeed, the past is so complicated and our knowledge so limited in many regards, that the task of writing a synthesis has been daunting in the extreme. The fact it has been accomplished is due wholly to Tim Fell, who, over the years, has developed a passion for landforms. It was his knowledge, enthusiasm and energy which resulted in the production of the series of programmes for Channel 4 entitled *Landshapes* which provided the stimulus for this book.

*Landshapes* has been written with a view to providing insights and knowledge without gobbledygook. The two of us designated to act as editors have endeavoured to curb the academics' natural tendency to retreat behind terminology and to use three long words when two short ones would do. In this we have been especially helped by Tim Fell and the series presenter, Tim Preece, both of whom have consistently tried to keep our feet firmly on the ground. We hope that the end product is a readable glimpse into what creates landshapes and how the variety of landscapes have evolved. If we have been unsuccessful in this, why not contact your local professional geomorphologist: most good university geography departments can still afford one or two.

Rita Gardner and David Jones
*June 1988*

The programmes entitled *Landshapes* were produced by Landmark Productions in association with Channel 4 Television.

**British Library Cataloguing in Publication Data**

Landshapes.
1.Great Briain. Landforms. Evolution
I. Brunsden, Denys II. Gardner, Rita
III. Goudie, Andrew IV. Jones, David.
551.4'0941

ISBN 0-7153-9216-6



Typeset by Typesetters (Birmingham) Limited
Smethwick, Warley, West Midlands
and printed in Great Britain
by Butler & Tanner Limited, Frome and London
for David & Charles Publishers plc
Brunel House Newton Abbot Devon

Published in the United States of America
by David & Charles Inc
North Pomfret Vermont 05053 USA

# CONTENTS

# 1

# LANDSCAPES, LANDSHAPES AND CHANGE

David Jones

## LANDSCAPES, LANDSHAPES AND CHANGE

*PLATE 1.1 The mountainous areas of the British Isles occur in the north and west. This winter scene in the North-west Highlands of Scotland shows the snow-covered ridge on the south side of Glen Shiel rising above the waters of Loch Cluanie. These are old, hard rocks that have been fashioned by ice. It is not difficult to visualise how further snowfalls could accumulate sufficiently to signal the onset of the next Ice Age.* (Full-size illustration on pp6-7)

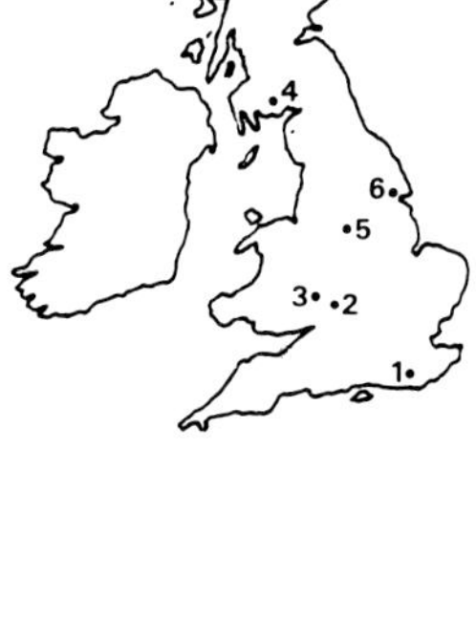

The British Isles are rightly famous for the variety and beauty of their scenery. Although small in area and lacking the grandeur of high mountains, great rivers or extensive plains and plateaux, these islands nevertheless provide an impressive array of landscapes which are both distinctive and contrasting. Compare, for example, the windswept, boggy mountainous moorlands of Scotland and Ireland (Plate 1.1) with the heavily populated, extensively farmed rolling landscape of south-east England and the flat expanse of the Fens[1] (Plate 1.8, see page 18). However, the feature that many visitors to these shores find even more striking is the variety of landscapes that can be encountered on a relatively short journey and the suddenness of the contrasts in scenery – the abrupt southern boundary of the Grampian Mountains[2] which separates highland moors from lowland farming; the unexpected arrival into the Lake District[3] that greets the traveller when driving southwards down the A591 in Cumbria; or the panorama that suddenly appears before the westbound motorist at the crest of Broadway Hill when miles of journeying across the gently rolling landscape of the Cotswolds[4] are replaced by a view over the Vale of Evesham to Bredon Hill[5], the undulating silhouette of the Malvern Hills and yet further to the Welsh Border Hills and the Black Mountains[6].

This scenic variety is an important asset which should not be taken for granted. Everyone has their list of favourite views which give them particular pleasure, especially as the colours change with the seasons or the mood of the weather. To the fortunate few these views may include the outlook from a window in the home or a vantage point in the garden. For the majority of us, however, they are composed of vistas seen from the roads or glimpsed from speeding trains, stopping places on walks, or those picnic locations that are returned to again and again because the combination of panorama and smell of warm grass or bracken always makes the food and drink taste that bit better. In virtually every case, no matter whether the vantage point be located high upon a lofty ridge or set in the more intimate surroundings of a winding valley, the pleasure of the scene is derived from the combination of two factors: the shape of the ground (the topography) which represents the flesh and bones of the landscape, and the way in which this physique has been variably clothed by nature and by man so as to create the patterns of fields, woods, heaths, moors, villages and cities that provide so much colour and contrast in the contemporary scene.

But it is often said that one should never judge a person simply by the clothes they wear. The same may also be said about landscapes. It cannot be denied that the nature of the vegetation cover and the patterns of land use greatly effect the *appearance* of the varied landscapes that each of us finds particularly pleasing, but we must also recognise that this pleasure is largely dependent on the way in which the surface covering is displayed to our gaze. In other words, vegetation and land use should not necessarily be considered as more important in the creation of an attractive landscape than the shape of the ground – indeed the two are normally mutually dependent.

Think how boring the landscape would be if the surface of the Earth was flat! There would be no viewpoints, no opportunity to look down on the pattern of fields with their bounding hedges or drystone walls, or to see the variety of greens and browns within a wood. The existence of topography is clearly essential to our appreciation of landscape. Indeed the character and distinctiveness of most landscapes owes much to the shape of land – the pattern of ridges and valleys (the terrain) – as well as to the underlying rocks, either because they break down to produce distinctive coloured soils (Plate 1.12) (orange in the Midlands, blotchy grey and brown on the South Downs[1]) or because they are extensively used as building materials which impart character to particular areas. Just think of the warm yellow-brown stone of the Cotswolds[2], the reddish-brown

building stone of Hereford[3] and Dumfries[4], and the 'white' drystone walls of the Peak District[5].

Unfortunately, the shape of the land often tends to be taken for granted by the beholder, especially in the gentler, lower-lying terrains of southern Britain. The pleasant gently rolling countryside induces the impression of unchanging permanence. A stream may be undercutting a bluff here or a slope has collapsed in a landslide there, but in general there is little obvious sign of change. Only along the coast where high, steep cliffs are battered remorselessly by the sea is the underlying geological bone structure of the country clearly exposed to view and the signs of erosion obvious. Cliff falls and landslides are common in such locations (Plate 1.2), especially after storms, and it is possible to measure the rate at which the crest of the cliffs retreats landward over time. Repeated surveys have revealed that retreat rates of over 1m (3.3ft) a year are by no means uncommon, and this has led to the widespread construction of concrete sea-defences which now fortify many of the more exposed coastlines. The most spectacular retreat rates were recorded along the 54km (34 mile) length of the Holderness coastline between Barmston and Kilnsea, Humberside[6]. Over the 46-year period 1852-1897 the whole of this cliffline retreated by an average of 65.5m (215ft) or 1.42m (4.6ft) a year (the width of a normal double bed), although there was some variation along the coast so that actual values ranged from 55.5m (182ft) to 83.2m (273ft). Erosion by the waves still

*PLATE 1.2 One end of Stonebarrow Hill, Dorset, is being rapidly eaten away by the sea. Erosion of the sea-cliffs on the left results in the development of huge landslides in the materials above so as to create the main landslide scar on the right. Between the two lies a great mass of debris that is moving seaward, including the building shown in Plate 7.5. The sea-cliffs are retreating fairly regularly; the landslide scar tends to move inland in jumps; but both types of movements average out at an inland progression of close to 1m (3.3ft) per year.*

*PLATE 1.3 The near vertical Chalk cliffs of Sussex have little beach and no concrete defences to protect them from the battering of waves. They are currently retreating at about 90m (295ft) a century. If this rate of retreat were to continue well into the future, which it probably will not, the whole of this part of the South Downs could be destroyed in 10,000 years.*

*PLATE 1.4 The Cuckmere Gap in Sussex, a large valley cut by a relatively insignificant stream through the Chalk uplands of the South Downs. The river is close to the sea and flows between banks (levées) to stop it flooding. It wanders about over a flat surface (floodplain), which it has created over the last 9,500 years by depositing up to 25m (82ft) of material. A section through a floodplain is shown in Figure 1.2. The river is relatively small compared with the valley it occupies and is doing little at present to*

continues today despite the efforts of engineers, with the highest values recorded on those stretches of coast that are without walls, groynes or those odd-shaped masses of concrete known as 'wave spoilers'. Even the spectacular, and often photographed, white cliffs of Sussex known as the Seven Sisters[1] (Plate 1.3) are retreating today at a rate that averages out at 0.91m (2.99ft) a year or 91m (299ft) per century.

If the white limestone known as Chalk that forms the Seven Sisters cliffline in Sussex, the White Cliffs of Dover[2] and other cliffs in Kent and Dorset, can be eroded by the sea, then surely the power of running water should be capable of sculpturing the same rock in inland areas where it underlies the downlands of southern England (eg the North Downs[3], South Downs[4], Chiltern Hills[5], Dorset Downs[6] etc). This is indeed the case, for the belts of high downland are not continuous but cut by major valleys occupied by rivers – for example, the River Thames flows through the Goring Gap[7] and the pronounced ridge of the South Downs is broken by four beautiful gaps used by the Sussex rivers Arun[8], Adur[9], Ouse[10] and Cuckmere[11] (Plate 1.4) on their route to the sea. These gaps are not merely being used by the rivers in question but have actually been excavated by the same rivers that now gently wind (meander) between the lines of willow. Clearly at some time in the past these rivers could achieve far greater tasks of excavation (erosion) than they appear capable of today. If this is true of the larger rivers then it must also be true of the streams. Similarly, if the Chalk that forms the upstanding ridges can be sculptured then surely the weaker clays that underlie the lowlands have also been shaped. Indeed the lowlands are lowlands because the forces of erosion (mainly running water, ice, wind

*PLATE 1.5 Upstanding masses of rock are known as tors. These examples from the Pennines are fashioned in Millstone Grit, a coarse sandstone that was used for making millstones in the past. The tors have been created by agents of change exploiting weaknesses in the rock (cracks) to form these sculptures in living rock. Frost, rock rotting, wind, gravity and water have all played their part in developing these land-forms.*

and gravity) have found these areas easier to excavate. Thus the surface of the ground is not permanent and unchanging, but has been fashioned to its present form and continues to experience change.

The processes of change that have shaped the landscape are not always dramatic features like breaking waves or grinding glaciers or torrents of muddy water; they may operate unseen and unsuspected. Those who live in areas with water supplies of 'hard water' are used to the accumulation of scale in kettles and hot-water cylinders. This scale is actually lime or calcium carbonate ($CaCO_3$) which is deposited when the water is heated because the amount of lime that water can hold is inversely proportional to the temperature – in other words cold water can hold more calcium carbonate than hot water. As falling rain contains no calcium carbonate, the lime in the water supplied through the taps must have been taken up into solution as the rainwater passed through lime-rich rocks (limestone) such as the Chalk. If you live in south-east England, the scale in your kettle indicates that the nearby Chalk downlands are being dissolved away before your very eyes, probably at a slightly faster rate than the writing is fading on the Victorian tombstones in your local churchyard.

As one moves westwards across the British Isles, the rocks become obviously harder, the hills tend to become higher, and steep slopes become relatively more common. The underlying rocks frequently appear at the surface to form steep cliff faces known as bluffs, scars or crags, and sometimes thrust upward above the ground surface in upstanding masses known as tors, some of which are carved into unusual shapes (Plate 1.5) so as to appear as if placed in the landscape by some sculptor. In these areas the scale of the topography often dominates the artifacts of man and the patterns of vegetation, although the sense of timelessness still prevails. Even along the coast, the hard rocks that often jut out into the sea appear well capable of repelling the power of the waves, despite the flying clouds of spray that are created during storms. However, appearances are once again misleading, for these rocks have also been sculptured by the same processes of erosion. The cliffs that often rise dramatically above the level of the sea exist because of erosion by the sea and are continuing to retreat before its attack, albeit very slowly.

In inland areas the power of running water and grinding ice have sculptured the terrain. In the north the valleys often have a pronounced U-shaped form (Plate 1.6) indicating the power of former glaciers now long melted away, while the steeper valley forms of southern areas signify erosion by water (eg the Wye Valley between Monmouth and Chepstow[1], and the Avon Gorge at Bristol[2]), and in both cases the accumulation of [illegible] the land surface is the product of erosion and subject to the processes of change.

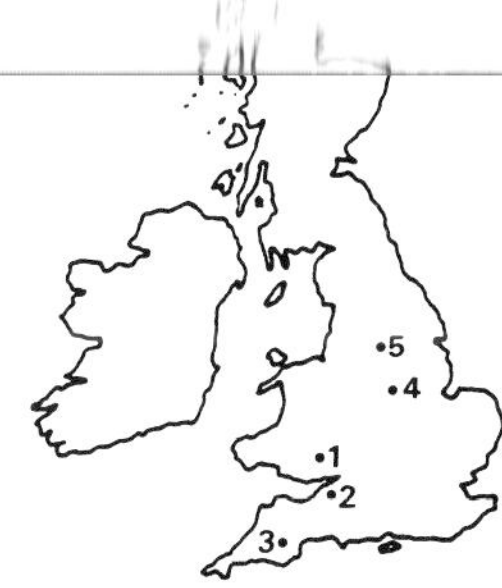


The shape of the ground is therefore not merely of interest as a backcloth for displaying the works of nature and human endeavour, but is worthy of investigation in its own right. There is in fact a branch of science devoted to the study of the shape of the Earth's surface and the processes that fashion it, which is known as geomorphology. Those who undertake such work are geomorphologists. Some concentrate on how the processes of change operate – how a glacier erodes, or the ways in which rivers actually move pebbles. Others investigate particular situations – what happens to the gravel on a beach or to the dunes in a desert. But one of the main underlying interests is how and why particular areas of land came to attain their current shape. These studies seek to establish the sequence of events which have resulted in the landscape patterns of today and thereby to account for the innumerable questions that occur to those who appreciate scenery. Why are the mountainous areas of the British Isles in the north-west and the main expanses of low, flat land in the east? Why do the Malvern Hills[1] look so different when compared with the nearby Cotswolds[2]? What causes rivers like the Trent[3] to have such strangely shaped courses and others, such as the Bristol Avon[4], to plunge through uplands in gorges rather than follow the lower ground to the sea? What made the Dartmoor tors[5]? How and when were dry valleys formed?

In order to answer these and many other questions it is necessary to search the landscape for clues as to what happened in the past. Many of the agents of change leave tell-tale indicators of their former activity, in terms of distinctively shaped ground or the debris that they left behind, which remain long after the process has ceased to operate. Fossil sand-dunes testify to dry periods in the past, scratches on rocks point to the passage of former glaciers. It is the use of such evidence that has led to the recognition that Shakespeare's Avon[6] originally flowed eastwards to the Trent and that a huge ice-sheet once stretched as far south as Finchley[7] in the east, while in the west the same ice-sheet overwhelmed the northern half of the Scilly Isles[8] but failed to reach the southern group of islands.

There is more to the landscape than at first meets the eye, and that is what this book is all about.

## CHANGE IN THE LANDSCAPE

While it is relatively easy to appreciate that the shape of the landscape may change over time, many people quite naturally find difficulty in appreciating the rates of change involved. Coastal erosion at over 1m (3.3ft) at year is easily understandable, especially if whole towns and villages have been destroyed in recorded time, as is the case with Dunwich[1], Suffolk, which was an important commercial centre in the thirteenth century with a dozen or more churches, a monastery, a school, market place, guildhall and several hundred houses and shops, now all lost to the sea. Similar tales of destruction can be recounted for other parts of the Norfolk and Suffolk coast (eg Aldeburgh[2] is a mere fraction of its original size), for the north coast of Kent (the loss of Reculver[3]), and the Holderness coastline of Humberside[4] where huge tracts of land have been destroyed since Roman times as is described in Chapter 6.

By contrast, the rate of sculpturing in inland areas is conspicuously slower, particularly where hard rocks reach the surface. Famous landmarks such as Haytor[5], the Stiperstones[6] and Cheddar Gorge[7] look roughly the same today as they did fifty years ago. Sometimes there are landslides, and rivers are clearly working in the landscape for they are muddy in flood, but there are few signs of change. Indeed, the accumulated limescale in kettles implies that the downlands of southern England are being lowered at a *maximum* rate of 1mm (.04in) per 20 years, which is an insignificant amount from the perspective of human life-span. However, this does work out to be the equivalent of 50m (164ft) per million years!

Thinking in terms of a million years is not easy for most people. The human time-scale is extremely short and anything over 500 years is generally considered ancient. In addition, the speed with which human societies have made dramatic changes to both the shape and appearance of landscapes has tended to blind us to the slower alterations that are being achieved by wind, water and gravity.

As recently as 10,000 years ago few humans inhabited the British Isles and their impact on landscape was minimal. However, population numbers have subsequently grown to over 60 million, in combination with truly amazing developments in organisation and technology, including the harnessing of energy sources of great power. As a consequence, there have been profound influences on the vegetation clothing the landscape, which were slow and modest at first, but which have increased in pace and scale as the population grew and technology developed. The early elements of this change were the 'clearance of the forests' and the 'drainage of the marshes', to which were added the more recent and far more dramatic impacts of urbanisation and industrialisation. As a consequence, there are few 'natural' landscapes remaining, for most reflect human interference. The extent of this transformation in appearance varies and is reflected in the four-fold division of landscapes into wildscape (eg Dartmoor[1], North-west Highlands of Scotland[2]), farmscape (eg East Anglia[3]), townscape (eg Dublin[4], London[5]) and ru-urban fringe, that untidy intermixing of urban and rural land uses that has developed around our cities and in areas of pronounced building activity. These processes continue today in many different ways, including the construction of new housing estates, the cutting down of woods, the grubbing up of hedges to create huge fields, the mining of minerals from pits and quarries, and the development of new roads that slice through hills and valleys by means of cuttings and embankments.

These changes are not merely cosmetic. The alterations in land use affect the underlying ground by varying its exposure to the ravages of wind and rain. As a consequence, soil erosion has become increasingly widespread over the last century, as is testified by the occurrences of small channels (rills) that can be seen scarring the surface of ploughed

SGG UNIT TITLE: WEATHER CLIMATE, ENVIRONMENT AND HUMAN ACTIVITIES. E105I1

KEY IDEA 12: FARMING SYSTEMS PROVIDE FOOD SUPPLIES AND RAW MATERIALS

STUDY THEME: Theory, case studies

## SCHEME OF WORK DETAILS.

### LEARNING OUTCOMES in terms of EGRC:

K/U a: factual work; K/U c: representing data in graphic and numerical forms; Ev a : interpreting information, both text and data; Ev c : expressing point of view; Ev d : identifying points of view.

### TYPE OF ACTIVITY:

Exposition and individual pupil work in co-operation with adjacent pupils will be assumed to be the norm. Additional or different activities are :-
answering questions based on text and illustrations
use of maps; completions/analysis of Wss; drawing map/diagram; study of . . slides..VHS..audio tape; group activity; discussion.

[illegible].

### CONTENT:

Introduction t[illegible]ation of f. F. as a system. Physical factor[illegible]ies in Europe. Current changes in f. Farm reor[illegible] policy.

### RESOURCES, PUPI[illegible]

R 86 on introdu[illegible]laborates this theme. Reading!

VHS 12 'Farmin[illegible]trate the factors in f (Ulster dairy f and E.A[illegible]

R 88 classific[illegible] orally; read R 89 for another classification.

R 90 F as a sys[illegible]ple explanation of the farm as a system.

R 92 physical f[illegible] written answer.

SELF-DIRECTED [illegible] A separate instruction sheet (E105I2) [illegible]d in this unit.

fields in winter and the recent rise in reported occurrences of dust storms in Yorkshire and Lincolnshire. To these indirect affects on the shape of the ground must be added the direct consequences of human activity in terms of excavation and dumping, which are fully described in Chapter 8. An excursion to any coalfield will reveal a legacy of heaps and holes of bewildering variety which bear testimony to the efficacy of human activity following the Industrial Revolution. The building of the railways also resulted in major reshaping on a grand scale with huge cuttings and long embankments, and such resculpturing continues today in excavations for housing and industry, port developments, motorway construction and the winning of surface minerals, most especially sand and gravel for concrete, limestone for cement, and clay for bricks. Human activity has become an important agent for change in the landscape, working in a similar fashion to running water, the sea, wind and ice, in that material is eroded (exca- [illegible]

[illegible] alterations to landscape. This can best be illustrated by any view across a city built on a river. We are going to use the panorama of London as seen from Parliament High Fields, Highgate (Plate 1.7).

Today the view southwards across the valley of the River Thames appears filled with an expanse of buildings that produce a skyline made

*PLATE 1.7 The view southwards from Parliament Hill Fields showing the Lower Thames Valley as it appears in 1988.*

both irregular and distinctive by the spires of churches, the majestic dome of St Pauls, the Telecom Tower and the high-rise tower blocks of the Barbican and other post-1950s developments. Here is an example of the most extreme level of change, where human activity has completely altered the shape of the land surface through construction using materials which were excavated from the ground elsewhere. Thus to build upwards, man has first to dig downwards.

But what was the panorama from the same viewpoint like in the past? A century ago a much smaller urban area with a lower and more uniform skyline would have been dimly visible through the shroud of smoke rising from thousands of chimneys. Fifteen hundred years ago the small ancestral town may have been glimpsed through the dense forests that blanketed most of the area. Five thousand years ago, one would have had to climb a tree to get a view across the seemingly endless forest of oak and beech. Go back 10,500 years and our hardy ancestors would have stood shivering in near arctic conditions as they surveyed a generally bare snow-covered landscape dotted with small pockets of birch trees; a landscape which to us would be more reminiscent of Siberia than the Home Counties. It would have been equally cold and bleak 18,000 years ago when ice stretched all the way from the present north coast of Norfolk to the North Pole!

Clearly the appearance of the area we now call London has altered dramatically over the last 10,500 years, but only part of the change is due to human activity. Climate has also changed greatly and with it the vegetation, the cold tundra having given way to the warm temperate conditions of today. There is nothing unique about London in this context, all parts of the British Isles must have experienced similar changes. But were these changes restricted solely to appearance or has the shape of the land also undergone significant alteration?

At first glance the topography of the London area would have appeared little different 10,500 or 18,000 years ago, for the pattern of hills and valleys would have been the same. Closer inspection, however, would have revealed significant differences. Small valleys which today have no running water (dry valleys) would have had seasonal streams on their floors because the water released by the melting snow in summer could not sink into the ground due to the frozen sub-soil (permafrost) and had, therefore, to flow over the surface (see Chapter 4). The existence of a permafrost layer within the ground also resulted in the widespread development of surface waterlogging during the summer months, the saturated layer often sliding and sludging downhill in a process known as solifluction, resulting in scars on the steeper slopes and aprons of debris (known as head) on the flatter ground below.

But the most noticeable changes would have been in the floors of the valleys. The River Thames and its tributaries would have looked very different. For a start they would not have flowed all the year round in a single well-defined channel set on a flat valley floor known as a floodplain (Plate 1.4). Instead, they would have had running water only during the summer thaw when large amounts of water were released from melting snow. In winter they would have been frozen solid. All the rivers would have flowed in well-defined, broad flat-floored troughs which now lie buried beneath the present floodplains – in the case of the River Thames through London, the river would have been up to 20m (65ft) below its present level. The rivers would have been much wider and shallower than their present-day equivalents, consisting of several threads of water continuously merging and dividing, separated by wide expanses of gravel (bars). Nor would the present-day tidal regime have existed because each time the climate deteriorated the ice-sheets accumulated, water became locked up as ice and the level of the oceans fell, often by more than 100m (330ft). As a consequence the floors of what are now the North Sea and English Channel became dry land (Fig 1.1). The ancestral River

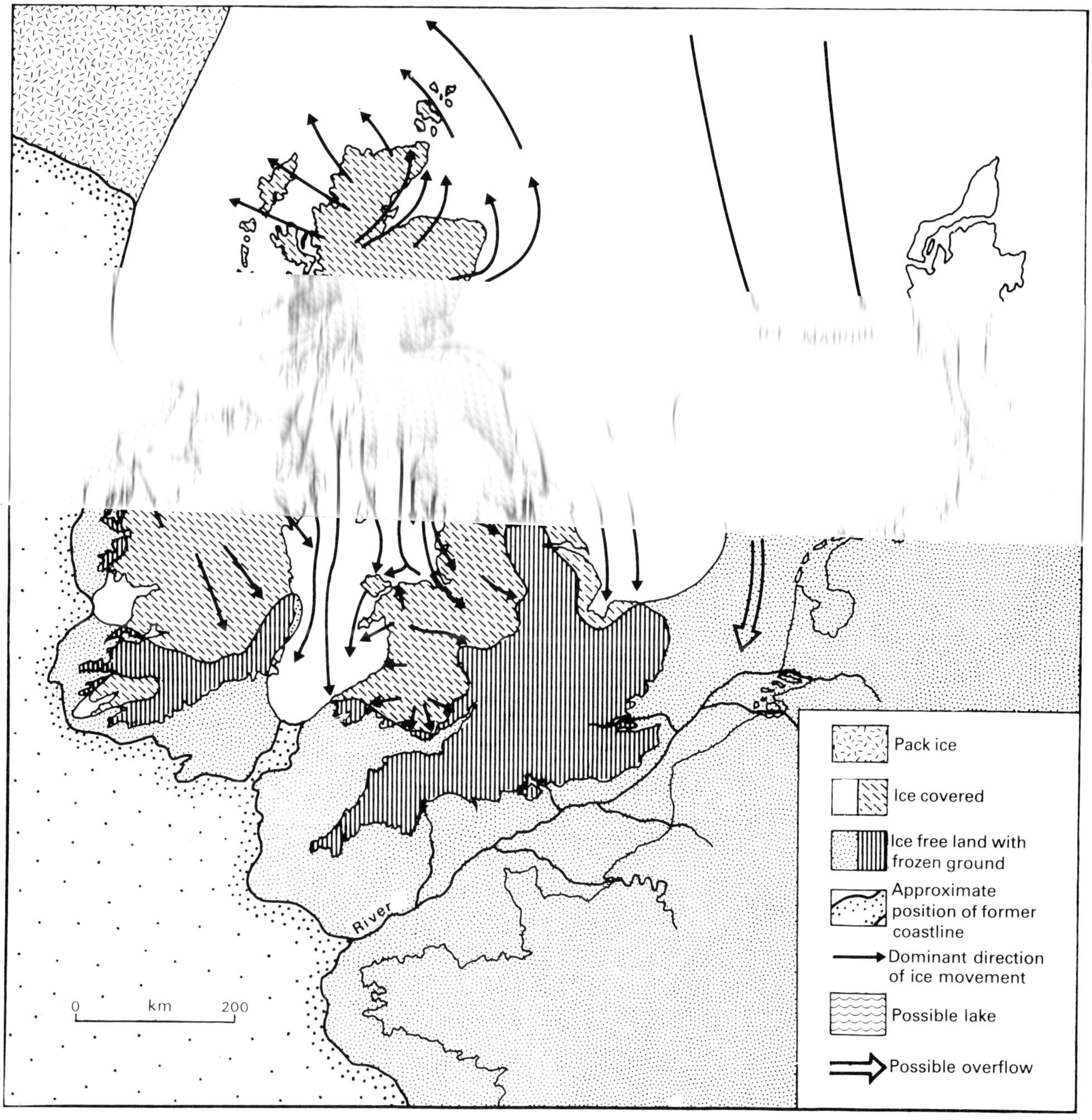


*FIG 1.1 Reconstruction of what the British Isles may have looked like some 18,000 years ago when the last major ice-sheet attained its maximum extent. While thick ice covered the northern half of the British Isles, the land to the south of the ice-sheet margin suffered varying intensities of ground freezing. The sea-level was probably lowered by at least 110m (360ft) which resulted in extensive parts of the present sea floor becoming exposed as dry land across which the rivers flowed in greatly extended courses – or at least they flowed during the summer months.*

*PLATE 1.8 The seemingly endless flat expanse of the Fens with its network of straight drains is one of the youngest landscapes, largely created by human endeavour. The underlying loose sediments are known as alluvium, and were laid down by rivers during the last 5,000 years. This whole area was a maze of winding rivers, swamps and tidal mudflats until the construction of embankments and the establishment of drainage schemes.*

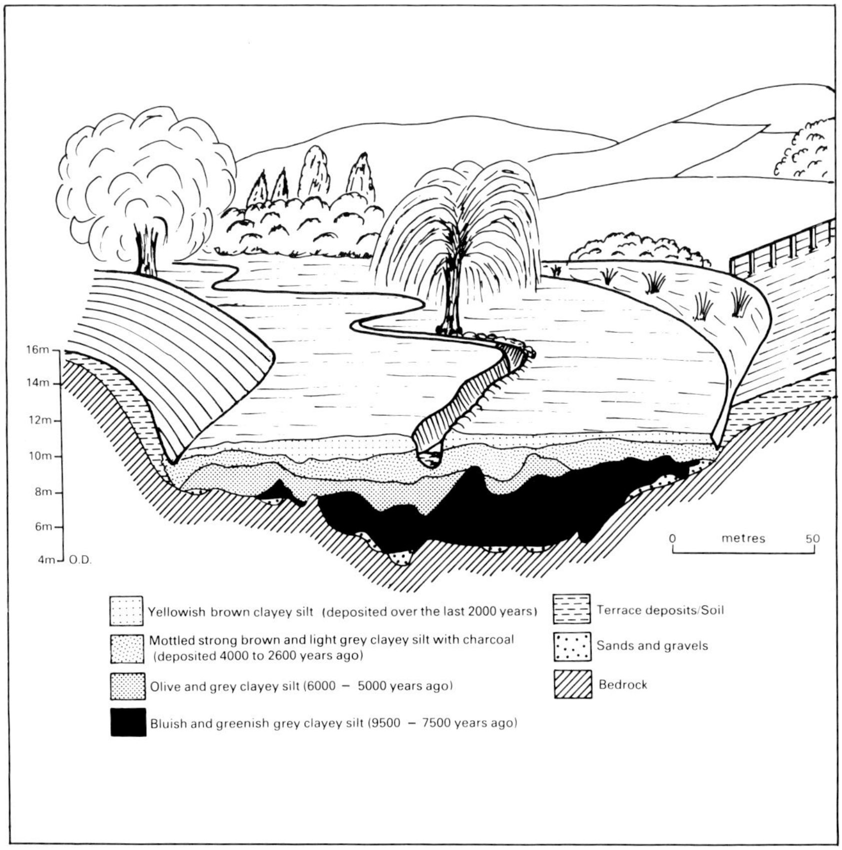


*FIG 1.2 The River Ouse and its floodplain at Sharpesbridge, Sussex. The flat surface of the floodplain conceals layers of deposits that have been dumped by the river over the last 9,500 years. During this time the River Ouse has changed from a broad shallow stream with a number of separate channels to the single-channel form visible today. The shape of the various layers of alluvium indicates that building of the floodplain was not a continuous process but undertaken in stages, with the river partly infilling its valley and then cutting back into the sediments before the next phase of infilling.*

Thames therefore had a much extended course, flowing eastwards and then southwards through what are now the Dover Straits to combine with the ancestral River Seine and so eventually reach the sea at some point between Plymouth and Brittany.

Thus if we stand back and adopt a perspective spanning 10,500 years, it is instantly apparent that there have been significant changes to topography in addition to those created by human activity. The most dramatic have been associated with the rapidly rising sea-level which caused the accumulation of mud and sand in the valley bottoms, thereby creating the belts of flat ground (floodplains) crossed by today's rivers (Plate 1.4 and Fig 1.2). Elsewhere in the British Isles, the same period of time has witnessed even greater changes. The Highlands of Scotland still had glaciers and small ice-sheets 10,500 years ago and England, Wales and Scotland [illegible] mainland of Europe by dry land, and continued to be [illegible]

[illegible] of the coastline was constantly changing. In many instances the lower portions of river valleys were flooded by the sea to form long, narrow inlets (rias) many of which were subsequently filled up with sediment (mud, silt and sand) carried by the rivers so as to recreate dry land in the form of alluvial lowlands. The Isle of Thanet[1] in Kent was a true island when the Romans arrived but has since been firmly reattached to the mainland; the great expanse of Romney Marsh[2] (Fig 1.3) was a shallow bay 3,000 years ago and one can still easily trace the old coastal cliffs from the hamlet of Cliff End, north via Winchelsea, Rye and Appledore to Hythe; the Fens[3] (Plate 1.7) and the Somerset Levels[4] have similarly silted up in the last 5,000 years, and up to 1km (.6 mile) of cliff retreat may have occurred in those areas of eastern England where the sea has attacked relatively weak rocks. Possibly the most dramatic example of such erosion was the destruction of the ridge of Chalk that formerly joined Purbeck[5], Dorset, to the Needles[6], thereby resulting in the isolation of the Isle of Wight.

These are dramatic changes achieved in about 10,000 years. Think what might be accomplished in a million years, especially if that period witnessed the expansion and decay of huge and powerful ice-sheets. But we must not be solely concerned with the most conspicuous forces of change, whether they be ice-sheets, the sea or human activity.

Even slow and pervasive processes can achieve much, given sufficient time. Let us return to the scale in kettles which is evidence that certain types of rock (limestones) can be dissolved by slightly acid rainwater. This process of solution weathering disfigures our statues, attacks the façades of our cherished ancient buildings (eg Canterbury Cathedral[7]) and reshapes portions of the landscape. Given enough time the effect of solution enlarges the cracks in the limestone so that the surface of the rock may become divided into blocks (clints) separated by deep narrow ravines (grikes) up to 0.5m (1.6ft) wide and 2m (6.5ft) deep. These are the famous limestone pavements that are such a feature of the Ingleborough[8] area of the Pennines and form the desolation of the Burren[9] in County Clare (Plate 1.11), where Cromwell's bloodthirsty troops claimed there was 'neither wood to hang a man, water to drown him, nor earth to bury him'. In other areas, solutional activity may be confined to specific locations because of the presence of cracks (joints) which allow the water to sink into the ground, thereby concentrating the dissolving action (Plate 1.9). Near-circular depressions

*[illegible] material infilling the pipes is a characteristic superficial deposit of chalklands known as Clay-with-flints and consists of a mixture of flints left behind after solution of the Chalk and clay with some sand derived from geological deposits that formerly overlay the Chalk.*

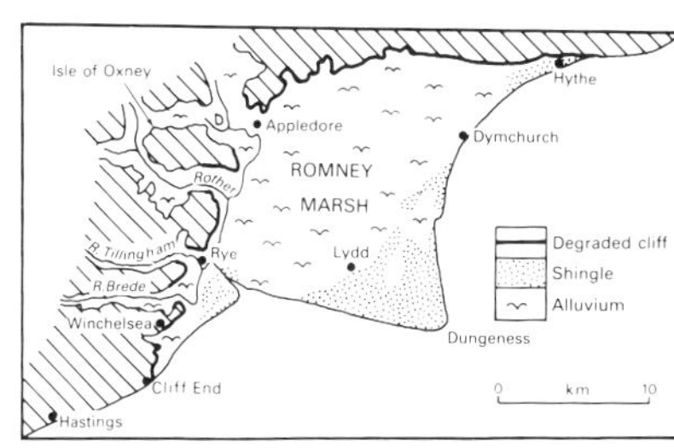


*FIG 1.3 The alluvium of Romney Marsh and the shingle of Dungeness together represent 250km² (96.5sq miles) of new land created over the last 3,000 years. Prior to this the area was a shallow bay bounded by cliffs, the remains of which can still be traced from Cliff End via Rye and Appledore to Hythe, although they are now much disfigured by landslides.*

can also be formed, known as dolines, usually up to 10m (33ft) deep and 30m (98ft) wide, although Culpepper's Dish, near Affpuddle[4] in Dorset, has a maximum diameter of 86m (282ft) and a depth of 21.2m (69.5ft). Similar features may form beneath streams where they are known as 'swallow holes'. They are well developed in the Mole Valley[5] to the north of Dorking, Surrey; frequently consume the whole of the summer months' flow of the River Manifold[1], Derbyshire, so that one can walk along the bed of the river yet remain perfectly dry; but attain their finest development in Gaping Gill[2], on the eastern slopes of Ingleborough in the northern Pennines, where an insignificant stream called the Fell Beck disappears down a vertical shaft up to 20m (65ft) wide and no less than 110m (360ft) deep, so as to reach the largest underground chamber in Britain, some 15m (50ft) long, 30m (100ft) wide and over 30m (100ft) high at one point – roughly equivalent to the interior of a good-sized cathedral. Such underground caverns, together with their linking passages, are also the product of solution by running water, and the collapse of such features can result in the formation of pits and gorges at the surface. All these dramatic features owe much of their shape to the dissolving action of water working at a rate that is incredibly slow from the human perspective. Analysis of the lime content in spring water issuing from limestone terrains indicates that the whole surface may be being lowered at rates of between 17mm (.7in) and 50mm (2in) per 1,000 years.

Fortunately, there is one area where these estimates can be tested. Around Ingleborough[4], North Yorkshire, there occur huge boulders of coarse sandstone (grit) which rest on low pedestals of limestone (Plate 1.10). The boulders have clearly been transported to their present locations and then dumped onto the limestone. It is now known that they were moved by an ice-sheet that melted away about 15,000 years ago, since when they have protected the limestone immediately beneath them while the surrounding surface has been lowered by solution. Thus the low pedestals of limestone up to 30cm (12in) high represent the amount of surface lowering that has taken place in 15,000 years. This works out at about 20mm (.8in) per 1,000 years or 41mm (1.6in) since Julius Caesar landed in 55BC, an incredibly slow rate when reviewed in historic perspective but attaining considerable significance if extrapolated over a million years.

The topography should not, therefore, be considered merely as background providing elevation, texture and sometimes colour to a vista but somehow static and unchanging, for nothing could be further from the truth. The topographic landscape is actually made up of a continuous cover of features (landforms) such as ridges, gorges, scars and valleys, whose very existence indicates that they have been shaped, and the process of shaping implies change. Obviously the topographic detail changes at a slower pace than do the more obvious variations in landscape appearance due to nature and to man, but given sufficient time the cumulative results of slow change can become surprisingly great.

While much has been written on the character of different landscapes (eg the Cotswold country[5] or the North Yorkshire Moors[6]), and the history of human involvement in fashioning the changes in landscape appearance, few have attempted to explain how and why the shape of the ground has evolved to its present form, and is continuing to evolve. This is the purpose of this book, and the examples and insights presented in it are the results of the efforts of numerous geomorphologists who have been concerned with establishing how landscapes evolve. Just as an art historian can tell at a glance whether an impressionist painting was created by Degas, Manet, Monet or Renoir, and can further quickly conclude whether it was created early or late in the artist's career, so the shape and composition of landforms provides geomorphologists with clues as to their age and origin. These investigations have revealed that in the majority of cases we are dealing with a long and complicated evolutionary history, and that in many instances

*PLATE 1.10 One of the blocks of sandstone dumped on the limestone pavement at Norber, near Ingleborough, North Yorkshire, by an ice-sheet that melted away about 15,000 years ago. The limestone immediately beneath the block has been protected from solution, while the surrounding areas have been lowered. The result is a small pedestal of limestone which represents the amount of solutional lowering that has occured since the block arrived. The answer appears to be about 20mm (.8in) per 1,000 years.*

the landforms that form the ground surface were fashioned under very different climatic conditions than those that prevail today. Indeed, much of the surface detail of inland areas appears to have been shaped under conditions of extreme cold, similar to those of the contemporary arctic and sub-arctic, and the clues to this cold ancestry exist for all to see once you know what to look for.

## WHAT CONTROLS THE SHAPE OF THE GROUND?

What actually determines the broad shape of the landscape with its framework of ridges and valleys within which lie small features – a bowl here, a terrace there? Many have pondered this problem, especially in those instances where a relatively 'ordinary looking' landscape contains [illegible]

[illegible] the steep west-facing slopes of Lincoln Edge[3]) to degraded coastal clifflines and thereby hypothesised that ancient inrushes of the sea had done much to shape the land. To many, such an inrush of the sea was easily explicable in terms of Noah's Flood or the Deluge.

Others sought for an alternative explanation involving ancient traumatic episodes in the early stages of Earth's history when great forces had left the ground buckled and torn. Exactly why and when these cataclysmic upheavals had taken place was a matter of speculation, for many had no idea of the Earth's age, while others still believed that the planet had been created in 4004BC. Nonetheless, the notion was considered useful in that vertical upheavals accounted for the frequent sudden transitions from mountain to lowland and the presence of major scars, while the existence of major tears in the Earth's surface determined those numerous instances where rivers plunge through ridges in narrow steep-sided valleys and gorges (Plate 1.4).

Despite these explanations there still remained a scattering of landforms of such unusual shape that their origins were ascribed to mystic forces. The Devil was a particular favourite, especially for short, narrow steep-sided valleys – the Devil's Punchbowl[4] near Haslemere, Surrey; the Devil's Kneadingtrough[5] near Wye, Kent; and the Devil's Dyke[6] north of Brighton in West Sussex, to name but three. The Devil's Dyke is a particularly well-known example, an enormous chasm cut into the face of the South Downs, supposedly by Satan who had become so enraged by the sight of the numerous churches on the low ground to the north, that he determined to cut a mighty trench to the sea thereby creating an inrush of water which would submerge the handiworks of God and drown the people who worshipped in them. Fortunately, the task was left incomplete because of the appearance of an old lady bearing a candle, which he mistook for the first rays of the rising sun, but not before he had cut the deep valley and deposited two mighty shovelfuls of earth in the nearby Ouse Valley where they form two low hills called the Upper and Lower Rises, just to the south of Lewes.

The Devil's influence was not seen to be restricted to valley features. The Stiperstones in Shropshire, a line of white teeth-like rocks (tors) that give the Stiperstone Ridge[1] an imposing skyline, are explained by two legends involving Satan, both connected with the highest tor which is known as

*PLATE 1.11 The Burren, County Clare, a desolate and barren expanse of limestone pavement formed in Carboniferous Limestone. The pattern of deep cuts (grikes) developed along the joints is well displayed, and shows how the limestone has been divided into blocks, known as clints.*

the Devil's Chair. One explanation is that the Devil constructed his chair here in the hope that his weight would eventually cause England to sink beneath the sea. The second legend involves the scattered boulders that surround the Devil's Chair. They were supposedly brought from Ireland by the Devil on one of his visits, but his apron string broke when he was getting up from the chair, scattering the stones.

Although such stories are of cultural interest, they clearly do not provide any scientific basis for the investigation of landscapes. This arose in the middle of the nineteenth century due to the growth of geological studies. It came to be recognised that the shape of the land's surface reflects the way in which different kinds of rock had been sculptured by processes of erosion, most notably the effects of running water. Soon other processes were identified including moving ice, the influence of gravity which makes material move downhill, and the wind, and it did not take long for the early investigators to realise that the shaping of the land involved three distinct tasks; removal of material (erosion), the carrying of the debris to some other location (transport) and the dumping of this debris (deposition). Thus it became possible to distinguish two main groups of landforms – those where rock had been carried away (erosional) and those where the shape of the ground reflects the way in which debris had been deposited (depositional, eg a delta in a lake).

In addition, it soon became apparent that rock was much easier to fashion if it was weakened prior to erosion. Such preparation is known as weathering and involves two main types of mechanism – 'rock rotting' where the strength of a rock is reduced by chemically induced changes and 'physical' or 'mechanical' weathering where the rock is fractured by the application of force (the freezing of water, the growth of salt crystals, an expanding tree-root). In the latter group, the repeated sequence of freezing and melting (a freeze-thaw cycle) is the most potent force for rock destruction.

By the close of the nineteenth century, therefore, the broad controls on landform creation had been identified and have subsequently been refined. Stated simply, the physical shape of the landscape is the result of '*agents of change* working on the *fabric of rocks* over very long periods of *time*'. Appreciation of this fundamental trilogy will probably be made easier by drawing an analogy with the creation of a sculpture. The nature of a sculpture is controlled by the type of stone that is being worked, especially the position and type of cracks (fractures), the skills, style and experience of the sculptor, including the tools available for use, and the time provided for completion of the task. Different sculptors working the same stone produce different results; the work of each individual sculptor can vary with the material that is being fashioned; and the longer the time available for the work, the more precise and defined the end product.

In the case of the landscape, the nature of the materials that form the [illegible]
[illegible]
[illegible]

[illegible]
[illegible]
[illegible]
[illegible]
[illegible]

which they are buried by loose debris (superficial deposits) produced by the agents of change, are all extremely influential in determining the shape of the ground as will be explained more fully in Chapter 2. It merely serves at this juncture to point out that the geological fabric of the British Isles is extremely complex, including as it does materials ranging in age from the young, soft alluvium of Romney Marsh[1] (Fig 1.3) which has been deposited over the last 3,000 years, to the ancient, gnarled and extremely hard rocks of the Outer Hebrides[2] which came into being 2,700 million years ago. There are literally hundreds of different rocks which have been variably buckled, bent and broken by folding and faulting. Many have been partly buried by superficial deposits so as to be only patchily exposed to view. With such a great variety of materials underlying the surface (see Plate 1.12), it is little wonder that the landscape of the British Isles is famous for its variety and contrasts in style.

### THE AGENTS OF CHANGE

The existence of a complicated geological fabric is insufficient in itself to create a varied landscape. The agents of change – wind, running water, ice, gravity, the sea – must be allowed to fashion the rocks because each imparts a distinctiveness to the landforms it produces due to the particular ways in which it shapes earth materials. Thus the landforms produced beneath a thick and heavy ice-sheet appear different to those produced by the sea along the coast, a river in its valley, or on a slope which has collapsed in a landslide. How these agents work and the features that they produce are fully explained in Chapters 3-7, while Chapter 8 discusses the works of the most recent, but now dominant, agent of change, humans.

It is also necessary to provide the agents of change with the opportunity to sculpture the rocks. Virtually all the processes are dominated by gravity. Material moves down a slope, either as a slowly creeping layer of soil, a bouncing boulder or a rapid landslide; rivers flow down valleys to lakes or the sea; glaciers slide downhill; wind-borne debris must fall to earth sooner or later. Only humans, the wind and glacial ice have the power to push material uphill. Thus to produce the dramatic landscapes associated with the mountains of Ireland, Wales, the Lake District and Scotland (Plate 1.1), requires that the rocks are first uplifted to a sufficient elevation so that they can be eroded to create the ridges and valleys of today. Tectonic

*PLATE 1.12 One should never underestimate the importance of rocks in creating colour and texture in the landscape. This view in the Mendip Hills clearly shows how two adjacent rocks produce very different surface characteristics. On the right is the Carboniferous Limestone which produces crags and grey soils. On the left the underlying Old Red Sandstone yields rich dark-brown coloured soils and building stones that are well displayed in the buildings of Hereford.*

uplift is therefore the necessary precursor to denudation. Only when the geological fabric has been raised can the strengths and weaknesses be exploited by erosion.

But what about the various agents of erosion that have combined to fashion our landscape – the sea, running water, ice, the wind and gravity. They are all very different in terms of how they work, the nature of the debris they produce, and the shapes that they create, as is fully described in Chapters 3-7. The rates at which they work also varies considerably, as is the case with humans. And just like humans, the rate at which each individual process will work depends on the suitability of the conditions. Some are naturally slow and persistent, such as the gradual downslope movement of the surface layer of soil on a hillslope (soil creep) which produces those small steps (terracettes) that are characteristic of many hillsides (see Chapter 7). But the operation of this process requires the existence of a slope, and the steeper the slope the faster the movement. However, plant trees on the hillside, and the roots will check the downslope movement.

The rate at which all processes of change operate in the landscape is controlled by such factors, which tend to be referred to by the grandiose title of 'environmental conditions'. If the conditions suit the process, it will operate relatively quickly, but if the conditions are not conducive to activity little will happen. Ice and snow are achieving virtually nothing in the present landscapes because the climate is not cold enough for snow to accumulate to form ice. But in the Ice Age, the growth of enormous ice-sheets ground down the rocks and huge volumes of water both beneath and in front of the ice achieved truely awesome feats of erosion, transport and deposition (see Chapters 3 and 4).

Climate is one of the most important influences on the operation of sculpturing agencies, but others include vegetation, rock type, vertical movements and slope steepness. These factors interact in a complex way with the result that the shaping processes do not work steadily in the landscape, but instead vary in intensity from place to place as well as with the passage of time. As a consequence, many processes are characterised by brief bursts of intense activity separated by peaceful interludes. For example, a hillslope may stand for thousands of years undergoing minor reshaping by soil creep and then, suddenly, it will fall in a huge landslide and millions of tonnes (tons) of material will move towards the valley bottom. The results of a few minutes' activity may include the reshaping of the hillslope to create a deep embayment, the accumulation of a chaotic jumble of moved material in the valley bottom, and possibly the damming of the river to form a lake which may survive for several years until it becomes infilled with sediment.

This variability is a particularly characteristic feature of rivers. Most rivers in the British Isles have permanently flowing water and have obviously eroded the landscape because they occupy valleys. Measurement of the debris being transported down rivers either in solution or suspension or by rolling and bouncing along the channel bed (traction), provides clues as to rate at which material is being removed from the land area drained by the river system (the catchment or drainage basin, see Chapter 5). If the values are extrapolated uniformly over the whole of the drainage basin, current estimates of land-surface lowering are in the range 4mm (.16in) to 200mm (8in) per 1,000 years – a large range but rivers differ greatly in their character and the nature of the rocks that they flow over. Given enough time it is not difficult to envisage the creation of the ridges and valleys of today's landscape. But the figures of 4-200mm (.16-8in) per 1000 years are generalised over the whole area from which the rivers draw water. The potential for downcutting available to the main rivers and their larger tributaries must be significantly greater, while the values along the ridge tops are minimal.

But anyone who has experience of rivers, either through fishing or sailing or walking, knows that moods change: the gently flowing waters of summer are frequently replaced by swirling muddy torrents after storms, prolonged rainfall or the melting of accumulated snow. As the ability of rivers to erode and transport material increases as their size increases, it should be obvious that most of the work is actually achieved during periods of flood. And not all floods are the same size; a few are very large and very powerful, but so infrequent as to be called rare. These are the so-called 'catastrophic events' which can result in major changes in landscape. If one travels to Exmoor[1], to the valley of the River Lyn[2], it is still possible to identify the features created on the fateful night of 15 August 1952 when torrential rain caused the little Lyn to swell to the size of the River Thames in flood (see Chapter 5). It is possible that the River Lyn achieved more work in those few hours of frenetic activity than it had achieved over the [illegible]

[illegible] particular combinations of shaping processes. Indeed, it is now recognised that the most rapid changes in the landscape were accomplished by running water and slope movements during those relatively brief periods of time between the melting of an ice-sheet and the arrival of a dense tree-cover. It was then that landforms which had lain frozen and immobile beneath a cover of ice for thousands of years were briefly exposed to the ravages of change prior to the arrival of a protective blanket of vegetation. These pulses of landscape change were extremely important and merely serve to emphasise the third element of the fundamental trilogy of factors – time.

TIME FOR A CHANGE

Time is of great importance to landform creation in two regards. First, the longer the time that a particular combination of sculpturing processes are allowed to operate, the greater the degree of change accomplished by the processes. For example, to create an interesting and varied tract of limestone scenery with its characteristic suite of landforms such as gorges, swallow holes, caves etc, takes hundreds of thousands of years. If there is insufficient time available, the end product is an immature landscape without the full range of landforms and with many features poorly developed.

The second aspect concerns the passage of time, in the sense that as time has passed so the conditions that influence the operation of sculpturing processes have changed. Climatic change has been especially important in the case of the British Isles, because the last 2.5 million years have witnessed repeated alternations between extremely cold conditions associated with the accumulation of extensive ice-sheets bordered by frozen wastes, and temperate conditions, sometimes slightly warmer than those prevailing at present.

During the past thirty years new techniques have allowed for much improved reconstructions of the sequence of past environments over the last 2.5million years, with the result that many ideas about the evolution of the British Isles have had to be rethought. It is now known that ice began to accumulate in the arctic as early as 5 million years ago and that the first really extensive glaciation of the North Atlantic region occurred 2.4 million years ago. Whether this glaciation affected the British Isles is unknown, but during the subsequent period of time there are thought to

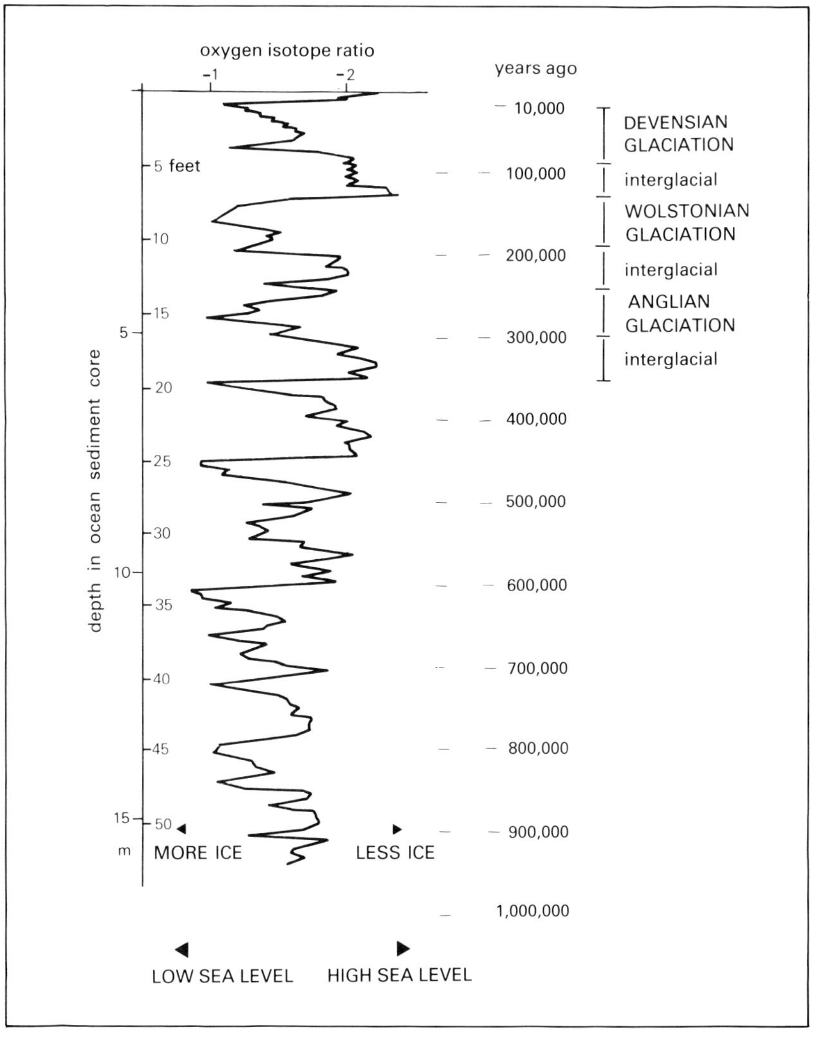


*FIG 1.4 Analysis of deep-sea cores has revealed that the lime (carbonate) content of minute organisms show variations in chemical composition with respect to the two isotopes of oxygen $^{16}0$ and $^{18}0$. It is argued that the lighter isotope ($^{16}0$) is more readily involved in evaporation than the heavier isotope. The growth of ice-sheets will therefore result in more and more $^{16}0$ being trapped as ice, so that the amount remaining in the oceans will decrease. Thus the carbon in marine organisms will show a smaller proportion of $^{16}0$ during cold phases than in the warmer interglacial episodes when much of the ice had melted and the water returned to the oceanic reservoir. The variations in the $^{16}0/^{18}0$ ratio therefore provide us with a guide as to the variations in climate in the past. This reveals a very regular alternation between warm and cold conditions as is predicted by the Milankovitch Theory (see Chapter 3). If you turn the graph on its side, the fluctuations give a general indication as to the changes in sea-level over the same period, with high sea-levels during the interglacials and very low sea-levels during the glacials.*

have been at least twenty cool or cold episodes, all of which would have been associated with the accumulation of snow and ice at high latitudes and altitudes, and the generation of glaciers and ice-sheets that spread to lowlands and towards the south. Why these events occurred is explained by variations in the Earth's orbit around the sun, the so-called Milankovitch Theory as described in Chapter 3, which has resulted in a fairly regular cooling and warming of the climate to yield a sequence of cold glacials separated by warm interglacials at intervals of about 120,000 years (Fig 1.4).

Each time the climate deteriorated, the arctic ice accumulated and spread southwards so that the level of the sea fell to a position at least 100m (330ft) below that of today. As a consequence, much of the surrounding sea floors became dry land across which flowed greatly extended rivers (Fig 1.1) – or at least they flowed in the summer months. At the end of each glacial episode the ice-sheets melted away so as to shrink northwards and into the mountains, the sea-level rose, and the amelioration of climate resulted in the northward migration of forests to recolonize areas until recently covered by ice and snow. Thus landscapes were subjected to a sequence of change with regard to the processes that were shaping them. The sequence may have begun with moulding under moving ice to be followed by fashioning under conditions of seasonal thaw, and then modification by the ravages of flowing water and landsliding before the healing blanket of vegetation could become established. Then, after about 20,000 years, the sequence

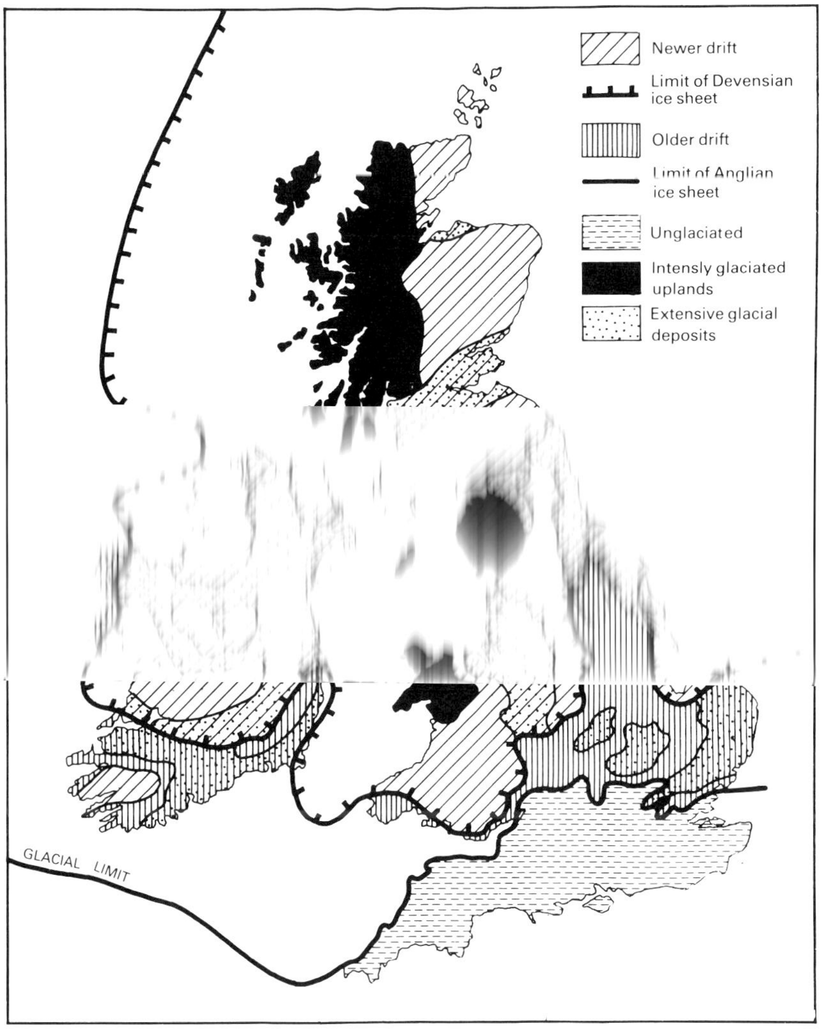


*FIG 1.5 The influence of ice-sheets in the British Isles. It is important to note that southern areas have never been glaciated while northern parts have been covered by thick, heavy, powerful ice-sheets on many occasions. Thus the degree to which landscapes have been modified by ice tends to increase northwards, although it must be recognised that the landscape of East Anglia, the Cheshire Plain and much of the East Midlands is largely developed of thick sheets of material laid down by*

would go into reverse, but quicker and with less sculpturing, as the next ice-sheet advanced to record yet another glaciation in the Ice Age.

Each ice-sheet tended to act like a giant bulldozer reshaping the pre-existing landscape by erosion and deposition and thereby destroying the evidence of earlier (older) glaciations. It should come as no great surprise, therefore, that we can only find convincing traces of four glacial episodes written in the landscape.

The oldest of the four recognised glaciations, the Anglian (270,000BP – Before Present) was also the most extensive (Fig 1.5) and defines the limit of glacial influence in the British Isles. This glaciation was of significance for two main reasons. First, it eroded the rocks of East Anglia[1] to such a degree that much of the area would now be beneath the sea if this same glaciation had not deposited huge volumes of debris called boulder clay which now underlie the ground over most of the area. Second, it dammed the ancestral River Thames[2] and diverted it south to its present route (see Chapter 5).

The succeeding glaciation, the Wolstonian, is dated at between 200,000BP and 150,000BP and is thought by some to have been almost as extensive as the Anglian. This is the ice advance that is considered to have caused the formation of a huge lake in the Midlands, known as Lake Harrison, which eventually drained to create the Warwickshire Avon[3] (see Chapter 5).

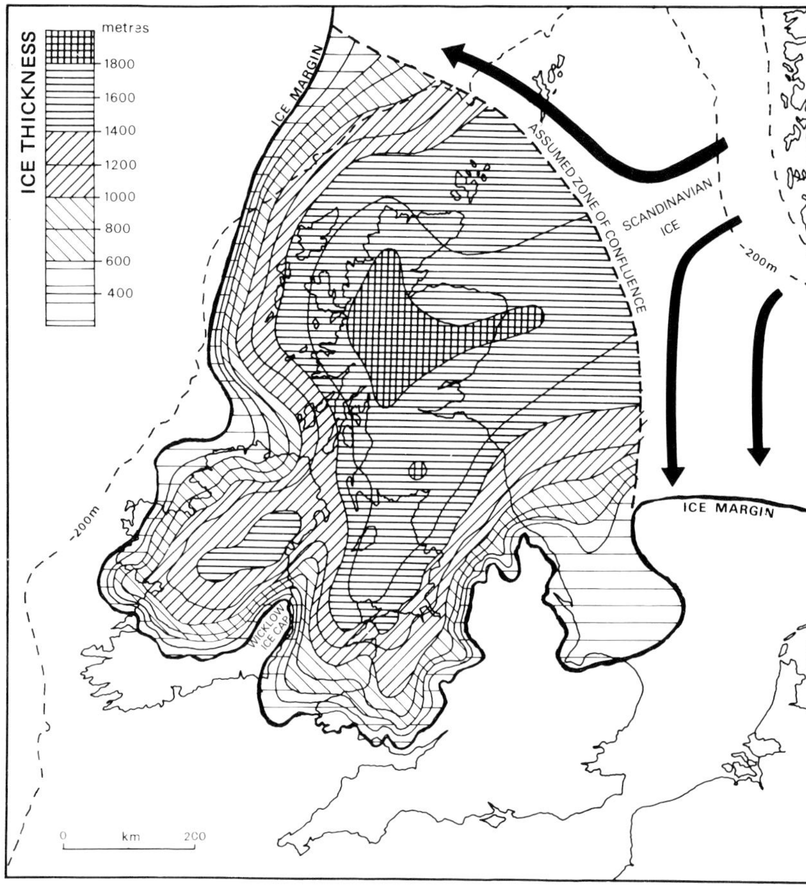


*FIG 1.6 A reconstruction of the Devensian ice-sheet showing its great thickness in northern parts of the British Isles.*

There then followed a period of warm interglacial conditions from 120,000BP to 80,000BP, after which the climate quickly deteriorated again and the ice of the Devensian Glaciation began to accumulate. The Devensian ice-limit (Fig 1.6) was reached as recently as 18,000BP, and is of special importance in the context of landscape, because it defines the boundary between the 'Newer Drift' terrains to the north and the 'Older Drift' terrains to the south. Thus to the south of this line, signs of glaciation are indistinct and blurred, but to the north the evidence of erosion and deposition by thick ice-sheets is clearly preserved for all to see (see Chapter 3).

After 18,000BP the Devensian ice-sheet rapidly melted away, thereby releasing huge quantities of water to indulge in the erosion, transportation and deposition of material, and it is thought that the whole of the British Isles were ice-free by 12,700BP. It is worth pausing here to assimilate the scale of this change. Because the Devensian is the youngest of the major glaciations – the following Loch Lomond re-advance only lasted from 11,500-10,800BP and was restricted to a local ice-cap in the North-west Highlands[1] and small pockets of ice in other highland areas (see Chapter 3) – it has been possible to reconstruct the shape of the ice-sheet (Fig 1.6). This has revealed that at the glacial maximum the northern parts of the British Isles were concealed beneath an ice dome whose surface rose to an elevation of 1,750m (5,740ft) over the Southern Uplands[2] of Scotland. Consider what the sizes of the ice domes must have been like during the earlier and more extensive Wolstonian and Anglian glaciations! The extent and thickness of these ice-sheets indicates that ice was frequently able to flow across mountainous areas, was capable of enormous erosive power, especially in areas where the rocks were not very hard, and equally capable

of dumping huge quantities of debris when the climate changed and the ice melted. The landscape must have looked very different during these phases of ice decay, with huge masses of melting 'dead ice' in the lowlands releasing vast quantities of water which busily reworked the freshly dumped glacial debris: a veritable lunar landscape of torrent tracts, saturated boggy soils and slope materials sliding and sludging towards the lower ground.

It is now thought that over 75 per cent of the last 2 million years of landscape history were characterised by cold conditions. It is no wonder therefore that the majority of the present landscape reflects fashioning under cold climate conditions, either glacial (see Chapter 3) or under the frozen ground conditions that bordered the ice-sheets (see Chapter 4).There simply has not been enough time for the current range of processes operating under temperate climatic conditions to accomplish the [illegible] evidence for this cold inheritance.

[illegible]

[illegible] longer operate (eg glacial ice), and [illegible] relics from times long past before the arrival of the first wintry blasts of the impending Ice Age.

That the landscape should be envisaged as a patchwork of landforms of differing age and origin should not pose any real problems. If the geological fabric is complex and the evolutionary history has been varied, there is no reason why the end-product should be uniform. New cathedrals, such as Coventry or Liverpool are built of an age and display single, although differing styles; but old cathedrals such as Canterbury or York are composed of elements of differing style and age – Norman, Perpendicular etc. Similarly, our more ancient towns consist of mixtures of buildings of differing styles and ages – Tudor, Georgian, Victorian, inter-war, post-war – which combine to provide the urban scene with variety. The landscape should be viewed in the same way, for it then becomes fascinating to analyse the component landforms with a view to distinguishing the ancient from the modern, the relic from the evolving, the shapes created by the fabric from the forms fashioned by glacial ice, running water, wind, the sea, gravity, intense cold, chemical alteration and human activity. The remainder of this book is devoted to examining the components that have gone into creating this variety, in the hope that others will seek out the clues for themselves.

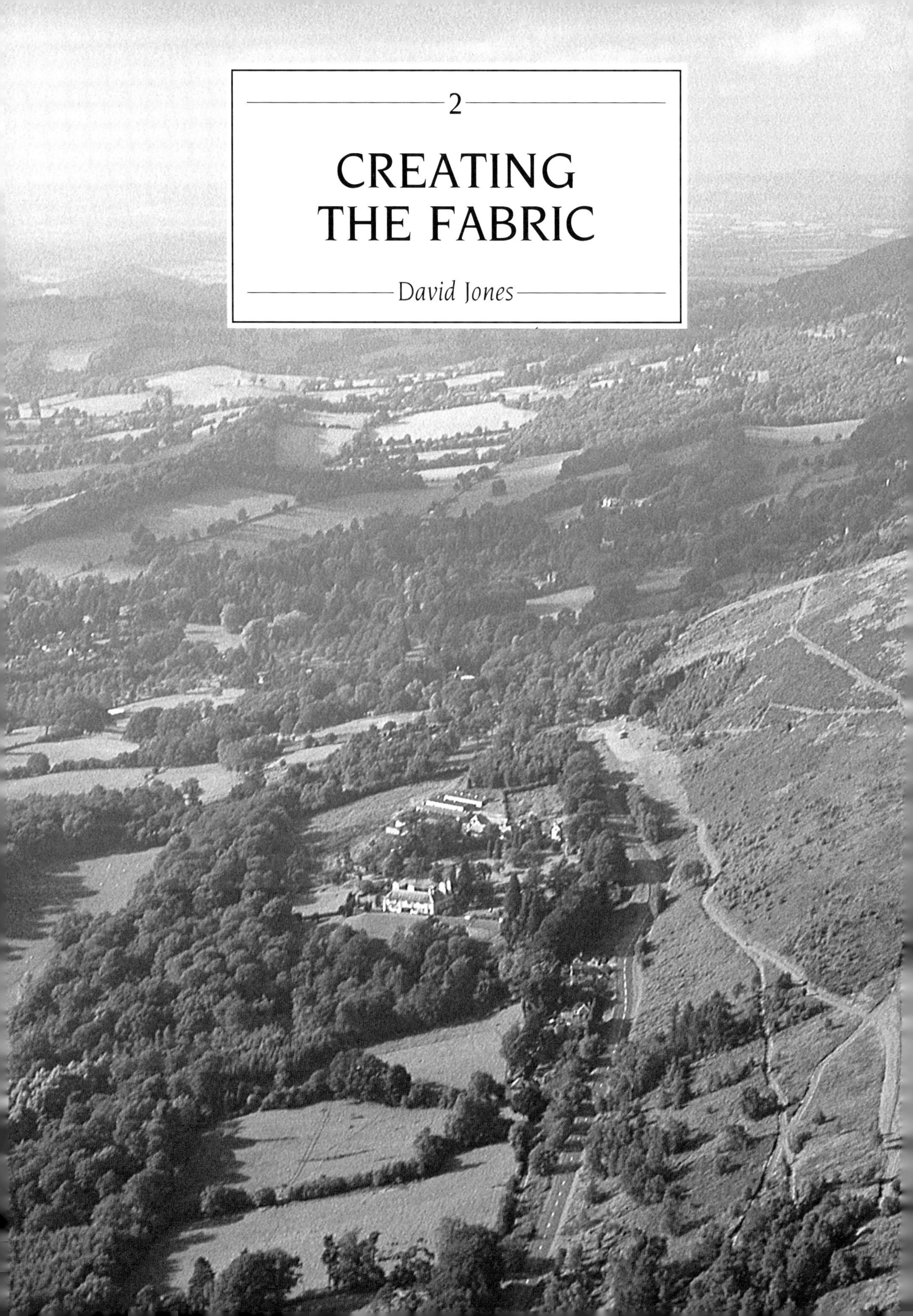

2

# CREATING THE FABRIC

David Jones

## PATTERNS AND CONTRASTS

When walking through the bustling streets of cities such as Glasgow, Newcastle, Leeds or Manchester, it is difficult to appreciate that a mere 20,000 years ago these areas lay beneath hundreds of metres of ice. And this was not the only occasion, for as was shown in the last chapter, there have been repeated occurrences of arctic conditions over the past 2 million years, when huge accumulations of ice spread southwards as thick, heavy ice-sheets, moulding all that they overran and achieving prodigious feats of erosion, transportation and deposition. But if this is the case, why have such a variety of glaciated landscapes survived? How is it that the three major peaks in the Lake District[1] – Helvellyn, Scafell Pike and Skiddaw – have such different appearances, a feature well known to fell-walkers, and that the Lake District itself is distinctively different from the nearby Pennines[2]? At the larger scale, how can one account for the differences in character between the flat, low-lying expanses of the Fens[3] (Plate 1.8) or the undulating plainlands of East Anglia[4] on the one hand, and the smoothed, rolling moorlands of southern Scotland[5] and the rugged, mountainous terrain of the Scottish Highlands[6] (Plate 2.1) on the other? Indeed, why are the most dramatic rugged landscapes located in the northern and western parts of these islands where the erosive power of ice was greatest, rather than in southern areas, such as Surrey, beyond the reach of glacial sculpturing?

But even in these southern unglaciated areas (see Fig 1.5) there exists equally dramatic contrasts in landscape. The flat low-lying expanses of Romney Marsh[7] and the Somerset Levels[8] have little in common with the rolling downland of Sussex[9], the high plateaux of east Devon[10] or the moorlands of Exmoor[11] and Dartmoor[12]. Here again, it is obvious that the terrain generally becomes higher and more rugged towards the west, and this feature requires explanation. Other questions no doubt also come to mind, such as why are there numerous excellent examples of upstanding masses of rock known as 'tors' on Dartmoor but none on Exmoor or in Hertfordshire? And why is Cheddar Gorge[1] where it is and not in Sussex?

Such questions draw attention to the fact that the nature of the materials underlying the ground exerts a profound influence on the way in which the ground can be shaped by the agents of erosion – wind, water and ice. Just as sculptors find it easier to fashion certain rocks than others, so it is with nature. The fabric of the underlying material therefore provides the constraints or ground rules for the development of landscapes, for some rocks are weak and can be easily moulded, while others are tough and resist change, standing out proudly as a skyline until eventually becoming worn down through the sheer persistence of denudation. The greater the complexity of the fabric, the more varied the shapes (landforms) that can be produced. Indeed, it is the inconsistencies or variations in the geological fabric that are exploited by denudation to create the ridges, hills, valleys and vales that provide interest in the landscape.

In this respect we must judge ourselves extremely fortunate, for the British Isles are made up of very varied materials, and it is this that largely accounts for the rich diversity of landscapes. Thus the fact that there are no mountains in Surrey and no tors in Hertfordshire, but excellent examples on Dartmoor, emphasises the need to appreciate something of the character of the geological fabric if the variations in landscape are to be understood.

Why then is there such a marked contrast in landscapes within the British Isles between the rugged and sometimes spectacular mountainous areas of the north and west (Fig 2.1), and the gently undulating lowlands characteristic of the south-east? The reality of this contrast is dramatically revealed in images obtained from spacecraft (Plate 2.2), which show that north-western parts appear wrinkled and creased as if aged, whereas the

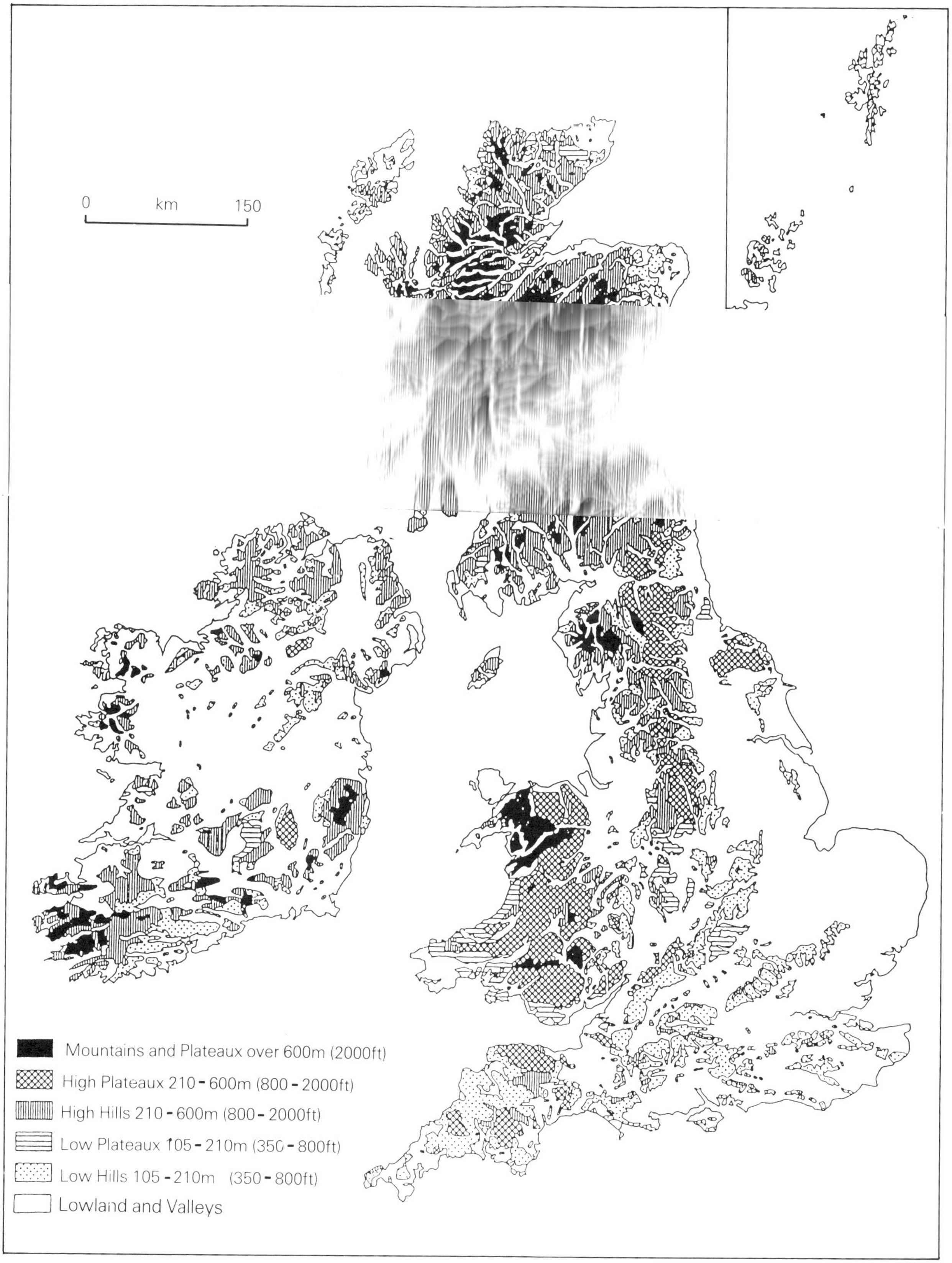


*FIG 2.1 The distribution of the main types of landscape in the British Isles.*

PLATE 2.1 *Loch Coruisg, Isle of Skye. A landscape developed on old, hard rocks which have been repeatedly smoothed beneath thick, heavy ice-sheets.*

PLATE 2.2 *LANDSAT satellite image of the British Isles. The upland areas show up very clearly, especially the North-west Highlands of Scotland with its western highly irregular fjord coastline and the numerous NE–SW orientated faults which have been eroded by rivers and ice to create valleys. The Great Glen, gouged out along the Great Glen Fault, is the most obvious of fault-guided valleys.* (Science Photo Library)

south-east looks fresh and unblemished by the rigours of life. This analogy with ageing is indeed generally correct, for the oldest rocks do appear at the surface in the extreme north-west of Scotland and in the Inner[1] and Outer Hebrides[2], and the youngest underlie the south-east. Between these two extremes, the rocks generally decrease in age south-eastwards almost as if they had been piled layer upon layer over time with the oldest at the bottom and the youngest at the top, and then pushed over and planed across. Once again this analogy is not misplaced, for there is convincing evidence that the British Isles have suffered tilting over tens of millions of years, with the north-western areas having physically risen while the east coast of England has experienced depression. Without this uplift in the north-west it would have been impossible for the rivers and ice-sheets to cut deeply into the ancient rocks and exploit lines of weakness so as to create the mountainous landscapes of today (Plate 2.1).

Similarly, the impact of subsidence is written clearly on the coast of the South East. The salt marshes on the Essex coast[3] and the extensive reclaimed swamps and tidal flats that now form Romney Marsh[4] and the Fens[5], represent the accumulation of material dropped by rivers whose flow has been checked by the rising level of the sea, and the continuing rapid rate of sea-level rise (between 2mm and 4mm (.08-.16in) per year) has posed such a growing threat to life and property that huge amounts of money have had to be spent on defences to keep the rising high tides at bay. These include high embankments (levées) and walls along the lower courses of rivers and the coast, and the construction of huge moveable concrete and steel flood-barriers at Hull[6], Yarmouth[7] and at Woolwich[8] on the River Thames. Only by these means is it possible to act like some latter-day King Canute and defend the line between England and the North Sea, thereby avoiding the possible repetition of the events that occurred on the fateful night of 31 January/1 February 1953 when high winds drove the sea inland, drowning 307 people. Indeed, the very existence of the North

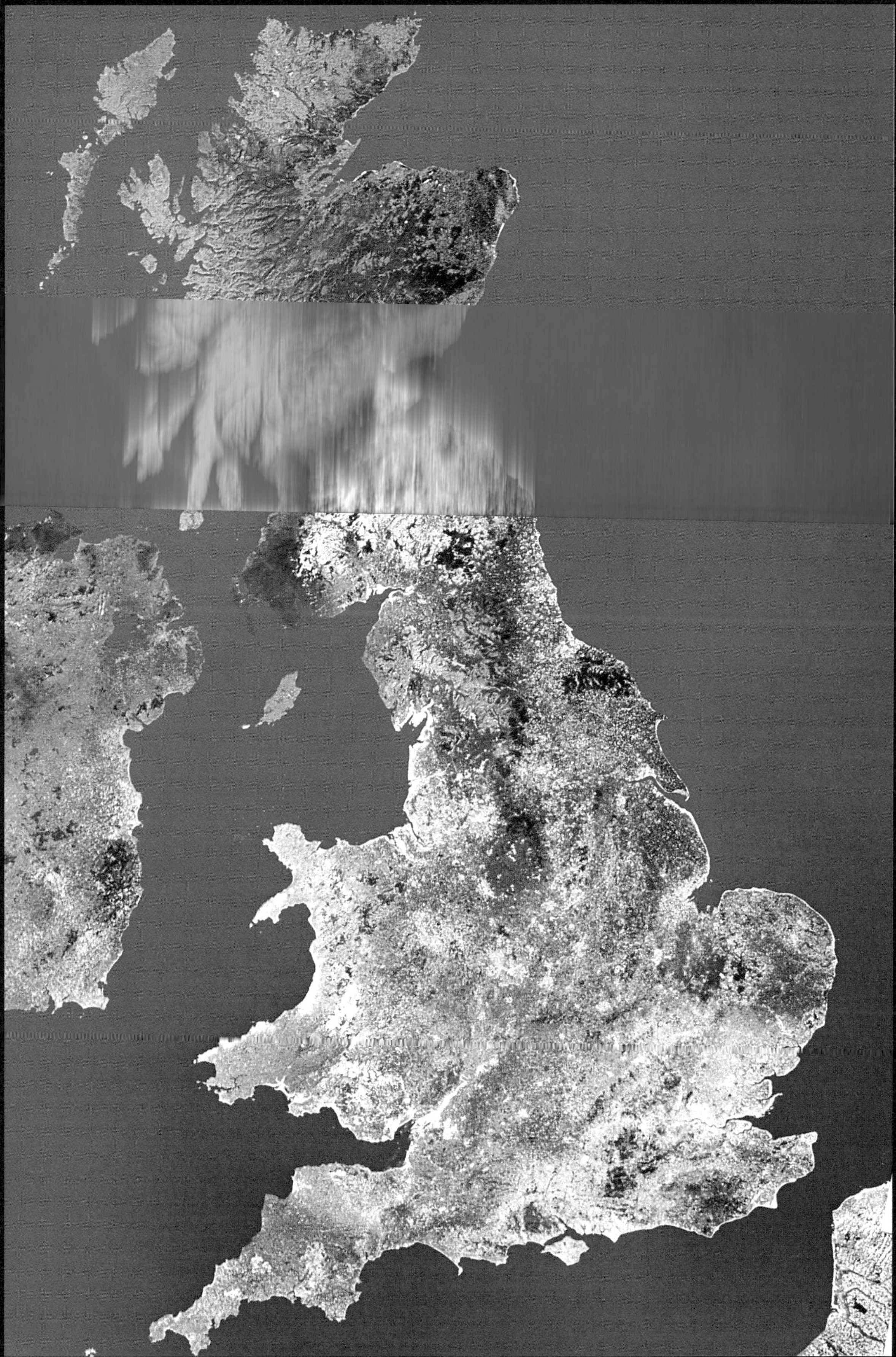

Sea is due to the presence of this zone of subsidence (the North Sea Basin).

Although the details of this seesaw action have only become known in recent years, the distribution of rocks of differing age has long been recognised. As long ago as 1909 Halford Mackinder in his book *Britain and the British Seas* observed that the British Isles appeared to have been 'built from the north-west and populated from the south-east'. He proposed a fundamental division of the British Isles into two parts on the basis of whether the rocks that directly underlie the surface are older or younger than a particularly significant point in the evolution of these islands, the end of what is known as the Carboniferous Period which occurred about 280 million years ago (Fig 2.2). The rocks that are older than 280 million years are for the most part hard, crumpled, crushed and torn due to their eventful history, and as a consequence are generally difficult to wear away so that they now form the highest and most mountainous areas. By contrast, the rocks that are younger than 280 million years are much softer and show fewer signs of wear and tear. Although the boundary between these two groups of rocks is very irregular in places (Fig 2.2), the reasons for which will be discussed later in this chapter, it is nonetheless true that Mackinder's famous Tees-Exe Line (Fig 2.2) effectively separates the ancient rocks of 'Highland Britain' to the north and west from the relatively young soft rocks of 'Lowland Britain' to the south and east.

Although this fundamental division is of great interest, it fails to provide the answer as to why there is so much variation in the scenery of Highland and Lowland Britain. Clearly to do this we must look more closely at the fabric and examine the details of composition and weave. This is most easily achieved if we begin by considering the different types of rock that combine to form the fabric.

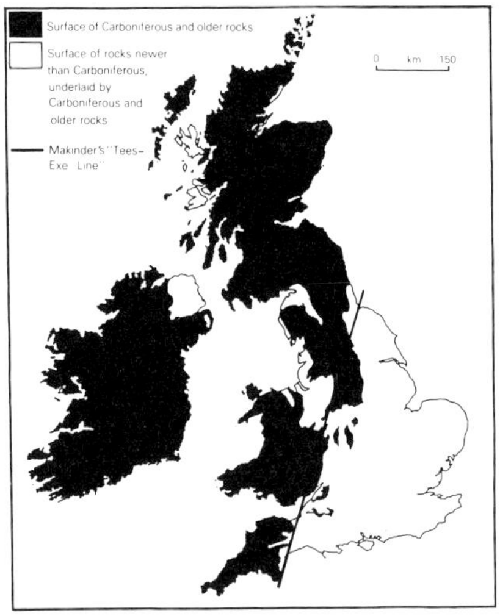


*FIG 2.2 The distribution of rocks that are either older or younger than 280 million years. The rocks that were created before 280 million years ago underlie the ground of Highland Britain, while those that are younger form Lowland Britain. Mackinder's Tees-Exe Line successfully approximates the boundary between Highland and Lowland Britain.*

## THE ROCKS OF THE FABRIC

The geological fabric consists of three main types of rock: **igneous** which are produced by the solidification of molten material or 'magma'; **sedimentary** rocks which represent the accumulated debris produced by the destruction of pre-existing rocks brought about by the operation of the agents of change (ice, water, gravity and wind); and **metamorphic** rocks which are formed by the alteration of any pre-existing rock, either igneous or sedimentary, through the application of great heat and/or intense pressure, but without remelting. These three main groups of rocks differ greatly in terms of their characteristics, distributions and the ways in which they are shaped by geomorphological agencies.

### ROCKS FASHIONED BY FIRE

Igneous rocks are considered the fundamental rock type because they have been created over virtually the whole length of Earth history, currently estimated at a staggering 4,600 million years or equivalent to 2.25 million times the period that has elapsed since Julius Caesar landed in 55BC! The first 700 million years of this evolution remains a mystery to geologists, but it is generally thought that our planet was created by gravity concentrating a cloud of dust orbiting the sun. This process generated great heat and the primitive Earth was undoubtedly a molten body which only gradually developed the surface scum of solidified debris that was to eventually form the foundation for the present continents. These earliest rocks would all have been classified as igneous rocks because they had been formed through the cooling of molten material or magma. Virtually none of this most ancient skin is exposed at the Earth's surface today, although rocks thought to be 3,900 million years old have been discovered in Greenland.

The gradual thickening of the Earth's crust to its present proportions (10-90km (6.0-55 miles) thick) was largely achieved by the further accumulation of igneous rocks through cooling. In many instances, the molten magma originating in the hot interior moved upward through the solid crust but failed to reach the surface. As a consequence, the huge ascending bubbles of molten material gradually cooled and solidified to create **intrusive** igneous rocks, of which the best known example is granite. Such rocks are hard and heavy and are referred to as crystalline because they consist of very tightly packed crystals of different minerals – three in the case of granite: white quartz, milky felspar and black mica. The size of the crystals in these rocks was determined by the rate at which the molten magma cooled; the bigger the crystals the slower the cooling.

Intrusive igneous rocks composed of large crystals (coarse-grained) therefore probably solidified many kilometres (miles) below the surface or in the heart of a huge slowly cooling mass of magma, while fine-grained examples may have solidified at shallower depths or within a small body [illegible]

[illegible] solidified about 280 million years ago up to 6km (3.7 miles) below the landsurface of that time. The Mourne Granite[2] in Ireland is much younger at 56 million years and probably congealed 800m (2,600ft) below the surface. However, the prize must go to the granite of northern Arran[5], in the Firth of Clyde, which was probably formed beneath a 2.5km (1.5 miles) thick layer of rocks a mere 58 million years ago but now forms the highest part of the island (see Plate 1.6) with summits rising to over 800m (2,600ft) above sea-level!

The process of gradual exposure by erosion assists in the creation of an important characteristic feature of igneous rock, a pattern of horizontal and vertical cracks known as joints which effectively divide the rock mass into rectangular blocks (see Plate 4.1). These cracks originally developed deep within the earth as the newly solidified material cooled and contracted, but were kept tightly compressed by the great weight of overlying rocks. However, the gradual removal of overlying materials results in a reduction of this load so that the joints are often relatively open when the igneous rock is finally exposed at the surface, thereby providing avenues of weakness that can be attacked by the processes of erosion. The most famous landform to be produced under these circumstances is the tor (see Chapter 4).

Not all the rising magma solidified within the crust. Sometimes the magma managed to reach the surface and pour out as lava which quickly cooled to form **extrusive** igneous rocks. Because of the rapidity of cooling, extrusive ingneous rocks are usually extremely fine-grained and sometimes resemble coloured glass (obsidian) which, in reality, is what they are. The character of volcanic activity depends on the chemical composition of the magma, and this, in turn, controls the nature of the rocks that are produced. Some magma is rich in iron (basalt) and this makes it extremely fluid and slow to cool. Huge eruptions of this type of lava occurred in western Scotland and northern Ireland between 66 and 58 million years ago, when the ground in these areas was riven by vast numbers of long cracks through which lava bubbled onto the surface (Fig 2.4). Eventually, an enormous expanse of solidified lava accumulated, up to 1,800m (5,900ft) thick in places, the largest portion of which survives as the plateau of Antrim[1], with its towering black cliffs. Occasionally, the rapidity of cooling resulted in the development of a particular pattern of

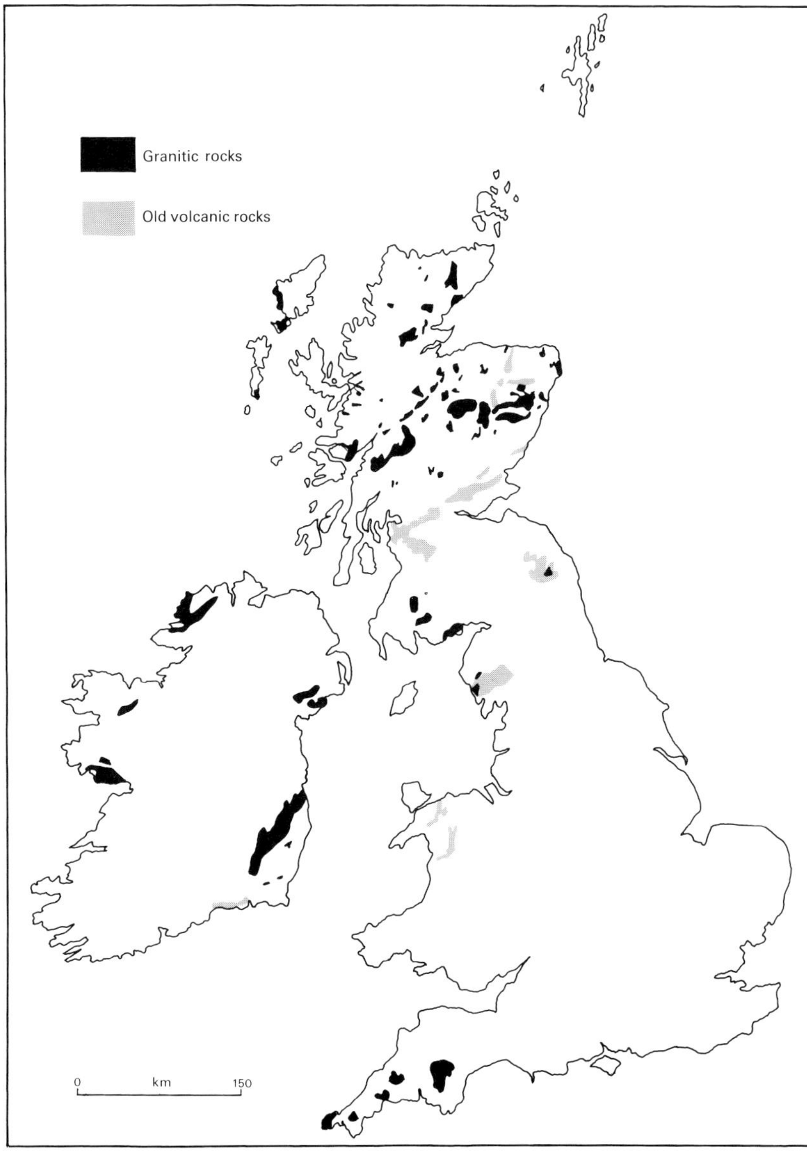


*FIG 2.3 The distribution of igneous rocks in the British Isles, excluding those dykes and lavas created when rifting separated the British Isles from Greenland which are shown on Fig 2.4.*

contraction cracks so as to produce the packed hexagonal columns that form the Giant's Causeway[1] and create the organ-pipe effect on the cliffs of the island of Staffa[2] (Plate 2.3). When these eruptions ceased, the feeder cracks became blocked with solidified magma thereby creating near vertical sheets of intrusive igneous rocks, known as dykes, which march in straight lines through the landscape of western Scotland (Fig 2.4). Sometimes these features form low walls, at other times shallow trenches; it all depends on whether the materials that form the dykes (dolerite) are tougher or weaker than the rocks on either side.

On other occasions the magma turned out to be deficient in iron so that the lava produced was much more sticky and cooled relatively quickly. This type of lava was usually extruded from a single hole, known as a pipe or vent, which became the site of a volcano. Although no such volcanoes occur in the British Isles today, they have left their mark on the landscape (Fig 2.3). The solidified materials in the vents of former volcanoes (plugs) still exist in the Central Lowlands of Scotland where they have been fashioned by erosion to form low craggy hills, eg Castle Hill[3], Edinburgh. The Cheviot Hills[4] have been carved from the remains of a huge ancient

volcano, and much of the more rugged scenery in Wales and the Lake District is developed on volcanic rocks.

ROCKS CREATED FROM DEBRIS

Once at the surface of the Earth, all rocks no matter their origin, are attacked by wind, water and ice, by frost and heat, and by the activity of organisms (eg tree roots, rabbits, worms). They weather and break into fragments which are carried away by water, wind or ice and deposited elsewhere in the form of sediments. Eventually such sediments will be deposited in an environment, often a shallow sea, which allows them to accumulate peacefully in huge amounts and eventually harden into sedimentary rocks. Gravel-sized material forms conglomerate (rounded pebbles) or breccia (angular pebbles); sand turns into sandstone; silt and clay are converted into shale or mudstone, and there is a full range of intermediate deposits. Dissolved substances removed by rivers in solution precipitate out to form what are known as evaporites, such as rock salt, while organisms can accumulate to form shell limestones, bone beds and coal. Clearly, therefore, the significance and variety of sedimentary rocks has increased over the last 4,000 million years as the oceans and atmosphere have developed and organisms evolved, for there could be no shell limestones before the evolution of organisms which could make the shells and no coal before there were tree ferns! Thus it should come as no surprise that the whole of Lowland Britain is underlain by sedimentary rocks (Fig 2.5) and that igneous rocks are of greatest importance in the oldest parts of Highland Britain.

Sedimentary rocks have a number of additional features of importance. They are generally weaker than igneous rocks but their toughness varies considerably depending on the hardness and chemical composition of

*PLATE 2.3 View of Fingal's Cave, Isle of Staffa, showing a sheet of columnar jointed (organ pipe) basalt lava overlain by a 'more normal' chaotic lava flow. This material was spewed out onto the landsurface between 66 and 58 million years ago as the crust began to stretch heralding the final opening of the North Atlantic Ocean Basin which was to separate the British Isles from Greenland.*

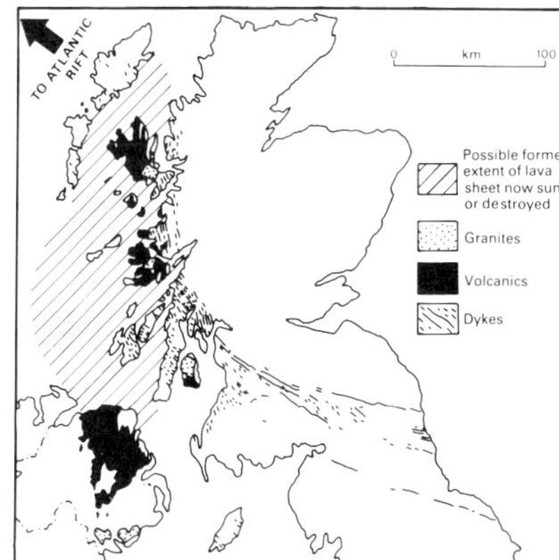


*FIG 2.4 The volcanic rocks created between 74 million and 53 million years ago when rifting of the North Atlantic Basin began.*

the particles that make up the rock and the cementing materials that bind these particles together. This is best seen in the coarser grained rocks such as sandstones and conglomerates. Sometimes the cement is the weakest link and the rock disintegrates to produce loose sand or gravel. On other occasions, it is the cement that proves more durable, so that individual grains and pebbles may be destroyed to create a pitted surface full of cavities (honeycomb weathering). Such features are especially well displayed on coastal cliffs where the salt spray readily attacks the rocks. The red cliffs of Dawlish[1], south Devon, provide excellent examples of the phenomenon. If both the minerals and cement are equally weak, then the rock is quickly worn down by erosion to form low ground but if both are strong, as occurs in a generally white-coloured rock called quartzite, the material resists being worn away and stands up as a ridge or crag (eg the Stiperstones[2]).

This idea of different resistance to erosion applies at all scales, from the minerals that make up a particular layer of rock to the relative durability of one mass of rock as compared with adjacent masses. Thus while shales and mudstones are composed of extremely small particles (clay-sized) that usually offer little resistance and are therefore worn away by erosion to create lowlands or vales, sandstones differ greatly in their resistance to erosion and can form both high and low ground. For example, a moderately tough sandstone layer will form a ridge if the rocks on either side of it are weaker, but the same rock could form a valley in another area if the adjacent rocks turned out to be more resistant. Limestones display similar variation in composition and hardness. Here again, the same limestone may form high ground in one area because it is more durable than the adjacent rocks, but low ground in another area because it turns out to be the weakest in that particular locale.

Because most sedimentary rocks originally accumulated as deposits on the floors of shallow seas close to existing areas of land, they frequently occur as sheets of material which display clear evidence of banding, or layering, known as bedding. Each bed is bounded by upper and lower breaks (discontinuities), known as bedding planes. These represent either a pause during the accumulation of the material, or a change in the character of the deposits (eg from clay to fine sand). As most bedding planes would have been almost horizontal when they were first formed, any tilting or bending observable today must be the result of earth movements following the formation of the rocks.

Bedding planes are most clearly displayed in coastal cliffs, and are easily seen in the Chalk cliffs of Sussex[1] (Plate 1.3) and Kent (eg the White Cliffs of Dover[2]), where they are picked out by bands of hard black nodules called flints. The bedding planes in the Chalk are rarely tilted very much, indicating that this rock has not been severely crumpled in the 70 million years since it was formed. This is typical of most sedimentary rocks in Lowland Britain, although there are exceptions, such as along the south Dorset coast near Lulworth[3]. For the most part these rocks have been piled one on the other over tens of millions of years as the sea repeatedly invaded and withdrew, rather like a stack of carpets in a warehouse with the oldest at the bottom of the heap and the youngest at the top. These rocks were then gently tilted to the east, so that the youngest is in the east and the oldest appears from beneath the pile only in the west. When the process of erosion set to work on such a situation, the tougher layers stand out as ridges separated by vales excavated in the weaker rocks. Each of the ridges is not symmetrical but has a gentle slope down the direction of tilting (down the 'dip' of the rocks) and a steep slope at its eroded limit (Fig 2.6). The steep slope is known as an escarpment or scarpslope and the shallow slope the dip-slope or back-slope. The same shape can be formed when magma is forced along the bedding plane separating two sedimentary rocks to form a sheet of intrusive igneous rock known as

*FIG 2.5 The distribution of sedimentary and metamorphic rocks in the British Isles.*

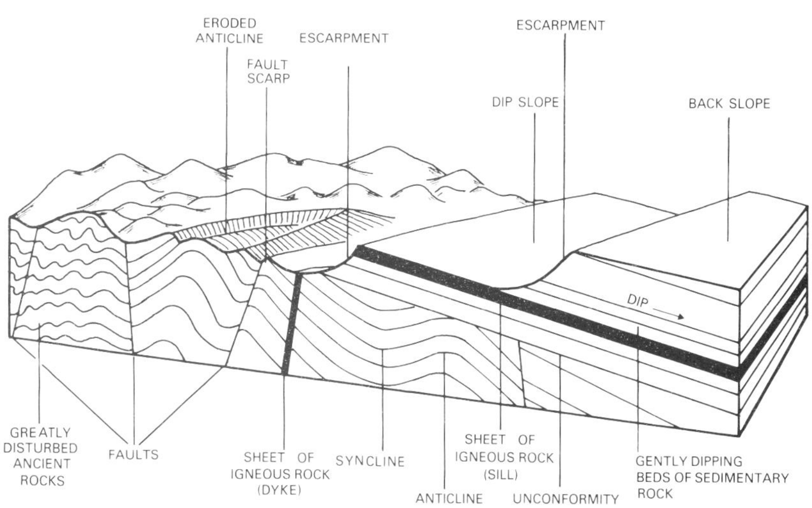


*FIG 2.6 The main landscape features associated with sedimentary rocks.*

*PLATE 2.4 The Whin Sill in Cumbria. A sill is a sheet of igneous rock which has been intruded between two layers of sedimentary rock. In this case all the rocks have subsequently been tilted downwards towards the right so that the sill comes to the surface at an angle. As a consequence, it now forms a 'cuesta', with gentle dip-slope declining to the right and much steeper escarpment or scarp slope falling away to the left. Similar shaped ground is developed on relatively hard sedimentary rocks. The crest of the Whin Sill provides an easily defended site with respect to attacks from the north (the left in the photograph) which is why the Romans built Hadrian's Wall along part of its length.*

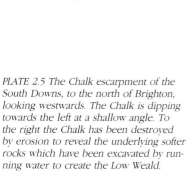

*PLATE 2.5 The Chalk escarpment of the South Downs, to the north of Brighton, looking westwards. The Chalk is dipping towards the left at a shallow angle. To the right the Chalk has been destroyed by erosion to reveal the underlying softer rocks which have been excavated by running water to create the Low Weald.*

a sill. The famous Whin Sill in Cumbria, as shown in Plate 2.4, is capped by Hadrian's Wall. The scarp is facing to the left, the dip-slope declining to the right, and it is clear that the molten magma was pushed in from right to left.

Sequences of scarps and vales are characteristic of Lowland Britain and any traveller should be well familiar with these 'belted landscapes' (Plate 2.5). Particularly fine bold west-facing escarpments occur where the Cotswolds[1] tower above the Vales of Severn[2] and Evesham[3], the Chiltern Hills[4] fall steeply to the Vales of Oxford and Aylesbury[5] and where the Lincoln Edge[6] stands like a straight wall above the Vale of Trent[7]. Indeed, most favourite viewpoints will be from the crests of escarpments (eg Leith Hill[8], Box Hill[9], Devil's Dyke[10]).

But travel further to the west, to the more ancient sedimentary rocks of Highland Britain, and the picture becomes confused. Here the contorted [illegible]

First, the bending and stretching of rocks when they are folded causes them to crack, as is shown in Plate 2.6, thereby creating complicated patterns of joints which can be exploited by agents of erosion. These joints differ from those most frequently seen in the gently tilted rocks of Lowland Britain (Plate 1.3), the majority of which were created when the material dried and contracted after being lifted up above the level of the sea in which it accumulated. Their presence is nevertheless of crucial importance, for they weaken the rock and make it vulnerable to destruction.

*PLATE 2.6 An upfold clearly developed in the hard rocks of the Pembroke coast. The bending of the rock layers and the cracks (joints) created by the stretching are both clearly visible.*

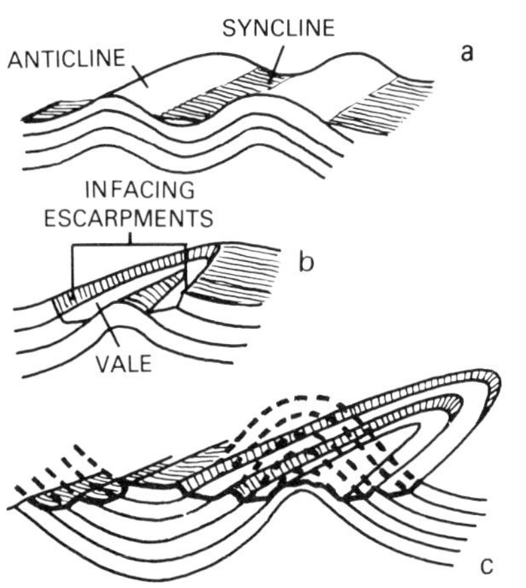


(a) Positive relationship between structure and relief
(b) Eroded anticline
(c) Eroded anticline with two sets of infacing escarpments and inverted relief produced by high ground preserved in syncline

*FIG 2.7 The patterns of topography that are created when erosion gnaws into folded sedimentary rocks. The right-hand part of diagram (c) is a simplified version of the structure-relief relationships displayed in the Weald of south-eastern England*

The second reason is that the presence of folds causes beds of rock to appear at the surface and then disappear again beneath the ground so as to produce complicated patterns of rock resistance. Sometimes the general shape of the landscape reflects the pattern of folds, with ridges formed by the anticlines and valleys following the synclines (Fig 2.7), as is well displayed in the Central Weald[4] of south-east England. At other locations erosion has gnawed through the arch of the fold to reveal softer rocks beneath. These have then been removed to produce a vale along the anticline bounded by high ground formed on the hard layer which continues to be preserved in the trough of the syncline (Fig 2.7). This is known as 'inverted relief' and is classically displayed in the Ouse Valley of Sussex, where the Vale of the Brooks[1] has been hollowed out of an anticline while the ridge of Chalk to the north, which terminates in Mount Caburn, is preserved in the complimentary syncline. Further erosion into the rock sequence may encounter another resistant bed of rock, so that a lozenze-shaped ridge appears within the core of the anticline, as in the Woolhope Dome[2] to the south-east of Hereford and at Crich[3], near Matlock. If denudation should continue yet deeper into the geological fabric, further weak and resistant layers will be encountered, so that a series of inward-facing scarps and vales will be created (Fig 2.7). Such patterns are classically developed in the Weald[4] and the Vale of Wardour[5], Wiltshire.

Features like these are widely developed in the highly disturbed rocks of Highland Britain, although the crumpling and crushing has often been so great that a good eye for landscape is required to pick out the scarps that reveal the presence of folds.

Sometimes the forces operating on the rocks were sufficiently powerful or sudden as to cause them to break. These breaks are known as faults (Plate 2.7) and can affect all rocks irrespective of nature or origin. Faults are not particularly common in Lowland Britain but are widespread in Highland Britain, especially in the areas underlain by the oldest rocks where they produce the aged appearance visible on space images (Plate 2.2). Occasionally one slab of the Earth's surface has been thrust over another, or the geological fabric has been ripped so that one area has slid past another like two pieces of an ice-flow that is breaking up in the spring thaw. The Great Glen of Scotland[6] marks the line of one such wrench fault – the Great Glen Fault (Plate 2.2) – for all the rocks on the northern side appear to have moved south-westwards some 105km (65 miles) compared with those to the south, so that the two sides of the valley do not match. However, most faults plunge steeply into the earth (gravity faults) which has the effect of bringing markedly contrasting rock materials together at the surface (Plate 2.7).

All faults represent lines of weakness that are exploited by erosion. Frequently they are followed by rivers so that excavation by water and by ice results in the creation of valleys whose direction is guided by the faults. Such fault-guided valleys are widely developed in Central Wales[7] and the Highlands[8] of Scotland, and it is this that accounts for the graining that is so apparent on the space image (Plate 2.2). In other instances, erosion may remove the material on one side of a fault more rapidly than on the other, and this will eventually create an escarpment (a fault-line escarpment). The most dramatic example of such a feature in the British Isles is in Cumbria, where the Cross Fell[9] escarpment towers up to 600m (1,970ft) above the Vale of Eden (Fig 2.8).

## ROCKS CHANGED BY EXPERIENCE

The scale and violence of the forces that must have gone into transfiguring the rocks of Highland Britain, in many instances also led to the original rocks being altered by the application of great heat or intense pressure to create new metamorphic rocks. Just as we turn clay into bricks, so convolutions within the earth changes the nature of existing rocks *but*

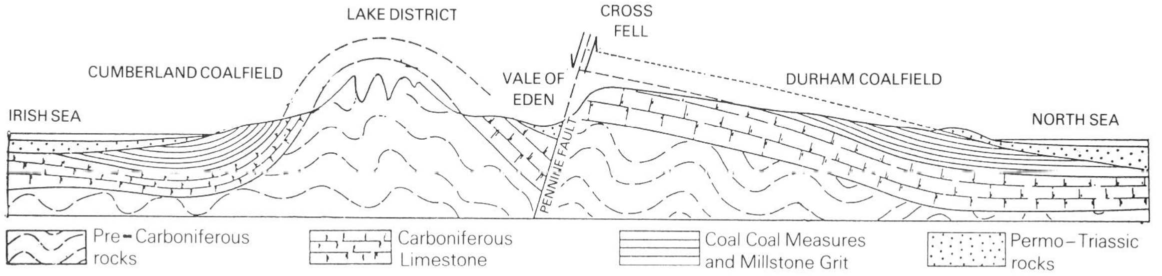


*FIG 2.8 A cross-section through the Lake District and Cross Fell to show how the Pennine Fault has greatly influenced the form of the landscape in this area.*

*without melting them* (if they were melted, new igneous rocks would be formed). Thus granite is converted to a rock known as gneiss which often appears spectacularly beautiful because of the complex banding of different colours; clay turns into slate; sands are altered to schist which [illegible]

[illegible]

[illegible] fabric of the British Isles, which is one reason why geological maps often appear like colourful abstract paintings. But don't be put off by the complexity, for there are patterns within the fabric. The most important of these is the change of rock character as one moves north-westwards. In Lowland Britain the fabric consists of young, relatively weak sedimentary rocks which have been but gently buckled. Over most of Highland Britain, a mix of igneous, sedimentary and metamorphic rocks have been crumpled and shattered on at least two separate occasions so as to provide the variable foundations that provide such scenic contrast. Travel to the extreme north-west and one passes onto terrains underlain by the most ancient rocks (up to 2,700 million years old) which have been so ravaged by events in the distant past that it is difficult to know what they were like before being repeatedly crushed and baked.

But do not consider for a moment that these variations in the character of the geological fabric means that Lowland Britain has been unaffected by major forces from within the Earth. Consider for a moment the white cliffs of Kent[1] and Sussex[2] (Plate 1.3) which mark the eroded stumps of the North and South Downs where they have been truncated by the development of the English Channel. The Chalk that forms these features rises high above present sea-level and reaches a maximum elevation of 297m (974ft) at Walbury Hill[3] in northern Hampshire. Yet the materials that form the Chalk, the remains of minute organisms similar to plankton, accumulated on the floor of a warm sea about 200m (650ft) deep. The rate of accumulation was slow, the thickness equivalent to the height of a man taking about 180,000 years to form, so there must have been relatively stable conditions for a long period of time in order that a layer of Chalk about 400 to 500m (1,300 to 1,650ft) thick could be created. However, since 70 million years ago when deposition ceased, the level of the sea in relation to the land must have changed dramatically, for the Chalk now forms hills (Plate 2.5). Indeed, in the case of Walbury Hill this change must have totalled about 500m (1,650ft). As the Chalk of southern England also shows some signs of buckling (eg the Weald, Fig 2.7), it has to be assumed that this alteration of elevation was largely due to tectonic forces from within the Earth's crust.

The geological fabric of both Highland and Lowland Britain contains many other signs of major changes in the relationship between land and

*PLATE 2.7 A steeply inclined gravity fault brings two very different rocks together on the coast at Portishead near Bristol. In this instance the rocks on the left have dropped several tens of metres (feet) compared with those on the right.*

*PLATE 2.8 An unconformity in the coastal cliffs at Newhaven, Sussex. The 'white' Chalk was laid down in deep water, the overlying brown Reading Beds were laid down in shallow water and the line separating the two is the unconformity. Unconformities are evidence for dramatic changes in the past. This unconformity is flat because it was trimmed by the sea before being buried by Reading Beds. By comparing the beds above and below the unconformity we can tell how old it is and what may have happened. In this case the Chalk is 80 million years old and the Reading Beds are 55 million years old, so the unconformity represents 25 million years of missing history, during which time the Chalk was physically raised by more than 200m (650ft) and the top 50m (165ft) was removed by erosion.*

sea which must be explained as the result of movements of the crust. The sedimentary rocks are not always laid one on the other in an orderly fashion: sometimes there is an abrupt change or break defined by a sharp boundary line known as an unconformity. The top of the Chalk is sometimes marked by the presence of such an unconformity, as at Newhaven[1] (Sussex) (Plate 2.8) where the line of unconformity clearly separates the white Chalk from the brown sand and gravels of the overlying Reading Beds. The Chalk was laid down in deep water (200m, 650ft), while the Reading Beds were deposited in shallow coastal waters (20-30m, 65-100ft). But there is more to the story. The Reading Beds have been dated as 55 million years old while the top of the Chalk visible in the cliff is about 80 million years old. Thus the line of the unconformity represents 25 million years of missing history! Only by studies of other areas with a fuller record preserved in the rocks is it possible to deduce what may have happened in those 25 million years. The most probable explanation is that the Chalk was uplifted to form dry land which was shaped by rain and rivers until the sea flooded the area again, trimming the surface flat and depositing the Reading Beds. Whatever the details, this series of events appears to have removed about 50m (160ft) of material, for that is the amount of Chalk that is missing.

As one travels westwards into Highland Britain, the unconformities change in appearance. The difference in character of the beds above and below the breaks becomes more marked, the time gap often stretches to hundreds of millions of years, thereby strongly suggesting that the amount of erosion increased to dramatic proportions. The one clear message that unconformities tell us is that erosion is not a new feature of the Earth's surface. Clearly landscapes have repeatedly evolved and been destroyed over hundreds of millions of years.

However, not all these ancient landscapes have been destroyed by the all-powerful sea. The huge outpourings of magma that flooded much of northern Ireland with lava some 66 million years ago (Fig 2.4), effectively buried the existing landscape of low hills and valleys beneath stone. The outpourings of lava were not continuous but came in three great pulses. Between each pulse, the surface of the newly solidified lava

sheet was sculptured by rivers, and weathered to produce soil upon which vegetation grew. These landscapes were also buried by the next flood of lava until exposed in quarries. They reveal leaf beds and red sub-tropical soils, which show that the climate was much warmer than today.

Two other examples, from England, are worth considering, because of their greater antiquity. Drive northwards along the M1 motorway and note how the landscape changes between Leicester and Nottingham. After miles of monotonous gently undulating 'scarp-and-vale' scenery, the motorway begins to climb over Charnwood Forest[2]: hills replace scarps, the orange soils of the Midlands become grey, dark rock appears at the surface and is well exposed in the road cuttings, huge quarries produce great noise and clouds of dust as machines break up the rock into usable-sized fragments, and the skyline is made irregular by upstanding masses of rock (tors). Clearly there has been a sudden and dramatic change in the [illegible]

The Malvern Hills[5] have a similar history (Plate 2.9). Here is another old hill chain composed of very ancient rocks which was also buried by Triassic desert sediments and has been exhumed by recent erosion. Both the Malvern Hills and Charnwood Forest are therefore ancient elements in a modern landscape. They are the oldest elements in the palimpsest, undergoing slow change under present conditions but mainly reflecting the circumstances of the past.

*PLATE 2.9 The Malvern Hills. This north-south ridge was shaped in ancient Precambrian rocks prior to being buried in the Triassic (225–190 million years ago). It is now being re-exposed at the surface by the action of erosion, which is stripping away the cover of weaker rocks to reveal the broad outlines of this ancient feature.* (Full-size illustration on pp 30-1)

Other examples exist, many of which are smaller in size. The shapes of some of the limestone hills in Derbyshire largely reflects the form of ancient reefs buried within the rock. The nearby Wynnats Pass[4], which looks for all the world like a gorge produced through the collapse of an underground cavern, is now considered to be an ancient sea-floor channel which was cut into the limestone as it accumulated over 300 million years ago. It later became choked with mud and has only recently been uncovered and the hardened mud removed.

Clearly there is more to the fabric than at first meets the eye, for the Wynnats Pass[4] appears similar to Cheddar Gorge[5] and yet their origins and ages appear very different. Thus similar looking landforms (features) can sometimes be produced by very different mechanisms. This often causes scientists to argue for years over the origins of features in the landscape.

## THE MANTLE OF SURFACE DEBRIS

The references to burial in the previous section should have struck a cord in the minds of many readers. This whole discussion about the complexity and significance of the geological fabric has failed to address the simple truth that in many areas of the British Isles the solid rock (bedrock) rarely appears at the surface. Indeed, over much of East Anglia the traveller has little or no idea what the bedrock may be, for the surface is shaped in sands and clays deposited by past ice-sheets, which although strong enough to form bluffs and cliffs where undercut by rivers and the sea, lacks the hardness of bedrocks.

These generally loose and varied materials that mantle the underlying bedrock are known as superficial deposits. They represent the debris produced through erosion in one area which have been dumped in their present location because the agents of change – wind, water, ice or the sliding and sludging of materials downslope – did not have the energy to carry them any further. They represent convincing evidence that sculpturing processes have been at work shaping the landscape, rather like the pile of wood shavings beneath a carpenter's bench. But just as the wood shavings will be swept away before much time has elapsed, so too will the superficial deposits be reworked by water, wind and ice to be dumped in new locations until eventually the material reaches the sea where it can accumulate in relative peace. Thus the superficial deposits of today are the rocks of tomorrow. They represent a stage in what is known as 'the rock cycle' which involves the accumulation of material to form rocks, the uplift of rocks so that they can be attacked by sculpturing processes, and the transport of the broken pieces across the earth to where they can accumulate and eventually become new rocks.

Superficial deposits are extremely widespread in the British Isles. It has recently been estimated that a mantling of material over 2m (6.5ft) thick covers 35 per cent of England, 30 per cent of Wales, 59 per cent of Scotland and 70 per cent of Ulster. In many areas, however, the blanket of superficial deposits exceeds 25m (80ft) in thickness so that the nature of the terrain developed on the bedrocks is completely obliterated. Remove these materials and the lower lying parts of Cumbria[1], Durham[2] and Northumberland[3] would look very different, much of the Cheshire Plain[4] and East Anglia[5] would be under the sea, and Romney Marsh[6], the Fens[7] and the Somerset Levels[8] would revert to bays and estuaries.

Nearly all superficial deposits are young by geological standards, most being the products of the repeated warming and cooling of climate that has characterised the last 2 million years of these islands' evolution (see Fig 1.4). Their character and distribution varies depending on the processes that created them and the rocks from which they originated. The most widespread is boulder clay, otherwise known as drift (Plate 2.10), a variable mixed deposit consisting of all sizes of material from clay through to boulders, which is what is left behind by an ice-sheet when it melts. The meltwater produced by the ice-sheet often reworked the boulder clay, so that the coarser materials were deposited as layers of gravel in the floors of valleys, while the finer materials were transported further downstream. Because of the lack of vegetation during the cold phases (see Chapter 4), much of the fine material (particularly the silt-sized particles) were picked up by the wind and deposited in thick layers of loess (Plate 2.11), rather like a covering of pale-orange snow. Later erosion has removed much of the original cover of loess from the slopes of hills and redeposited it on the valley floors where it is an important component of alluvium, the loose fill of sediment that forms the flat-floor (floodplain) of many lowland river valleys (Fig 1.2). The extensive and thick (up to 30m, 100ft) alluvial spreads that form the Fens, Somerset Levels and Romney Marsh have also accumulated in the last 9,000 years and consist of redeposited loess, fine-grained materials eroded by rivers, silts brought in by the sea, and organic remains (peats).

*PLATE 2.10 A characteristic deposit of boulder clay as seen in County Down. Boulder clay is a very mixed deposit consisting of all sizes of material from clay to boulders, which is dumped by ice-sheets. It is very widespread and in some areas exceeds 30m (98ft) in thickness (Fig 1.5).*

Landsliding has affected many escarpments in the past and left a chaotic jumble of debris on the lower slopes. The passage of time has smoothed over many of the features (see Chapter 7), but the presence of irregular, 'rippled' slopes is a good indicator of past ground movement. Material also slipped and sludged downslope during periods of permafrost, leaving a mixed deposit known as head in valley floors and along the base of escarpments (see Chapter 4). In the case of the Chalk, the head produced is white in colour and known as 'coombe rock'.

The Chalk downlands also contain two further superficial materials of interest. The dissolving action of rainwater removes the limestone but leaves behind the impurities, including the flints. These impurities, when mixed with the remains of any overlying deposits such as the Reading Beds

shown in Plate 2.8, produce a deposit known as Clay-with-flints (Plate 1.9). It is the occurrence of Clay-with-flints which accounts for the blotchy colour of ploughed fields in chalklands.

The other chalkland superficial material of interest is much more fascinating and enigmatic. Visitors to the famous stone circles at Stonehenge[1] and Avebury[2] (Plate 2.12) are often impressed by the great size of the up-ended blocks of material known as sarsen stone. Sarsens are a form of very hard sandstone, and blocks can be found littered on the surface of some downlands (eg the Marlborough Downs[3]) in such profusion that they appear from a distance like a flock of sheep, hence the old name 'grey wethers'. Although many have been cleared for use as building stone, they can still be seen on pastures and in those valleys where they have been concentrated by slope movements (eg Piggledene and Lockeridge, [illegible]

[illegible]

It is clear that the geological fabric and the superficial deposits that mask it, contain evidence of a long and complex evolutionary history involving a succession of traumatic episodes. The rocks show signs of being uplifted, buckled, crushed and torn; of enormous volcanic eruptions and deep innundations by the sea; and of ancient climates ranging from tropical to arctic. To describe in detail the full complexity of this evolutionary history requires greater time and space than is available here, but it is nevertheless possible to provide a general guide to the sequence of events that have led to the development of such scenic variety (Table 2.1). However, an appreciation will only be gained if four key aspects are understood from the outset.

First, geological time appears virtually endless from the human perspective. The Earth's age is estimated at a mind-boggling 4,600 million years. Of this time, the first 700 million years of the youthful, hot Earth's existence will always remain a mystery as no evidence can possibly have survived. Doubtless the surface was a most hostile place, contorted by huge volcanic upheavals and bombarded by meteorites and comets. Indeed, in the case of the British Isles, little evidence has been found to help us understand what happened before 1,000 million years ago, and the real record of the rocks only begins about 600 million years ago. If we draw an analogy with a 24-hour clock and make the history of the Earth fit into one day, this means that the day has been a virtual blank until early evening between 6 and 7 o'clock (18.47) and there are only very hazy recollections before about 9 o'clock (20.52 to be exact).

It is this last relatively brief episode of Earth history that has been subdivided to form the geological time-scale (Table 2.1, see page 52). Everything prior to 600 million years ago is normally lumped together under the name Precambrian, although other divisions do exist. The last 600 million years has been divided into a hierarchy of units by geologists in just the same way as the history of a country is divided by a historian. Thus, the three main lengths of time known as the Palaeozoic, Mesozoic and Caenozoic – the eras – are the equivalent of the Dark Ages, the Middle Ages or the long periods when monarchs of the Houses of Tudor or Hanover occupied the throne of England. But in the case of the geological time-scale, the divisions are based on the state of evolved life. *Palaeo-* means 'time of old life' when organisms developed in the oceans and then colonised the

*PLATE 2.11 During the arctic phases of the Ice Age, the lack of vegetation meant that the wind could relatively easily move small particles. Dust storms must have been fairly frequent because thick surface deposits of silt-sized material are common on the Continent. This material is called loess although the term 'brick-earth' has often been used. It forms the orange layer at the top of this cliff at Pegwell Bay, Kent, where it locally exceeds a thickness of 6m (20ft). However, patches of loess are not common in the landscape and it is thought that most of the original material has been removed by erosion and deposited in the floors of river valleys where it helps make the floodplains (Fig 1.2).*

land; *meso-* refers to 'middle life' which culminated with the land areas dominated by huge reptiles such as Brontosaurus and Tyrannosaurus that now provide the focus of attention in museums of natural history; finally, *caeno-* indicates 'present life'. It was during this last-mentioned brief span of time beginning a mere 65 million years ago, or at 23.40 on our clock, that two very important things happened. Man first appeared on Earth about 10 million years ago (23.57) and the Ice Age began 2.4 million years before present (BP), or the equivalent of a mere 47 seconds before midnight!

These 'eras' are then divided into shorter units of time known as 'periods' (eg the Jurassic), equivalent to the reign of a monarch in history (eg Henry VIII), and finally epochs.

The second point concerns the fact that the British Isles have not always been their present shape. Indeed, over the majority of geological time there existed dramatically different patterns of land and sea. At many times the present land areas were flooded by the sea, and it was during these occasions that most of the sedimentary rocks that underlie the contemporary landscape were deposited.

The third dimension, and one that many readers may find difficult to grasp, is the ability of the Earth's surface to experience vertical movements of enormous scale. The throwing up of huge mountain ranges the size of the Alps or Himalayas requires considerable feats of imagination, but to suggest that events of a similar magnitude may have occurred in our record often leads to exclamations of disbelief. And yet the highly contorted and altered rocks of Highland Britain suggest that this is indeed the case. There are, in addition, signs of spectacular vertical movements which are quite separate from those involved in the building of mountain ranges. For example, the North Sea Basin between these islands and Scandinavia has subsided by over 3km (1.8 miles) in the last 180 million years. Similarly, the present extent of the Irish Sea[1], Cardigan Bay[2] and the Bristol Channel[3] have all been determined by vertical movements on a grand scale, with the collapse of portions of the Earth's crust to create the present sea floors.

But the fourth point is without question the most challenging. It involves the appreciation that the British Isles have not always been where they are today.

One of the most exciting scientific developments of the last twenty-five years has been the discovery that the Earth's crust is not continuous and stationary, but consists of a number of rigid slabs (plates) about 100km (60 miles) thick which slide over a hot, weak 'plastic' layer called the asthenosphere. These plates are in fact composed of three layers of rock which together form the lithosphere. The bottom is formed of heavy, dense material known as the upper mantle. Above this lie the two layers that make up the crust. The lower crust is composed of a dark, heavy rock similar in composition to basalt and generally known as 'sima', which underlies the floors of the oceans but is elsewhere concealed beneath a discontinous, lighter, 'granite-like' material which forms the continents (usually called 'sial').

Heat generated within the Earth causes material from the underlying soft asthenosphere to push upwards, as magma, along some of the boundaries between plates. The heat causes the edges of the plates in these areas to turn upwards and so form the network of huge mid-oceanic ridges. The cracks caused by this bulging allow the magma to reach the surface and cool to form new ocean floor, thus accounting for the name 'constructive margins'. This, in turn, causes great pressures to build up in the plates. As the Earth does not appear to be expanding, it follows that the creation of new crust in these areas must be balanced by destruction in others. In these areas of destruction (subduction zones), the leading edge of one plate is pushed down beneath another so that material can be returned to the asthenosphere. These 'destructive margins' are the sites of consid-

*PLATE 2.12 Upended sarsen stones forming part of the megalithic stone circle of Avebury. These sarsens were once part of a sheet of cemented material that developed within the soil 30 to 50 million years ago when the British Isles had a tropical climate.*

erable convolutions because the movements involve thick slabs of cold, rigid material. There is much friction (earthquakes) and considerable crumpling (mountain building), together with volcanic activity where the sinking material is remelted to form magma. The Andes Mountains of South America are an excellent example of what can happen along an active destructive margin.

Thus the plates are in continual motion, being created in some areas, destroyed in others or simply sliding one against another along huge tears in the Earth's crust like the San Andreas Fault in California. As the plates include both continental blocks (sial) and underlying ocean floor material (sima), their motion results in the phenomenon known as 'continental drift'. Should a continental block be moved to the edge of a plate it may be involved in a collision with another continental block located at the edge of the other plate, in which case enormous mountains are created (eg the Himalayas were squeezed up as a result of India colliding with the southern margin of Asia). As it appears to be very difficult to drag continental material down into the earth, such a collision stops the system operating. This leads to overheating within the asthenosphere and new areas of upward moving magma are created (hot plumes) which break through the lithosphere to create new plate boundaries and new directions of movement. Thus the fabric of the continents which merely sit on these plates are moved about over the surface of the globe, sometimes coming together via a number of collisions to be welded into a super-continent, at other times being broken up into smaller and smaller fragments which drift apart and become separated by ocean basins.

When these notions are applied to the British Isles, the results are truly startling. The northern part of the Atlantic Ocean has only been in existence for the last 100 million years (since 23.29 on our clock). One could have walked from Ireland to North America 150 million years ago, or Scotland to Greenland for that matter, and the journey would not have taken long for they were both located adjacent to the British Isles (Fig 2.9). Then came the hot plumes from the asthenosphere, the crust bulged and split, huge

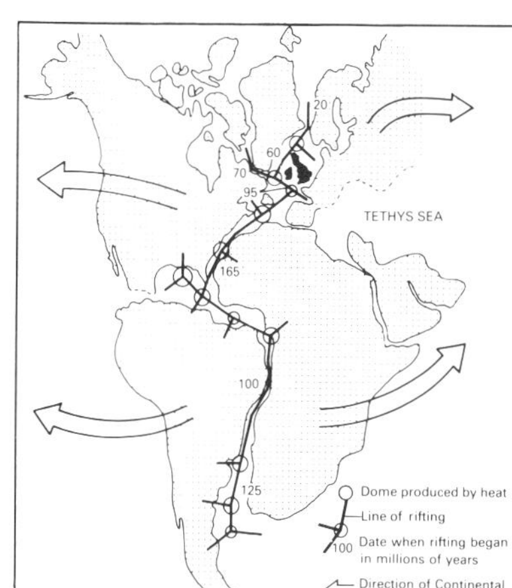


*FIG 2.9 The Supercontinent of Pangaea as it appeared 200 million years ago just prior to the start of rifting that was to create the Atlantic Ocean Basin of today.*

upswellings of magma spilt onto the earth (the plateau basalts of Antrim, northern Ireland) and the plates moved apart to create the Atlantic Ocean Basin which has been widening ever since at a rate of 2-3cm (.8-1.2in) per year.

But this is not the first Atlantic Ocean. Around 500 million years ago (ie 21.23 on our clock) there had existed another 'Atlantic Ocean' which is known as the Iapetus Ocean (Fig 2.10). But in this instance, what are now Scotland and Northern Ireland were attached to Greenland and Canada on one side of the ocean, while England, Wales and Eire were on the other. Thus there is basic truth in the observation that northern Scotland has a greater similarity to eastern Canada than to England! It was only as a consequence of the closing of this ocean basin that the underlying foundations of the British Isles became welded together about 400 million years ago (21.55). And what a powerful weld it was. The collision threw up an enormous mountain system – the Caledonian Mountains – equal in size to the Alpine-Himalaya chain of today, remnants of which stretch from Norway, through Scotland and eastern Greenland to the Appalachian Mountains of the USA.

These are merely episodes in a long sequence of rupturing and collision that have affected the British Isles. Mountains have been thrown up and then destroyed by erosion to create huge volumes of debris. This debris has accumulated in shallow seas only to be thrown into new mountains by collisions caused by the restless motion of the Earth. It is the power from within that causes the repetitive cycle of mountain building, and although the mountain ranges are destroyed in time, the signs of their

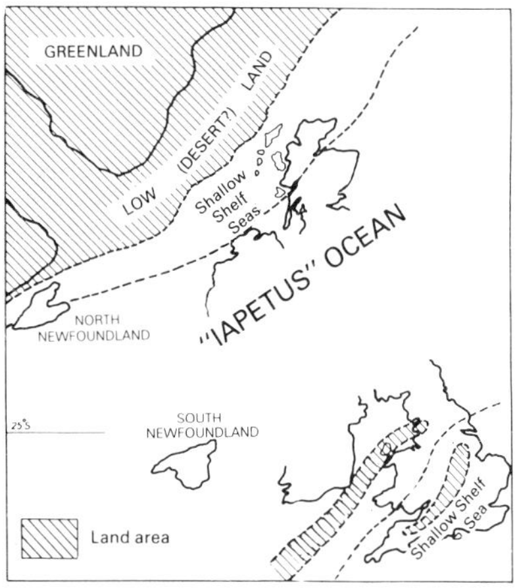


*Fig 2.10 Reconstruction of the earlier Atlantic Ocean or Iapetus Ocean as it is known, which finally closed with a collision of continents about 400 million years ago and so created the Caledonian Mountain system.*

*Table 2.1. Geological Time*

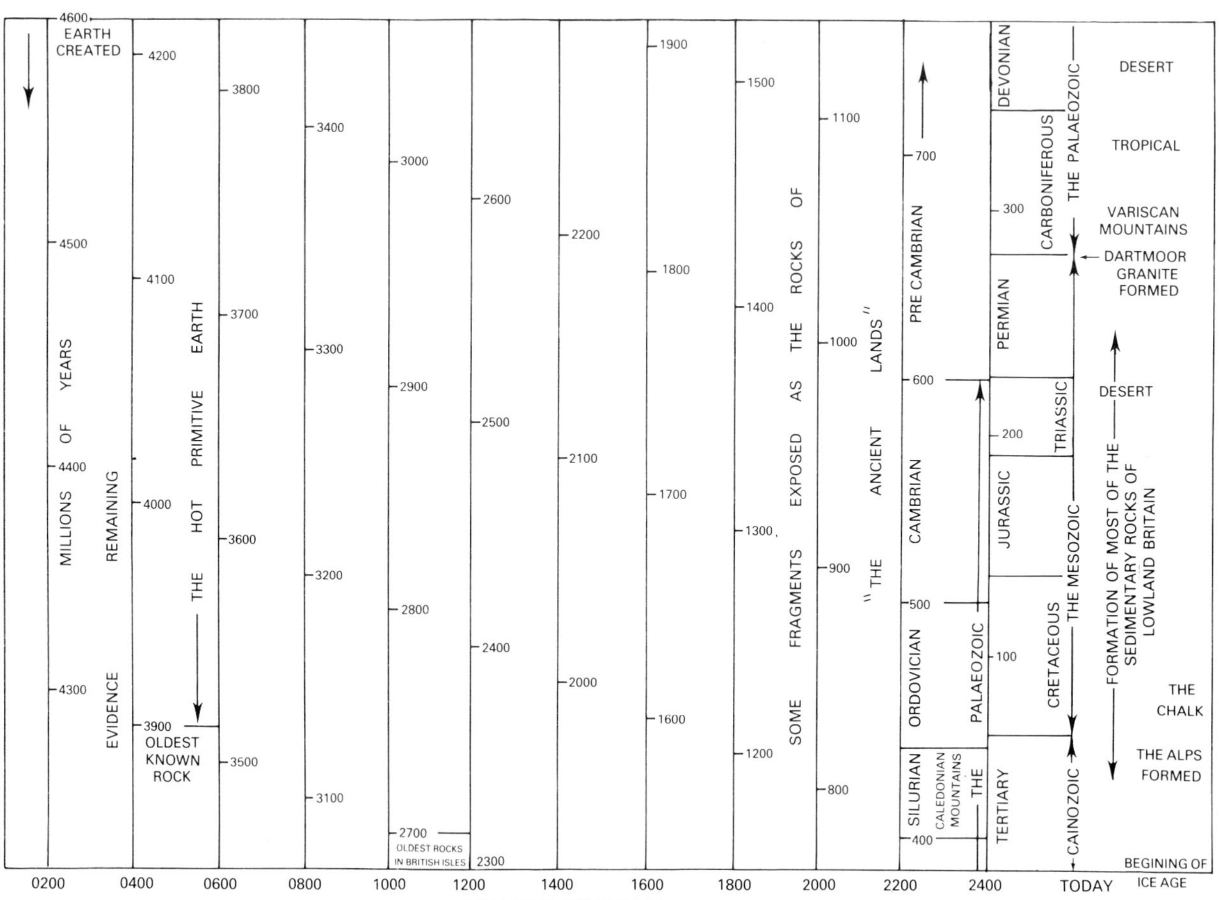

former existence lives on in the folds and faults within the fabric. These are the scars of happenings long past and their presence provides lines of weakness and strength in the land and therefore greatly influences the form of today's landscape. Thus the Great Glen has been gouged out along the Great Glen Fault[1] which last moved in that calamitous collision over 400 million years ago.

It would be arrogant to assume that the southern half of the British Isles has remained stationary, motionless, while the rest of the world jostled about on their moving plates. Where these islands were before 500 million years ago, or 21.23 on our fateful day, seems to have slipped their memory, for the first recollections as pieced together by eminent doctors, places them deep in the southern hemisphere at a latitude of about 45 degrees. Since then, they have drifted northwards and westwards to their present locations, while at the same time colliding with and moving round other [illegible] and the red muds of the Midlands accumulated. By then we had reached a position equivalent to that occupied by the present Sahara.

This northward drift was to continue to the present, slowly taking these islands from tropical conditions through to temperate climes. Indeed, it is continuing today with a northward movement of about 11km (7 miles) every million years. But it had another, far more significant implication. This northward motion was to carry these islands within striking distance of the huge ice-sheets that were to develop in the forthcoming Ice Age. Indeed, the slow encroachment of land areas into high latitudes may well have been an important contributory factor in the development of the extensive Pleistocene ice-sheets.

## THE DIVISIONS OF THE FABRIC

We have already observed that the geological fabric of the British Isles is composed of rocks that become younger as one travels from north-west Scotland to south-east England, almost as if succeeding layers had been piled one on the other and then pushed over so that they became inclined towards the east. This is roughly what has happened, for the western parts of the British Isles were raised by the pressures created as the Atlantic Basin opened over the last 100 million years, while the east has undoubtedly sunk because of the subsiding North Sea Basin.

The various layers of rock that are now exposed differ depending on what they are made of, how they were formed, when they were formed, and the way in which they have been crumpled and torn in later life. Scientists can use these criteria to make innumerable divisions, but for the purposes of understanding the landscape, four basic groupings will prove quite satisfactory (Fig 2.11). The main distinguishing features of each group are the age of the rocks and the ways in which they were contorted and altered by the three mountain-building episodes that have affected these islands.

### THE ANCIENT LANDS

Ancient (Precambrian) rocks undoubtedly underlie the whole of the British Isles, forming what some geologists call 'the basement' upon which later

*FIG 2.11 The fundamental four fold division of the geological fabric of the British Isles.*

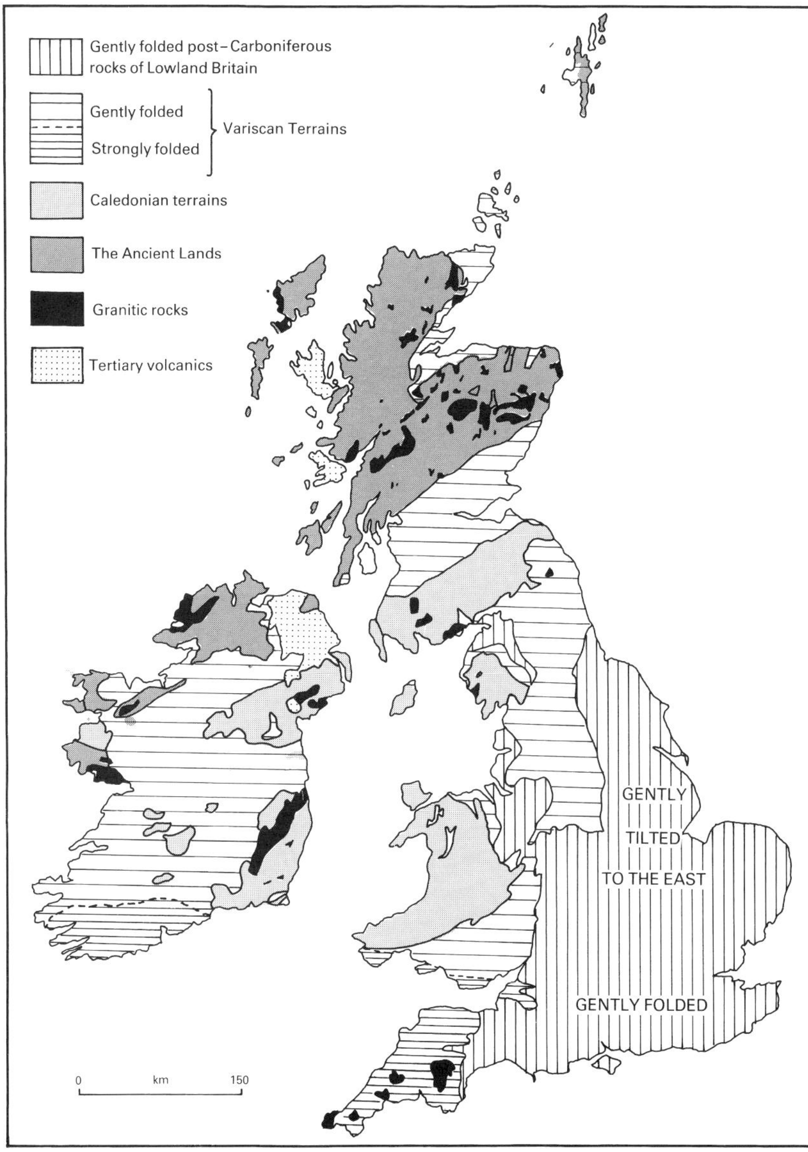


(younger) rocks have been piled. This basement appears at the surface in the Scottish Highlands and Islands (except the Orkneys), Ulster, Donegal and parts of County Mayo, and includes the oldest part of our rocks, the gnarled Lewisian Gneiss of Sutherland and the Isle of Lewis, which has been dated at 2,700 million years or more than half the age of the Earth! These are the rocks that were originally attached to Canada and Greenland (Fig 2.10), and they still bear the scars of the calamitous collision that caused them to become welded to the remainder of the British Isles some 400 to 500 million years ago. They were intensely heated and crushed at that time so that the original rocks were converted to metamorphic rocks. They were also severely buckled as the two continents came together, throwing up the huge Caledonian Mountain range in a similar fashion to material being squeezed between the jaws of a vice. The original mountains have long since been removed by erosion so that all we see today are the foundations dotted with masses of granite where bubbles of magma cooled several kilometres below the surface 400 million years ago. But the patterning of folds still remains, and their alignment NE – SW provides a graining to the landscape because it controls where harder and softer bands of rock appear at the surface to be exploited by wind, water and ice. The most pronounced NE – SW graining, however, is provided by the huge tears (faults) that were developed at the same time and which have been exploited by the ice-sheets to create the Great Glen[1] and other valleys clearly visible from space (Plate 2.2).

These tough, ancient rocks of our foundations impart a quite distinctive character to the landscapes developed upon them, although the nature of the rocks themselves create variety. Thus the more rounded outlines of the Cairngorms[2], developed on granite, cannot be confused with the jagged peaks formed by quartzite or with the incredibly steep-sided 'island mountains' of Sutherland[3] developed on the ancient Torridonian Sandstone.

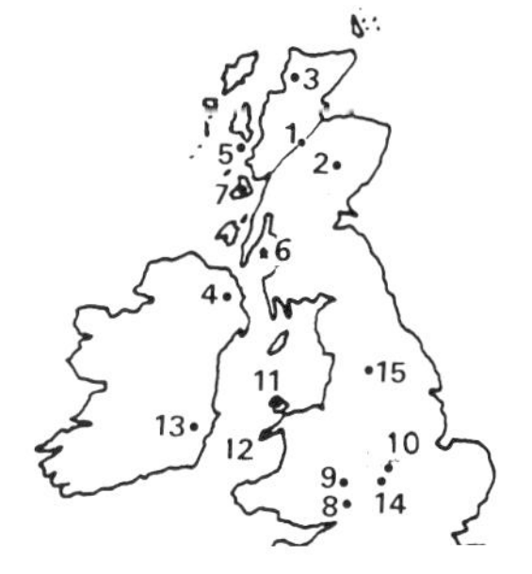


That there are still 'mountains' in this area, albeit dwarfs by comparison with the great ranges of towering peaks created after the original colli- [illegible] on Arran[6] and Mull[7], now wholly destroyed except for their roots.

Those who are fascinated by these ancient foundations do not necessarily have to travel to the north-west fringe of the British Isles to see rocks of Precambrian age. The Precambrian basement underlies the whole of these islands at depth, and occasionally pokes up to the surface through the cover of younger rocks. It forms the Malvern Hills[8], the Longmynd[9] and Charnwood Forest[10]. It can also be seen in Anglesey[11], the Lleyn Peninsula[12], and at Rosslare[13] in south-east Ireland. A splinter comes to the surface as the Lizard Peninsula in Cornwall, and further glimpses can be obtained at such unexpected locations as Nuneaton[14], Warwickshire, and Ingleborough[15], North Yorkshire.

CALEDONIAN TERRAINS

When North America-Greenland collided with Europe about 400 million years ago, the materials that had accumulated in the ocean that formerly separated the two continents were crumpled and crushed to create the Caledonian Mountains. These materials are now exposed as the Southern Uplands of Scotland, the Lake District, the Isle of Man, much of Wales and in eastern Ireland (Fig 2.11). We are, of course, looking at the foundations of the former mountain system, for the granites of Dumfriesshire (Criffell)[1] and Wicklow[2] solidified from magma deep below the surface. The shock of the collision was less severe in these areas than in the ancient terrains further north, so only a few of the rocks were altered by heat and pressure, the most notable example being the clays that were squeezed to form the famous slates of Blaenau Ffestiniog[3]. For the most part the rocks are sedimentary rocks (sandstones, shales and limestones) with occasional masses of volcanic lava (eg the Borrowdale Volcanics that form the Langdale Pikes[4] in the Lake District). They are crumpled and torn with the same NE – SW orientation as the rocks further north, and this has imparted a distinctive graining to many of these landscapes. Indeed, the main river valleys of south-central Wales show this alignment very clearly because they have been gouged out along major faults.

VARISCAN TERRAINS

Following the Caledonian upheaval, the extensive ranges of true, high mountains were eroded under desert conditions. Huge spreads of sand

and gravel accumulated in lowlands and can be seen today in the red soils and building stones used in Herefordshire[1]. Later, much of the British Isles was invaded by the sea and thick limestones accumulated. This is the Carboniferous Limestone that now underlies much of southern Ireland and also forms the Northern Pennines[2], the Peak District[3] and the Mendips[4]. Huge deltas then built out into the sea, the mixtures of sand and clay eventually becoming the Millstone Grit which forms much of today's Pennines. Eventually, the deltas were colonised by swamp forest and the accumulated vegetation debris survives as the Carboniferous Coal Measures.

These events were to set the stage for the next great upheaval about 300 million years ago. This time the collision zone was in the south. The restless movement of the crustal plates caused Africa to collide with Europe, resulting in the creation of a major range of mountains – the Variscan Mountains – stretching from eastern USA via southern Ireland and southern England to the Ardennes and central Europe. The folds and faults were orientated approximately E–W, a graining that is still clearly developed in the sequence of headlands and bays that make the south-western coast of Ireland so distinctive. Further east, a huge bubble of magma solidified deep beneath these Variscan Mountains some 280 million years ago, to form a mass of granite known as a batholith. This batholith underlies virtually the whole of Cornwall and much of Devon, and erosion has revealed upstanding projections to create a number of famous granite landscapes including Dartmoor[5] and Bodmin Moor[6].

Further to the north, the effects of this mountain-building episode were more complex. This was due to the presence of buried folds and faults dating from the earlier Caledonian mountains which had, by this time, been ground down to mere stubs. The most prominent development was the creation of the Pennines – the backbone of England.

## LOWLAND BRITAIN

The remainder of the British Isles is covered by young, relatively weak sedimentary rocks laid down over the past 250 million years. This is Mackinder's Lowland Britain, a gentle landscape developed on the sands, limestones and clays which were deposited in the shallow seas that repeatedly invaded this part of the British Isles. Over most of the area the rocks are gently tilted to the east so that the harder bands create belts of higher ground with escarpments (the Cotswolds[1], Lincoln Edge[2]) separated by lowlands excavated in the weaker clays. In the south, however, the rocks have been gently buckled, possibly as a consequence of the forces that have so recently thrown up the Alps. The great arch of the Weald[3], and the corresponding depressions of the London[4] and Hampshire Basins[5], bear testimony to these forces, and smaller folds can be clearly seen in places such as Stair Hole[6] in Dorset.

All these folds were formed in the period 70 to 20 million years ago. In some cases the arches have been completely destroyed, which points to the effectiveness of erosion in shaping the landscape. Take the Weald as an example. The Chalk that forms the North[7] and South[8] Downs is actually the eroded remnants of a continuous layer of rock that originally stretched over the Weald in the form of an irregular dome. Since the Chalk was uplifted from beneath the sea 70 million years ago, erosion has cut through the arch and into the older rocks below. Up to 1,050m (3,450ft) of rock has been removed. This works out at only 1.5cm (.6in) for every 1,000 years – insignificant from the perspective of human history but dramatic in the context of geological time.

There is one final point worthy of consideration. The boundary between Lowland Britain and the harder rock terrains of Highland Britain is irregular (Fig 2.2). Here we see further evidence of major vertical movements of the Earth's crust.

The landscape of the British Isles about 250 million years ago would have been unrecognisable. The Variscan Mountains stood like a huge wall across the south. In the north were the denuded stubs of the Caledonian Mountains, and between the two lay a jumble of huge tilted slabs of rock separated by hilly country where the rocks had buckled under the stress. The climate was arid, so the scenery would have been reminiscent of the south-west USA. When the forces that had created the Variscan Mountains began to relax, vast areas of the crust bounded by huge faults began to subside under the force of gravity. This was to establish the major patterns of highland and lowland that we see today. The various portions of Highland Britain have stayed relatively buoyant, while the intervening tracts of Lowland Britain and many of the adjacent areas, now covered by sea, represent areas of crust that have subsided over the last 250 million years. Thus Wales is a buoyant block surrounded by subsiding basins: Car- [illegible]

The creation of the geological fabric of the British Isles has been a long and complex process. Rocks have been repeatedly created, distorted and then partly destroyed. The debris produced through the destruction of rocks in one area has been used to create new rocks in other regions, and so the cycle has continued through the eons of geological time, slowly and remorselessly building up an ever increasingly complex fabric. Periodically, this fabric has been affected by cataclysmic changes involving the creation of mountain systems or the establishment of huge networks of cracks (faults), so that some areas have sunk dramatically compared with adjacent areas. It is this fashioning on a grand scale that has prepared the bold outlines and variable textures that have been fashioned by wind, water and ice to create the landscapes that we love. But remember this is just one assemblage of landscapes in a long and evolving sequence that have been developed since a recognisable crust formed in the dim and distant past: one frame in a very long and intricate movie that is actually only about halfway through its complete showing.

But why is the fabric of the British Isles as complex as it is? The answer lies in the fact that these islands have often lain on the margins of important events. Just as they lie today between a major ocean and a huge continent, so in the Ice Age they frequently lay partly beneath ice and partly under snow. The same is true of the geological past. A new ocean basin has been created immediately to the west of these islands in the last 100 million years. Mountain ranges have been thrust up in the north and the south, some areas have been disturbed by folding associated with the recent creation of the Alps, and the North Sea Basin to the east has steadily subsided over the last 180 million years. It is a complex history involving huge forces, but events have tended to affect different portions of these islands in turn – and here is the secret behind the amazing variety of scenery. Much of Scotland and northern Ireland are geologically similar to Norway, Greenland and eastern North America. The South West Peninsula is similar to Brittany and the Ardennes. Parts of southern England are like Picardy, the Brecklands could be mistaken for a minature Lüneburg Heath, and the Fens are for all the world like Holland.

The major belts of differing landscapes that occur within Europe come together in these small islands, and it is this that provides the basis for scenic variety.

3

# THE POWER OF ICE

Andrew Goudie and Rita Gardner

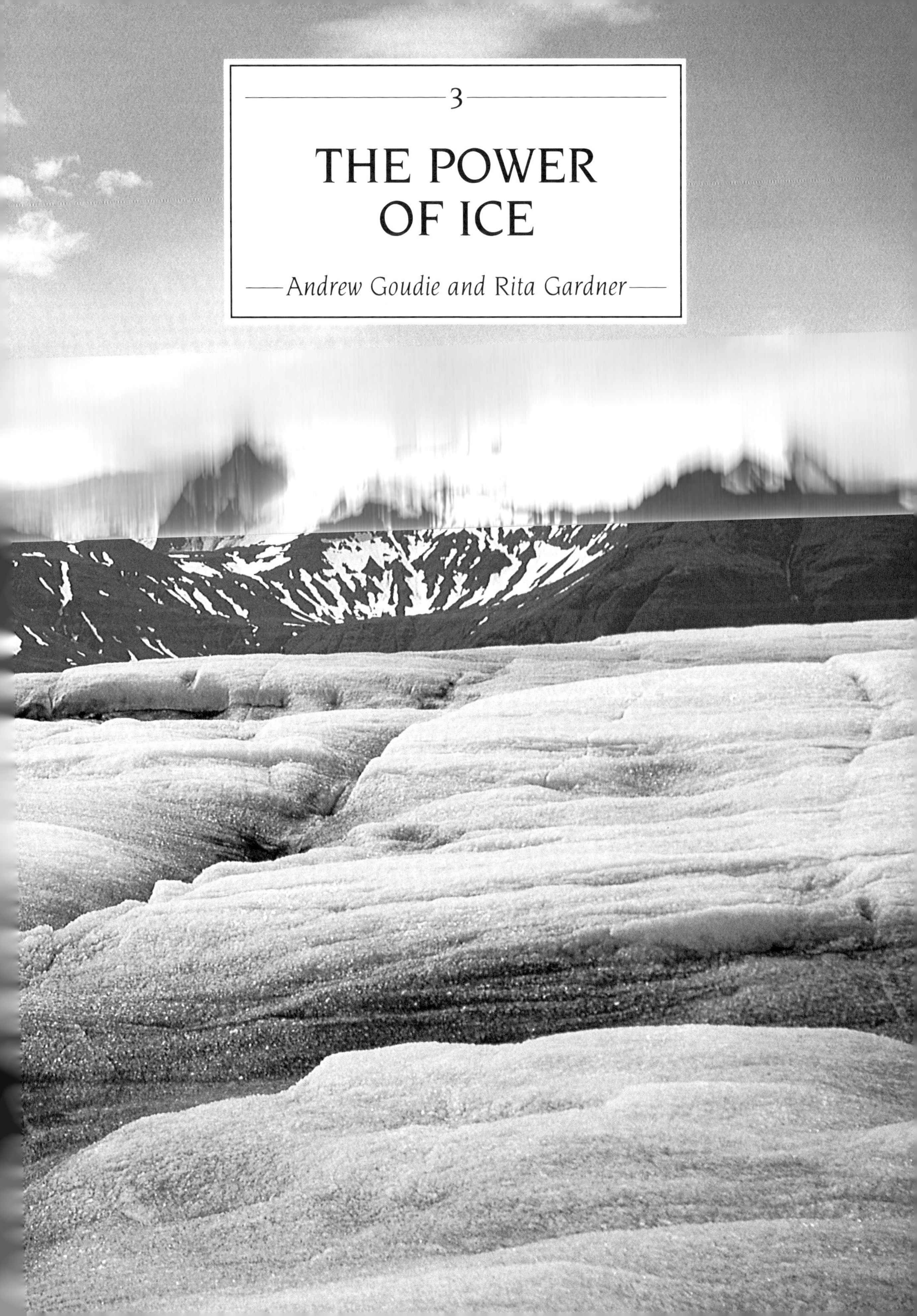

## THE POWER OF ICE

The Ice Age was not a single cataclysmic event but several separate periods of deep freeze which utterly transformed great tracts of the British Isles. The onset of each separate episode of harsh conditions witnessed the accumulation of truly enormous quantities of snow and ice, completely altering the appearance of these islands. Scotland, Wales, Ireland and northern and central England were at various times rendered unrecognisable by enormous blankets of ice. The scenery at these times would have been reminiscent of contemporary views of Spitzbergen or Antarctica: seemingly endless expanses of glistening white ice dazzlingly bright when the sun shone, with here and there small patches of dark, jagged rock rising above the surface where the summits of present-day hills and mountains had failed to be totally overwhelmed. Even as recently as 18,000 years ago the majority of the British Isles lay beneath hundreds of metres of ice (see Fig 1.6). One could have walked across the surface of the ice-sheet above the Lake District and not seen a single piece of rock – even the summit of Ben Nevis[1] was immersed by over 400m (1,300ft) of ice.

At the base of the ice the landscape was being transformed. On the one hand great valleys and hollows were being gouged out of tough rocks by its grinding power, elsewhere the debris quarried by the ice was being smeared over the landscape. Ice is capable of wholesale demolition and plastering on a scale that no other agents of change in the landscape can match. For example, Nant Ffrancon valley[2] in north Wales was carved out by ice, and much of the landscape of East Anglia[3] was built up by material being dumped by ice as it melted.

What made ice an even more potent force in fashioning the landscape was that the conditions existing 18,000 years ago were by no means unusual. Similar harsh conditions have persisted, on and off, for at least three-quarters of the last 2.5 million years. The degree of cooling and the extent of the ice varied. The most extensive ice accumulation is thought to have occurred about 270,000 years ago, when ice reached from the Highlands down to Essex[1], London[2], Oxfordshire[3], Bristol[4], north Devon[5] and the Scilly Isles[6] (Fig 3.1). Compare for example, the northern, smoothed and formerly ice-covered parts of the Scillies with the southern, craggier parts that were never covered by ice.

The last ice advance spanned the time from about 70,000 to 13,000 years ago. Although the landscape was cold and barren in the earlier stages, it was not until between 30,000 and 25,000 years ago that substantial glaciers developed in the highland valleys. By 18,000 years ago these had developed into large domes of ice, capping the highlands and extending as sheets of ice over the lowlands to the south and east as shown in Fig 3.1. At times the highlands would have looked like Iceland today (Plate 3.1).

It is rather surprising to learn that by 13,000 years ago the ice had largely disappeared – such a dramatic change in a mere 5,000 years. A short-lived cold hiccup from about 11,000 to 10,500 years ago then saw the return of ice to parts of the Scottish Highlands[7], the Lake District[8], Snowdonia[9] and the Brecon Beacons[10]. Over the past few thousand years conditions have been similar to those at present with the exception of short periods of slight cooling, such as between 1750 and 1850. These phases were not cold enough to lead to the formation of glaciers, but in the coldest winters the Thames froze over. The climate would only need to cool about 3°C for small glaciers to form again in the Scottish Highlands.

Relatively short warm interludes – like that of the past few thousand years – have separated the long periods of icy conditions. Indeed, it is likely that the ice will return once again in about 3,000 years' time, disrupting the landscape and freezing out any inhabitants in the north.

Given our icy history it is hardly surprising that much of the landscape was fashioned by glaciers and sheets of ice. But why did the ice only start to accumulate and invade our landscape about 2.5 million years ago? And why has the climate changed repeatedly from cold glacial phases to warm, ice-free interludes during this period?

The answer to the first question lies in the distribution of land masses around the surface of the Earth. As explained in Chapter 2, the Earth's crust is made up of a set of jigsaw-like plates of varying sizes – about twelve large ones and many smaller ones. Whilst some of the plates consist entirely of either ocean floor or of continent, most contain parts of both continental and ocean floor areas.

These plates all move relative to each other, very slowly, at no more than a few centimetres a year, but the effect of this over millions of years is to redistribute the land masses. About 50 million years ago Antarctica separated from Australia and slowly moved south to its present position over the south pole; at the same time the giant continent of Europe and Asia and the north American continent both moved towards the north pole. [illegible] and the cooling brought about by the ice itself, was sufficient to sustain the growth of ice-caps as far south as the British Isles.

Perched right at the limit of ice growth, our islands experienced the full impact of the fluctuating growth and melting of the ice. But the rapid fluctuations between warmer and colder conditions that were responsible for the growth and decay of the ice are caused by other factors, superimposed on the general cooling in climate.

It is known that the Earth's orbit around the sun changes in small, but regular and predictable ways. There are three aspects that change. The first is the path of the orbit, which varies from near circular to more elongated, and then back to near circular, and so on. One cycle of change takes 96,000 years. It has little effect on the total annual amount of sun's energy received, but it does affect the length and intensity of the seasons. The second aspect that changes is the angle of tilt of the Earth's axis. This varies from about 21.5 to 24.5 degrees and back again over a period of about 40,000 years. This too affects the intensity of the seasons, making winters colder and summers warmer when the tilt angles are high. This change is felt most intensely at higher latitudes. The last aspect of change is that the Earth wobbles like a top on its axis – the angle of axis stays the same but the axis swivels round. It takes between 19,000 and 23,000 years to complete one full swivel. A combination of swivel and change in the path of orbit determines the seasons at which the Earth is closest to the sun and furthest away.

All these factors taken together alter the seasons subtly; lengthening some seasons and shortening others, and intensifying some whilst weakening others. The effects vary depending on the stage in the various cycles that the Earth has reached at any particular time. It is thought that cool summers are most likely to lead to ice accumulation in the northern hemisphere. This is because snow falling in winter will not melt entirely in a cool summer, thus helping the snow to accumulate year after year. The bright snow cover, in turn, aids the cooling, as described before. Such cool summers occur when the angle of tilt of the axis is relatively low, and when the Earth is furthest away from the sun in the northern hemisphere summer.

The known variations in these factors in the past coincide remarkably well with the timing of warm and cold fluctuations on Earth. The best record of the climatic fluctuations comes from the materials that have

FIG 3.1 The extent to which ice covered Britain at three different times: the maximum extent; the last great advance around 18,000 years ago; and during the short cold hiccup around 11,000 years ago.

*PLATE 3.1 A glaciated landscape in Iceland. The photograph is taken standing on the Breidamerkurjokull (jokull means ice cap/glacier in Icelandic) and in the distance, behind the mountains, can be seen Oraefajokull.* (Full-size illustration on pp 58-59)

accumulated undisturbed on the sea floor. Unfortunately much of the direct evidence of ice growth and retreat on the land has been destroyed by later ice advances.

In the ocean it is the marine organisms that live close to the surface of the sea that best record temperature changes. They do this in two ways. First, the type of species or the proportions of different species can change as the oceans cool and warm up. Secondly, the detailed chemistry of their shells varies slightly, but in a regular way, according to the temperature and composition of the water that the shells grow in. Once the small creatures die, their shells sink to the ocean floor and accumulate in layers; oldest at the bottom and youngest at the top. This geological thermometer awaits the intrusion of man. By carefully extracting a core of material from the ocean floor, and then dating it, he can work out fluctuations in temperature of the surface waters at the times when the organisms were alive, by analysing the type of shells and their chemistry. More than 20 cold-warm-cold cycles have occurred in the past 2 million years, each one taking an average 100,000 years (see Fig 1.4). They look set to continue well into the future unless man alters the climate to a profound degree.

## THE FORMATION OF GLACIERS

If enough snow falls, and if it does not all melt during the heat of summer, gradually a glacier will form. But how does this remarkable transformation take place? The process starts when, as soon as snowflakes are buried by other snowflakes, they start to lose some of their delicate tracery. As the weight of snow above increases, the flakes are more and more compressed and air is expelled from between them; making a snowman has the same effect. As the ice crystals in the flakes are packed ever more densely together, typically the crystals amalgamate and grow, and individual crystals can eventually grow to be larger than tennis balls. In a matter of a few hundred years at most the snow is transformed into true, dense glacier ice. The transformation takes place most rapidly, sometimes in less than ten years, when the snow partly melts and refreezes directly to ice.

Once the ice has formed, gravity starts to play a role, and the ice slowly moves downslope. It does this partly by sliding, jerkily, over the rock beneath it, the sliding being facilitated by meltwater between the base of the ice and the rock. The film of water only needs to be a few millimetres thick for this to happen. The meltwater is formed by a combination of the heat given out by the earth, the pressure of the ice above, and the friction of ice moving across the rock. But the ice also moves by deforming inside the mass, in response to the pressure created by the weight of ice above. Particularly high pressure occurs when the ice is thick or where the slope of the ice is great. The ice responds to this pressure with a creeping movement – individual ice crystals move relative to each other, and the crystals themselves shear internally. The rate at which the ice creeps downhill depends on the amount of pressure and the temperature of the ice.

Considering both the sliding action and the creeping action together, it follows that most of the movement occurs at or near the base of the ice. The top layers are carried along on this conveyor belt. Where parts of the ice mass are moving at different speeds, or where not all the pressure can be absorbed by creeping, stresses are set up. These result in fractures (crevasses).

The glacier grows and advances so long as the supply of snow exceeds the rate of melting. Generally most of the snow accumulation takes place in the colder, upper parts of the glacier, whereas the melting dominates in the lower, end-portions, particularly at the snout. The glacier is like a giant sluggish machine in which snow is transformed to ice and then slowly transported down from the area of accumulation to the area of melting. In the process the glacier may emerge from its confining valley and coalesce with other streams of ice to create ice-sheets that spread across lowlands and even onto the sea's surface. As a consequence, ice may travel for thousands of miles before melting. The health of a glacier or ice-sheet thus depends on the amount of incoming snow, on how much of the incoming snow is transformed to ice, and on how much melting is taking place. It adjusts in extent and thickness according to the balance between accumulation and melting. As the climate changes so too does the balance, and the glacier/ice-sheet responds.

The rate at which glaciers move is controlled partly by the rate of accumulation. The thicker the ice, the greater the pressure, and the faster the movement. Where the ice is accumulating, the rate of movement generally speeds up downslope: but it slows down again towards the end of the ice [illegible]

On average, measured flow rates today can vary from 0.1m (4in) per day to 6m (20ft) per day on glaciers that are warm enough to have meltwater at the base. In general, ice-sheets, where the ice spreads out over the landscape and is not confined to valleys (as it is in glaciers), move more slowly. In extreme cases glaciers can advance more than 8km (5 miles) per year. In 1963 the Bruarjokull glacier in Iceland advanced at a startling rate of 5m (16ft 8in) per hour at times. This dramatic surging tends to occur after dramatic increases in accumulation or after rapid melting. At these times the normal balance between the amount of ice in the accumulation and melting zones is upset.

Although the ice clearly moves forwards and then melts and 'retreats' backwards, what does it achieve in shaping the landscape? The Victorian writer John Ruskin once remarked that a glacier was no more able to erode its valley than custard could erode a custard bowl. But he was wrong. Glaciers are not impotent masses of ice sitting in valleys, as is evident from the quantities of debris being continually carried out of the mouths of glaciers and ice-sheets by meltwater streams. The debris has to come from somewhere, and it indicates that glaciers are very effective at eroding the rocks over which they pass. In fact the volume of debris is enormous; the rate of erosion by ice is usually many times greater than that for rivers draining a similar area.

One of the most effective means of erosion is by meltwater, at the base of the ice, refreezing around protruding pieces of rock. As the ice moves on, the rock is plucked from its bed and incorporated into the bottom of the ice. Obviously it helps if the rocks have been weakened or loosened before the passage of ice, but even solid blocks can be removed in this way. Localised melting and refreezing often happens around small irregularities in the rock; the increased pressure in being forced against the rock causes the ice to melt, and the water then refreezes on the other side of the irregularity.

Once these boulders are incorporated into the base of the ice they act like landscape-sized sandpaper, scouring and grinding away at the rock beneath as they are dragged over the surface. Other material that happens to fall onto the surface of the glacier may be incorporated into the ice mass as it falls into crevasses, or it may sit passively on the ice, being carried on its cold conveyor belt. All this debris bound up in the

*PLATE 3.2 Great armchair shapes carved out of mountainsides in the Lake District by ice. In places all that remains of the former mountain slope is a razor-sharp ledge of rock. In the right background can be seen a U-shaped trough, formerly cut by ice.*

ice explains why glaciers so often appear a dirty grey colour, especially near their snouts.

Beneath many glaciers there are not just films of meltwater between the ice and the rock, but also concentrated streams of water that are confined into tunnels in the base of, and beneath, the ice. The water is under great pressure and flows at high speed, and is capable of eroding huge gorges out of the rock in some instances.

Glaciers are thus capable of great erosion. Moreover, they act as huge debris transporters, both in the ice and in the meltwater streams beneath. Eventually this debris must be dumped, either beneath the glacier or ice-sheet or at its margins. The erosion and the dumping create an array of landscapes unsurpassed in terms of grandeur, size and variety by any landscapes formed by rivers, the sea, the wind or gravity alone.

and all that remains of the former mountainside are the thin ledges along which the paths wind precariously. Imagine the sheer power needed to have carved these huge corries out of solid rock; yet it was all achieved by the ice plucking off rock fragments and grinding away at the rock, and by frost shattering the rocks above the level of the ice.

Characteristically, the result is a flat-floored hollow surrounded on three sides by very steep side and back walls (Plate 3.2). The smoothed shape has been likened to a giant armchair and, rather like a cushion in the chair, there is sometimes a small lake in the floor of the corrie. This happens either when the ice hollows out a basin in the rock floor, or where debris dumped as the ice melted creates a small natural dam across the entrance of the hollow.

Today the reshaping of corries is limited to a little gullying of the steeper slopes by rainwater, and perhaps a few rock fragments prized off the slopes in winter by water freezing in cracks in the rocks (see Chapter 4). But even as recently as 15,000 years ago many of the corries were occupied by small glaciers similar to those present today in mountainside hollows in the Alps, Pyrenees or Himalayas (Plate 3.3). The former limits of ice in the corries is normally marked by the sharp distinction between the ice-smoothed rock surfaces and the jagged, frost-shattered rocks that stood up above the ice.

The slow accumulation of snow and its transformation into ice was described earlier, but we still have to explain the locations of the small glaciers. A glance at a map of Snowdonia, for example, will show that the number of large corries found on north and east-facing slopes is far greater than the numbers facing west or south. This is because of local variations in the climate. North and east-facing slopes are colder; they receive less sun and they face the directions from which the coldest winds blow. The snow was carried in on the prevailing westerly winds. It swirled up over the mountains and accumulated on the more sheltered slopes on the lee side of the mountains. These slopes were also the coldest, east-facing ones, so the accumulated snow in these locations tended to last through the summer months without melting, thereby building up year on year so as to eventually form ice.

PLATE 3.3 A modern corrie glacier, perched high above the Valley of Flowers in the Central Himalayas, at an altitude of approximately 16,000 feet. On the valley side below the small glacier the smoothed rocks have been deeply dissected by gullies, and rising above the corrie are the typical jagged mountain peaks shattered by the action of frost.

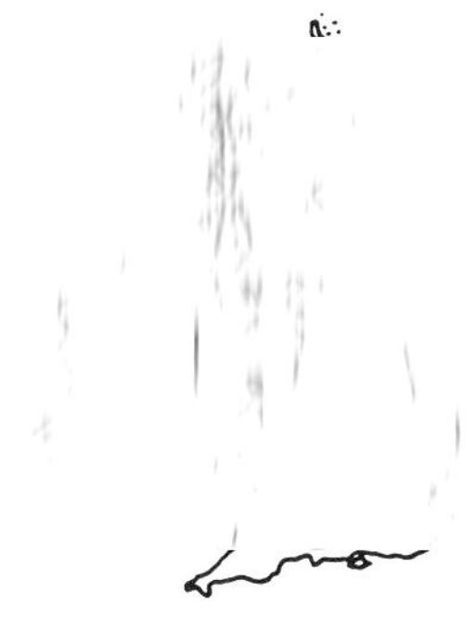

CONCENTRATED ICE EROSION: GLACIAL TROUGHS

Anyone who knows one of our highland areas will realise that corries and formerly glaciated valleys differ in terms of size, shape and location. Corries are cut into the sides of mountains; glacial troughs are in the valleys. Ice flowing off a mountainside scoops out a hollow, but ice moving down a valley carves a huge, smooth trough with a flat floor and steep valley sides. Valley glaciers are masses of ice restricted to the valleys and usually fed from an area of snow and ice accumulation on nearby higher ground.

The creation of glacial troughs requires more ice than that needed to carve a corrie. Often as the corrie glaciers outgrow their hollows they extend down into the valleys below. Ice from several corries may join together to create a small valley glacier which, as it grows and extends down valley, carves a trough (Fig 3.2). A view over the Lake District[1] or [illegible] the flow of ice outwards and downwards in all directions from the dome. Some of the troughs, such as Windermere[3] and Wastwater[4], were gouged very deeply down to levels well beneath present sea-level, although at the time they were carved, sea-level was about 100m (330ft) lower than present.

Troughs can also be carved out beneath a large ice-sheet, hundreds of metres thick, when a stream of the ice is confined to a channel or valley in the rocks. Often these troughs are open at both ends, unlike those cut by valley glaciers, where the troughs taper upwards into the higher ground that supplied the ice. Ice-sheet cut troughs are not necessarily controlled by former valleys; there are many instances in Scotland of troughs cut through the boundary of higher land that separates two adjacent sets of river valleys. This leads to the fragmentation of the highland areas, as seen, for example, to the north-west of Fort William[5] in Scotland. Here, too, the power of ice to erode huge troughs is obvious. They are mostly filled in their deeper parts by lochs, and some of these are well over 200m (650ft) deep – Loch Morar[6] and Loch Ness[7] to name but two.

Many troughs were carved to depths below present sea-level. Those that had direct access to the sea were flooded as the seas rose when the ice melted, giving rise to dramatic fjords. Whilst our fjords are not as grand as those in Norway or New Zealand, they are nonetheless one of the prime reasons for the beauty of the west coast of Scotland.

Regardless of whether the troughs were gouged from beneath huge ice sheets or carved by small glaciers occupying only the valleys, they look very similar. But the shape of ice-carved troughs is very distinct from that of river-cut valleys (Fig 3.2). Where rivers weave through highlands, the valleys have spurs of rock projecting into them. But these spurs are no match for ice, which planes them off with the ease of an electric sanding machine on a piece of rough pine. The result is a beautiful, straight-sided valley with no spurs of rock to interrupt and spoil the clear view.

Ice also usually widens a valley more than running water, which, in the highlands, tends to erode vertically downwards. So, a river-cut valley is a steep 'V' shape in comparison with the more flattened and wider 'U' shape of an ice-carved trough. The 'U' shapes are very easy to spot even today (Plate 3.4), for the action of water since the ice melted has done little to modify them. Britain has a wonderful legacy of troughs gouged out of hard rocks in the highland areas – the Glens of Scotland;

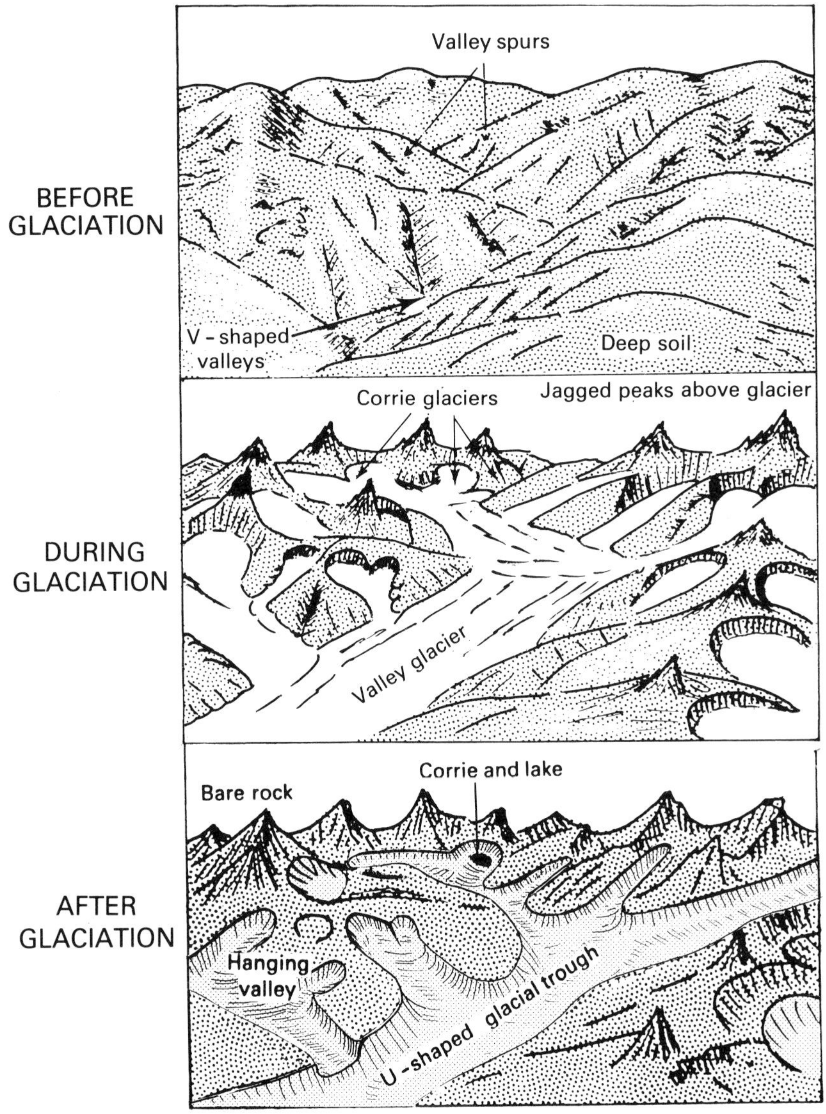


FIG 3.2 The effects of glaciers eroding valleys and mountainside hollows on the land shapes of a highland area.

English Lakeland[1] valleys; Nant Ffrancon[2] and Llyn Peris[3], amongst others, in Snowdonia[4]; and innumerable valleys in the Black Mountains[5], Brecon Beacons[6] and the Pennines[7]. Sometimes you will see smaller 'U' shaped valleys entering the main trough, not at the level of the valley floor but, perversely, perched high up on the sides of the trough. Waterfalls often cascade majestically down from these valleys that have been left 'hanging' in mid air. The answer to this landscape puzzle is that the main trough was carved by a larger and more powerful glacier, whereas the tributary valleys only contained small glaciers, which could not erode so deeply.

Having admired the troughs from a distance, let us now see what smaller features the ice has carved on the valley floors and sides. Examine the bare rock surfaces and you will often see great grooves and scratches that make the rock surface appear like a well-used cutting board. This is a fairly accurate impression; for the grooves were produced by boulders, embedded in the base of the ice, being dragged across the rock as the ice moved. Look a little further afield and you may notice that the rock floor of the trough, where not covered up by debris, is irregular, with sudden steps, small basins and even areas that trend uphill. These are probably the result of local changes in the power of the ice or in the strength of the rock. For example, where two glaciers join there will be a sudden increase in erosive power and the trough will be deepened. If the valley narrows, perhaps owing to an area of more resistant rock, the ice will also erode downwards more deeply. If the rock is weaker at a particular point, the ice will find it easier to erode, so forming a small basin in the rock.

Occasionally you will also stumble across small rocky hills, usually several metres high. These are strangely asymmetrical – smooth and gently sloping on one side but very jagged and steep on the opposite one (Fig 3.3). These are remnants of resistant rock that failed to succumb to the erosive onslaught of the ice, and so the ice only managed to subdue their surface shape. The smoothed side always faces the direction the local ice travelled from; the great pressure of ice and its bouldery load against this surface sandpapered it smooth. But the pressure also caused a little local [illegible]

[illegible] knoll or crag of rock with softer rocks behind, the ice will streamline the softer rock leaving it as an elongated tail gently sloping away from the hard upstanding rock (Fig 3.3). Edinburgh Castle[1] stands on one such crag and the Royal Mile runs down the streamlined tail.

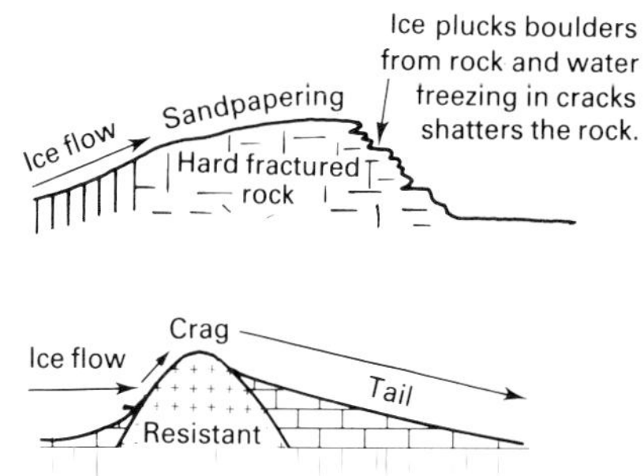


[illegible]

## ICE SCOURING A WHOLE LANDSCAPE: 'KNOCK AND LOCHAN' AND LIMESTONE PAVEMENTS

When the erosion beneath ice-sheets is not concentrated into troughs, but causes scouring of the whole landscape, the land is shaped a little like the rocky bottom of some glacial troughs but on a much larger scale. The result is an irregular, bare rocky landscape dominated by hills. Some of the hills may be quite large, perhaps 100m (330ft) high, but many are much smaller than this. Whilst some of the smaller hills are smoothed all over by the sandpapering ice, many others have ice-smoothed surfaces on one side and jagged, frost-shattered slopes on the other. In between the hills lie numerous ponds, lakes and boggy depressions. These were the sites of weaknesses in the rocks, such as faults and cracks, that were ruthlessly etched out by the ice to create rock basins. It was the action of ice picking out the variability in resistance of different areas of the rock that created this unusual landscape. The most striking example in Britain is on the ancient metamorphic rocks – the Lewisian gneiss – of north-west Scotland[2] and the outer Hebrides[3] (Plate 3.5). These areas are known to the Scots as 'knock and lochan'.

It is at first difficult to see what this landscape and the bare expanses of grey limestone found in parts of the Pennines and Ireland, for example, have in common. The answer is scouring by ice. If you have ever walked across the Burren[4] in County Clare, Ireland, or Hutton Roof Crags[5] near Morecambe Bay, Lancashire, or around the Ingleborough[6] area of north-west Yorkshire, or the south Wales coalfield[7], you will know how spectacular the effects of ice-sheet scour on limestones can be. The Burren from the air (Plate 1.11) is a fascinating landscape – a huge, bare white pavement created naturally in the limestones. On Hutton Roof Crags the surface of the pavement is divided into intriguing diamond-shaped patterns (Plate 3.6). But why are rock pavements not found in the limestone uplands of Derbyshire[8] or the Mendips[9], when these areas are both composed of the same tough limestone? The answer is that they were not covered by ice

PLATE 3.5 In the foreground is an ice-smoothed, rocky landscape, complete with ponds in small depressions, and behind lies the majestic, resistant, but nevertheless smoothed, pinnacles of Suilven.

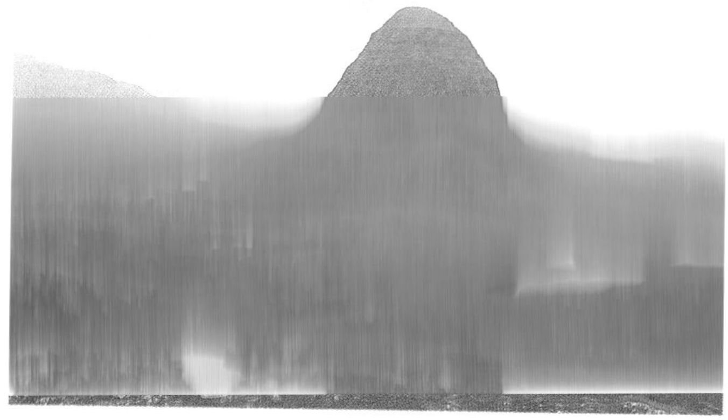

PLATE 3.6 Diamond-pattern shapes in the sloping limestone pavement at Hutton Roof Crags in Lancashire. Ice hoovered clean the surface of the limestone, so forming the rocky pavement. Water then enhanced the diamond pattern.

PLATE 3.4 A classic U-shaped valley in the Black Mountains of Wales; a reminder of the power of ice in sculpting the landscape.

during the last main glacial advance, some 18,000 years ago. Hence the limestones are covered over by soils and rock debris, and the rock itself is rarely seen at the surface, except on steep valley sides. The implication is that the ice acted like a landscape vacuum cleaner, clearing up the surface of the limestones.

The type of limestone is also important, for pavements are rarely formed in other than the Carboniferous Limestone. What, then, are the important characteristics? First, the limestone needs to be pure, otherwise the weathering of the rock since the ice melted would have left the surface covered with a coating of impurities. Secondly, it needs to be resistant to frost attack, so that a layer of angular debris will not accumulate and obscure the rock surface. Lastly, it needs to occur in thick and extensive enough layers for a good expanse of limestone to be exposed at the surface of the ground. The slope of the pavements usually relates to the layers that occur naturally in the limestones; so if the rock layers are dipping, the pavement too will slope at roughly the same angle, as at Hutton Roof and Newbiggin Crags[1] in Lancashire. In contrast, the pavements around Ingleborough[2] are more or less flat.

As well as hoovering the limestone, ice may also scratch and groove the rock surface, and dump foreign blocks of rock onto it. At Norber[3], near Ingleborough, there is a multitude of ice-carried boulders dumped on the pavement surface (Plate 1.10). The boulders, of Millstone Grit, were only carried down from nearby hilltops onto the limestone; but elsewhere in Britain and Ireland foreign blocks (erratics) have been carried hundreds of kilometres before being dumped. On the rocks around Croyde Bay[4] in Devon, for example, there are blocks that have been carried down from Scotland!

The boulders at Norber act as umbrellas, protecting the limestone beneath from the dissolving action of the rain. This explains why they are now perched on pedestals of limestone, left as the rock surface all around has been lowered by dissolution, as explained in Chapter 1 (Plate 1.10). But this is not the only effect of the rainwater. Looking at Plate 3.6 you will notice the intricate patterns on the limestone pavement – patterns of narrow, deep crevices that join together and separate the blocks of limestone. The crevices are natural features but they have been widened by the rain draining off the surface of the rock and down into the cracks. As this happens, the water may also dissolve small channels into the edge of the blocks of limestone near the cracks. These are beautifully developed where the pavements are inclined, as near Morecambe. Thus limestone pavements are the surfaces of tough limestones that have been wiped clean by the passage of ice, and dissected into blocks by running water.

## ICE DUMPING THE ERODED LOAD

What happens to all the debris the ice picks up as it carves great troughs and smooths the landscapes of the highlands? Inevitably it has to be dumped, either beneath the active ice, or as the ice withers away when the climate warms up again. This constructs a whole new set of landshapes: small and large, boring and spectacular. Because glaciers and ice-sheets are so effective at eroding and transporting debris, it is scarcely surprising that they are also very effective at smothering and masking the landscape with load after load of it.

If you live in East Anglia you may be forgiven for thinking that the debris is all dumped anyhow to form flat to irregular, low hummocky landshapes. But fortunately there are a multitude of interesting landscapes of deposition depending on how and where the material is dumped. The greatest difference in shapes is probably between material dumped beneath the moving ice compared with that dumped at the ice margins.

In all cases the material dumped is a regurgitated mixture of all the rocks and materials the ice has eroded on its journey out from the highlands. This mixture is usually a variety of differing rock fragments embedded in a mass of finer sands, silts and clays (Plate 2.10), traditionally known as drift but now more generally called boulder clay.

DUMPING AT ICE MARGINS
If you have ever seen a glacier or ice-sheet you will know that its ends are usually crammed full of murky-looking debris and more closely resemble the contents of a building-site waste heap than one's image of clean ice. When the ice melts, this debris is left as a ridge (moraine) marking the former extent of the ice. The ridges in Scandinavia can reach heights of 200m (650ft) and more, but in Britian and Ireland they are usually much [illegible]

[illegible] slowly incorporated into the side margins of the ice, and was left as ridges when the ice melted.

DUMPING BENEATH ICE
Dumping beneath ice happens in four main ways. First, the high pressure of the ice at its base causes a little melting, which in turn frees small particles from their icy prison. The particles are plastered onto the rock bed beneath the glacier. This happens where the ice is becoming less active, losing its power to erode, but it is not necessarily related to the retreat of the ice. Secondly, the frictional drag on particles in the base of the ice moving across rough rock may be greater than the force of the ice pushing the particles, and so they are plastered on the rock surface. Thirdly, fracturing and shearing in the base of the ice, because of the huge pressure of the ice's weight, gives off heat. This melts some ice locally and leads to deposition of a little of the load. Lastly, there is melting at the top and base of the ice mass as it finally wastes away.

Much of the material that is dumped in these ways forms undulating, hummocky deposits and occasional ridges of debris. But in some places the debris is shaped into beautiful clusters of small hills, all roughly the same size and shape, and all pointing in the same direction. In most cases the hills (drumlins) are a few hundred metres long and tens of metres high. They are elongated, and have a round blunt, front end and a long, tapering rear. Looking from above they appear like a load of eggs in the landscape basket (Plate 3.8). In the Eden Valley[2] there are more than 600 hills. In Clew Bay[3], in County Mayo, the hills rise out of the sea like a set of great dolphins. In Scotland, Glasgow[4] is built on and between them, and in north Wales they lie crammed between the mountains and the sea[5] (Fig 3.4). The two most extensive belts of these hills are in central and northern Ireland, and encircling the uplands of the North Pennines and Lake District. They tend to occur in the lower-lying areas.

The distribution of the drumlins suggests that they were formed in areas where the ice movement was constrained by gentle slopes and where ice-flow was interfered with by other ice masses. In such situations the thickness of the ice or its speed would be increased, creating pressures on the soft debris dumped beneath the ice – pressures great enough to deform and streamline the material into drumlin shapes. It is ice flowing over and around the material that streamlined it, and thus the

PLATE 3.7 A ridge of moraine in the foreground dams the serene lake at Llyn Llydaw in Snowdonia. Lakes dammed by moraine are common in formerly glaciated highlands.

PLATE 3.8 Looking like eggs in basket, these small hills were formed beneath a mass of moving ice. By flowing over and around the soft material, at just the right velocity, the ice streamlined the material into these distinctive hills.

*FIG 3.4 The location of drumlins in the British Isles in relation to the extent of ice 18,000 years ago.*

orientation of the drumlins shows the direction the ice was moving in – from rounded head to streamlined tail. The faster the ice flow, the more elongated the drumlins probably became; but where velocities were too high, the deposits beneath the ice were removed altogether. This may explain why there are no drumlins on the east coast of England.

Thus in Britain and Ireland we have three distinctive types of landscape created by ice dumping its load. The vast drumlin fields are landscapes formed as active ice moved over the terrain and shaped the malleable debris dumped beneath the ice into clusters of hills. These form usually beneath the middle parts of ice-sheets. In contrast, there are flat, lowland areas of subdued hummocky landscape characterised by thick accumulations of dumped debris, boulder clay, and the occasional ramparts of moraines. These are landscapes formed at the wasting margins of ice-sheets and are typical of East Anglia and Lincolnshire. Lastly, there are the more localised moraine and dammed lake landscapes found in the glaciated valleys and corries of the highlands. These were, for the most part, fashioned by valley glaciers rather than ice-sheets.

## MELTWATER IN THE ICY LANDSCAPE

Until now we have looked at landshapes directly formed by ice, either eroding or dumping. But water is also a potent force in the icy landscape. We have seen that the thin films of water at the base of ice help it to slide,

*PLATE 3.9 A strange, sinuous ridge stands out from the surrounding landscape. Once it was a tunnel in the bottom of a great sheet of ice. The tunnel partly filled with gravels and sands dumped by meltwater, and when the enclosing ice melted away, the debris was left as a ridge.*

that local melting and refreezing helps ice to erode, and that melting ends in the dumping of all the debris load. But water does much more than this. Streams of meltwater flow in tunnels in the base of most ice-sheets and glaciers. The water is confined and flows under great pressure; the flow velocity is high, particularly during the warmer summer months when more meltwater is produced. These streams issue from the front of glaciers and ice-sheets onto the barren, arctic landscapes beyond and, when the ice finally melts, huge flows of water tear across the landscape.

But what landshapes did the water, and its heavy load of sands and gravels, create in our islands? Plate 3.9 shows a strange, sinuous ridge meandering across the landscape. Inside the ridge you would not see a jumbled-up mixture of rock fragments and fine materials, as found in boulder clay. Instead, you would see thick layers of rounded gravel separated by layers of sand and the occasional layer of finer material. Ice is not capable of sorting materials in this way, so we have to turn to the role of water to explain the feature.

In fact, the ridge started life as debris being transported by streams of meltwater in tunnels in the base of an ice-sheet or glacier. The debris was en route to the ice margin, but it did not get there. The coarser debris was dumped in the tunnel itself, probably as the velocity of the water was falling after the summer peak flow; but for the debris to be preserved, it is likely that this particular tunnel was then abandoned. It is this old, partly infilled 'tunnel' that we see today as the ridge of gravelly material (the esker). This, like all other eskers, was aligned roughly parallel to the direction of ice-flow and so it is a good indicator of the direction the ice moved in at the time. Eskers are particularly common on the plains of Ireland, to the south of the drumlins.

Features that look similar to eskers also form along the front of a gradually decaying ice-sheet. They too are composed of sands and gravels, but they [illegible]

where ice is wasting away rapidly, its margins may break up leaving detached masses of soft decaying ice. These are often covered by the sands and gravels washed out of the ice front. However, when the lumps of ice then melt, the gravels over it subside, and a small hollow is left in the landscape (a kettlehole). Plate 3.10 shows a kettlehole containing a small pond.

*PLATE 3.10 (below) Not a manmade pond, but a hollow that once housed a huge chunk of decaying ice, as an ice-sheet melted away. Today, the steep banks of loose material show signs of instability, and minor landslips can be seen.*

*PLATE 3.11 (pp78-9) The impressive channel of Newtondale was carved relentlessly by great floods of meltwater, but now houses little more than a small stream and the railway line.*

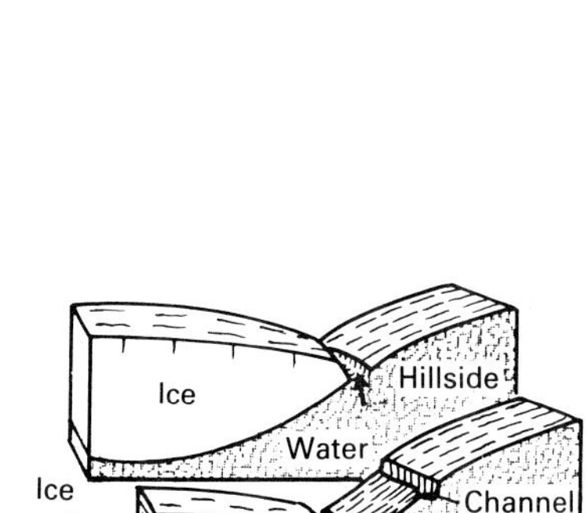

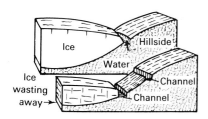


*FIG 3.5 How channels are carved into a hillside by meltwater at the edge of a mass of ice.*

Thus, at the decaying margins of ice-sheets much activity is taking place; boulder clay is being dumped as moraine ridges, masses of debris is being washed out by meltwater streams to give deltas at the ice front and plains of debris beyond, and stagnating lumps of ice are being buried by debris. It is no wonder that the landscape legacy of these great melts is a jumbled mixture of gravel plains, hillocks, hollows, ridges and mounds. These features are less commonly seen in formerly glaciated valley troughs. This is partly because the glaciers were still active as they retreated, and partly because the features have been eroded away or covered up by later river activity.

Although these landscape features are undoubtedly interesting, they cannot compete in sheer size and splendour with the giant troughs carved into the landscape by huge, concentrated flows of meltwater generated by the rapid decay of ice-sheets. For example, snaking across the North Yorkshire Moors there is a deep sinuous trench, like a leviathan railway cutting, as much as 250m (820ft) wide and 100m (330ft) deep. It is a winding valley of great magnitude, and yet it, Newtondale[1], contains no more than a miniscule stream. (Plate 3.11).

The classic suggestion as to its origin was made at the turn of the century by Percy Kendall. He imagined that in the Ice Age a large ice-sheet advanced from the north and east, abutted onto the high land provided by the Cleveland Hills[2], and then encircled them. This prevented rivers from the hills and other unglaciated areas from draining away to the sea. As a result of this ponding, large lakes were formed in Eskdale, Glaisdale and Wheeldale. They became progressively deeper until their level reached that of the surrounding countryside. Then, Kendall believed, the lakes overflowed as great torrents of water, carving an enormous channel to the south – Newtondale[1]. The water from Newtondale emptied into the low-lying Vale of Pickering[3] and perhaps formed another lake. Kendall argued that when the water reached the vale it deposited its load to form a large delta of sediment.

Subsequent to Kendall's work, other great lakes were postulated for various parts of Britain and Ireland. Southwards from Lake Pickering, two huge lakes were proposed, which together extended almost as far south as Cambridge. In the English Midlands, Lake Harrison[4] may have occupied a large area between Gloucestershire and Leicestershire (Fig 5.5). In north-western England and the Welsh Borderland, Lake Lapworth[5] was supposed to have innundated an area from north of Manchester to south of Shrewsbury.

More recently, these explanations have been questioned. Research has failed to locate reliable evidence for old lake shorelines and lake sediments in many cases other than in the Highlands of Scotland where there are the famous parallel roads of Glen Roy[6]. People have also questioned whether ice is quite as leak-proof and effective at damming up water as Kendall proposed, and they have suggested other ways in which channels like Newtondale could have been formed. More recent theories are based on the idea that as the climate warmed up at the end of the glacial period, the great ice-sheets decayed and released large amounts of meltwater. This water flowed over, under and around the ice mass, and carved the channels such as Newtondale[1]. Many meltwater channels are easily recognisable, for they form deep gashes in the crests of hills, in locations where under present conditions no large river could exist. Other channels descend hillslopes obliquely or run in groups along the hillsides – behaviour that is also not normal in rivers. Some of the channels are single, such as Newtondale, whereas others, notably in the Cheviot Hills[7], are complex systems.

Two main types of channel have been identified. They form in different locations in the ice mass. First, there are those that are cut against hillsides by water flowing along the glacier or ice-sheet margin. This occurs frequently,

for the simple reason that, when a glacier rests against a valley side, the absorption of heat by the rock causes melting of the glacier surface. This creates a depression between the valley wall and the ice. Meltwater from the ice surface and any water flowing down the hillslope will tend to drain into this depression, and will carve it deeper, creating a definite channel cut into the hillside. When the surface of the ice mass is being slowly lowered, as it finally wastes away, several parallel channels may be cut, one after the other, each representing a lower glacier margin against the hillside (Fig 3.5). Even more spectacular, are the huge channels carved beneath the ice mass. These are cut by very large meltwater streams flowing at the bottom of a rapidly decaying mass of thick ice. Sometimes the deep, box-like channels have complicated links between them, as just south of Fishguard[1] in south-west Wales. Newtondale[2] was also probably [illegible]

[illegible]

[illegible] ern England, Scotland and Wales, whereas landshapes of dumped debris dominate in the lower lands of East Anglia, the Midlands and Ireland. The former extent of the ice combined with its persistent attack for most of the last 2 million years leaves little doubt about its role in shaping the landscape of Britain and Ireland. You only have to look: a landscape of rocky hills and ponds in north-west Scotland; great troughs in Snowdonia; mounds, ridges and hillocks in East Anglia; and many more landscapes from the Scilly Isles to the Shetland Isles, attest to the power of ice.

# 4

# BEYOND THE MARGINS OF ICE-SHEETS

Rita Gardner

## A FROZEN LANDSCAPE

On a warm summer's day on Dartmoor[1] the narrow lanes are packed with tourists keen to admire the open views of rounded granite moorlands punctuated by great heaps of rocks – the tors – that stand out majestically on the skyline. In winter it is a stark and bleak landscape, but nowhere near as inhospitable as when the tors were excavated by the forces of nature from the surrounding rock. Then Dartmoor shivered under intensely cold conditions similar to those experienced around the polar ice-caps today in Siberia, Canada and Scandinavia. The landscape was stark, windswept, and could support little in the way of vegetation. Plants flowered briefly during the short summer thaw but for most of the year the ground was frozen completely with ice extending tens of metres below the surface. It was as if the landscape had been put into a huge fridge. The short summer thaw only affected the surface layers, creating a quagmire of sludge and debris-laden water which slid and flowed downslope; whilst later refreezing of water in cracks and pores exerted great pressures on the rocks causing them to shatter along planes of weakness.

If you climb over a tor on Dartmoor (Plate 4.1), remember that you are probably perched on remnants of rock more resistant to the potent pressures exerted by water freezing in cracks than the surrounding rocks. What then determines whether a rock will be resistant? The most likely cause lies in the spacing of the joints, or fractures, in the granite. Where the joints are closely spaced, the rock is more easily shattered into small fragments that can be carried away in water during periods of thaw. Where the joints are widely spaced, the rock is more resistant to this form of attack. This explains why the tors are made up of huge 'boulders' that appear to have been carefully stacked one upon another. In reality you are looking at a mass of rock with very widely spaced horizontal and vertical joints that divide the rock into large blocks. The joints themselves formed millions of years ago as the original molten material cooled, contracted and solidified into granite, deep within the Earth's crust, and also as the weight of overlying crustal rocks was slowly removed by erosion over a period of more than 270 million years, so releasing the pressure on the granite mass beneath.

It is fascinating to think that the rocks forming Dartmoor originated deep within the Earth's crust and have been slowly revealed at the surface by erosion. The hardness and general resilience of the rock meant that the granite stood out in the landscape, forming the moorland, as the softer sedimentary rocks around it were more easily worn away by the action of wind and water. Then, in the geologically very recent past, the action of ice and seasonal meltwater under harsh arctic conditions has finely chiselled the moorland, leaving the most resistant areas of rock as the sculptured tors (Plate 4.2). The waste produced in the sculpturing process, called clitter, is littered around the slopes below the tors. You may notice that sometimes the clitter is not scattered randomly but occurs in lines and lobes downslope. These mark the former pathways of the sludging process – solifluction – in which the blocks were carried downhill in a mass of debris that slid over the permanently frozen ground beneath. Rough Tor[1] on Bodmin Moor in Cornwall gives a dramatic illustration of the volume of angular clitter that can result. Some of the boulders were made use of in prehistoric times for the construction of nearby stone circles.

Not everyone believes that freezing conditions have been solely responsible for creating the tors, but all agree that arctic conditions in the recent past have been very important in shaping them as we see them today. Some believe that the granite was also weakened at an earlier stage by intense chemical rotting either just after its formation or when the British Isles experienced a tropical climate over 30 million years ago. Either way, the

tors are the resistant remnants of granite from around which the chemically rotted or ice-shattered debris has been removed.

In summary, tors are generally formed in hard rocks, but rocks in which some areas are more resistant to attack than others. The tors themselves are the tough remnants, the resilient parts, from around which the weaker, often ice-shattered, debris has been removed. It follows that tors can form in any relatively tough rock that has local differences in resistance; they are not only found in granite. Other examples include the quartzites of the Stiperstones[1] in Shropshire, and the sandstones of Brimham Rocks[2] in North Yorkshire.

But it was not only Dartmoor that suffered the arctic onslaught. In every major cooling of the climate, the Scandinavian ice-sheets expanded and advanced southwards, combining with the ice-sheets produced in our own uplands and engulfing much of these islands. Less dramatic cooling resulted in smaller, more localised [illegible]

[illegible] years the landscape has been at the mercy of an arctic, but not ice covered, environment. As the ice-sheets melted and retreated northwards at the onset of the warmer – interglacial – phases, so the arctic environments followed them, sweeping across Wales, Ireland, northern England and Scotland. It is hardly surprising then that arctic conditions have been one of the more potent influences shaping the landscape of the British Isles, particularly in the south. Imagine, for example, Kent looking like Siberia does today. Not only were dramatic landscapes created at these times, but the shape of every hillslope was modified. These far-reaching effects were brought about mainly by the actions of water freezing and melting in the ground.

When most people think of the Ice Age, images of vast ice-sheets hundreds of metres thick and of devouring glaciers spring to mind (see Chapter 3). Here, beyond the margins of the ice-sheets and glaciers, we are concerned with the less spectacular, but none the less effective, growth of ice in the ground. Two aspects of this are especially important in shaping the land. First is the pressure caused by the freezing of water into ice, as many will know from the problem of burst pipes. It is pressure that can shatter hard rocks and contort soft ones. Secondly, there is the sealing effect; water freezing in permeable rocks – ones that normally allow water to drain through – changes the whole character of the rock by sealing up all the cracks, fissures and pores. This is like a sponge becoming clogged with soap.

These two aspects alone are enough to cause havoc in the landscape, but further devastation takes place when the top layers of the ground thaw rapidly in summer. This suddenly generates large volumes of water, but the ground beneath is still frozen and incapable of absorbing it. Not content to let ice and water reshape the landscape, the wind also gets to work. Whistling unimpeded across the barren landscape it sculpts the rock and blows away any loose, fine material – dust and sand. So, far from being inactive in the 'deep freeze', the landscape is shattered, sealed up, bombarded by summer meltwater and scoured by the wind. We need to consider these activities in more detail (Fig 4.1) before turning to the landshapes that they created in the British Isles.

The very low winter temperatures of 1986 and 1987 gave some idea of the air and ground temperatures that would prevail for much of the year

PLATE 4.1 The bouldery remnants of granite, that form the famous Dartmoor tors, look as though they have been carefully stacked one upon another. In reality the tors are the most resistant parts of the granite, left standing up in the landscape as the weaker granite around has been eroded away.

PLATE 4.2 Water freezing in fractures in the granite prized off the great blocks of rock that litter the slopes around Rough Tor, perched on the skyline of Bodmin Moor.

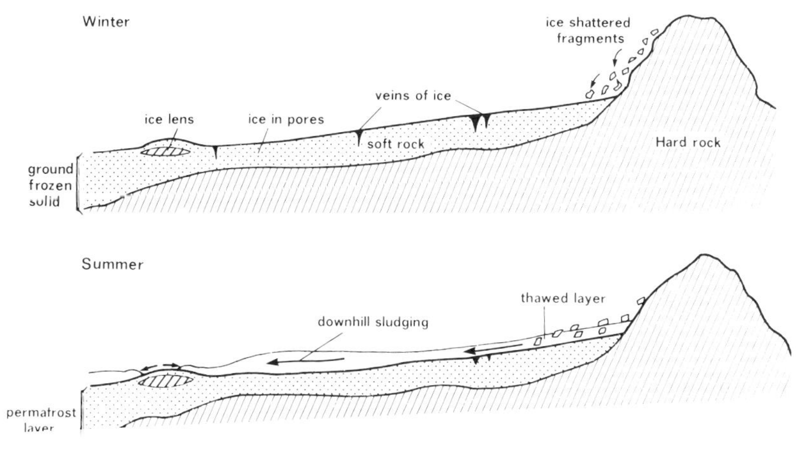


*FIG 4.1 Arctic activities in the landscape in winter and summer, beyond the margins of the ice-sheets.*

[illegible] from the top downwards in the autumn. This top layer is the only one showing much sign of activity in the mostly frozen landscape.

Ice in the ground can exist in several forms, such as horizontal lenses, as veins filling vertical cracks in the soil, or simply filling pores in the soil and rock. The form depends on the amount of water available, the rate of freezing and the characteristics of the rock or soil. For lenses to form there has to be a constant movement of water into the area. As the ground freezes, from the surface downwards, the surface supply of water is sealed off, and so the water is drawn up by tension from the still unfrozen material below. Continual sucking of water not only feeds the growth of the ice lenses and veins, but also dries out the unfrozen material, which then contracts and cracks. The cracks are typically arranged in an interlocking pattern of five- or six-sided polygons. In contrast, ice growth in pore spaces comes largely from the water already held in the pores.

The freezing of water in the ground can have several dramatic consequences. Water as it freezes expands by roughly 9 per cent of its volume. When the ice is confined to cracks in the rock, the pressure of expansion may be enough to force the rocks apart, shattering them noisily into small angular fragments. This happens even today on high mountain tops such as Snowdon[1], Scafell[2] or Ben Nevis[3]. If the water is concentrated as a lens of ice, the growth of the lens may lead to the doming up of overlying soft rocks or soils. The land is heaved up as if several hydraulic jacks had been placed in it. In cases where the overlying weight is too great to be heaved up, the expansion causes compression and contortion of the surrounding materials. If this is not enough, the ice in pores seals up the ground, rendering it impermeable. This sealing effect is, perhaps surprisingly, particularly important during the brief summer thaw. This is because although the thaw penetrates only a few metres into the frozen ground, over an entire landscape this can generate a lot of meltwater, quite suddenly, and this water cannot sink into the frozen ground beneath. So the meltwater, and any summer rain, is forced to run off the surface of the landscape. In flowing off downslope it carries with it soil, and any rock debris shattered by the earlier action of freezing. Sometimes the debris content is so high that the meltwater appears more like a slurry of liquid mud than a flow of water.

On steep slopes, the movement can be very rapid indeed. But even on gentle slopes of no more than a few degrees, the same mechanism is capable of moving large blocks of rock, albeit at a much slower rate. Anyone who has played hockey or football on a semi-frozen pitch will know how slippery it can be. Imagine the whole landscape like this. Not surprisingly, the material that is finally dumped, as the sludging comes to a halt, looks like a higgledy-piggledy mixture of rock fragments, sands and muds. But careful inspection reveals that the rock fragments are all aligned with their longest dimension pointing downslope, in the same direction as the material slid. This phenomenon can often be seen at the top of cliffs where the rock fragments in the, so-called, 'head deposit', all point out to sea as at Croyde Bay[1] and Baggy Point[1] in north Devon.

When the summer thaw takes place at the same time over a large area, huge amounts of running water can be generated. This concentrates into swollen streams and rivers capable of eroding the landscape and carrying away tonnes of debris. Floods are common at such times. But these rivers only flow in the summer across their wide, gravelly beds. For the rest of the year the river beds lie empty, dormant, and frozen solid by ice.

Refreezing of the thawed top layers in autumn sometimes gives rise to a very strange effect indeed. The colder surface layers freeze first and this leaves a sandwich of unfrozen material beneath the frozen surface and the permafrost at depth. Often the unfrozen layer is squeezed and buckled as it becomes more and more confined. Any water seeping along in the unfrozen zone is also confined by ice above and below. This hampers the drainage, causes the water to pond up beneath the surface, and often eventually leads to such high water pressures that the ground above is domed upwards under the pressure.

In short, the effects of water freezing in various forms in the ground can turn the landscape into a pattern composed of irregular domes, giant hexagons of ground outlined by cracks, and heaps of frost-shattered rock debris. Every year the summer thaw then wipes clean many of the surface features and the sludging redistributes the soil and rock debris in preparation for the following winter of upheavals. The rivers have a brief spell of glory before the winter shutters down the landscape and all is once more frozen.

In all this we have not yet thought about the wind. In general the climate was not only colder but also drier during the arctic phases. This is because the sea was further away, and the air was colder and could not carry as much moisture. Also less evaporation took place owing to lowered land and sea temperatures, and to the presence of ice and bare ground. Such light-coloured, bright surfaces reflect more of the incoming sun's rays back into the atmosphere than a darker vegetated surface does. This in turn left the land surface even colder, as less of the incoming solar energy was absorbed into the ground. A dry land surface, and one on which the soil is not protected by a dense plant cover or bound together by roots, is an easy target for wind erosion. A modern example is the bare exposed surfaces of the East Anglian fenlands in spring. This tendency for greater wind erosion was heightened by increased wind velocities at times during glacial phases, and by a supply of loose, sandy sediments washed out of the mouths of glaciers and ice-sheets by meltwater. These all combined to provide an abundant supply of material ideal for the wind to work on, and perfect circumstances for the wind to pick up and transport it. There is no doubt that dust storms were a common event in the arctic landscapes of the British Isles.

## CHANGING SEA LEVELS

Whilst these dramatic events were taking place on land, the sea too was responding to the expansion of the ice-sheets. In order to generate such huge ice-sheets in the northern hemisphere, a vast supply of water, falling as snow, was necessary, and most of the water that was locked up as ice was originally evaporated from the oceans (see Fig 5.2). This depleted the ocean stock, leading to lowered sea-levels worldwide. When the ice-sheets were at their maximum extent, sea-levels fell to more than 100m (330ft) below present levels. This meant that the British Isles were truly a part of Europe, as the falling seas exposed much of the floor of the North Sea and English Channel as land. For example, the 'Channel' shoreline lay between Cornwall and Brittany, and across the exposed channel floor flowed a huge river system created by the Seine, Solent, Thames and Rhine joined together. At times of lowest sea-level, the floor of the Irish Sea was uncovered and Ireland and Wales were joined together. Exposure of new land all around the coastline meant that the British Isles 'grew' by several thousand square kilometres during each glacial phase (Fig 1.1). The coastline then retreated back to roughly its present position during the warmer, interglacial phases [illegible] locked up in the huge Antarctic and Greenland ice-caps, it is estimated that world sea-levels would rise by a further 60m (197ft) or more. There is, however, no evidence that this has happened in any of the warm, interglacial phases during the past million or so years.

## THE ARCTIC LEGACY

The legacy of icy arctic conditions in the British landscape varies from one part of the country to another. Most of the effects of the early cold phases have been wiped away, like chalk being erased off a blackboard, either by subsequent glacier or ice-sheet advance across the area or, beyond the ice-sheet margins, by more recent arctic conditions overprinting the landscape. The most recent major cold phase in the Midlands and southern Britain and southern Ireland spans 70,000 to approximately 10,000 years ago, but can be subdivided into phases of greater and lesser intensity. Even over this time-span it is very difficult to date precisely the age of particular features; some may be composites of several events, and many have no material that is suitable for dating.

By now we know that for much of the past 2 million years the climate and landscape of the British Isles was dramatically different. Huge ice-sheets in the north gave way to the growth of ice in the ground beyond their margins. But what were the effects of the changing environment on the shape and character of today's landscape?

### SCREE SLOPES

In the colder highlands the arctic processes only began to operate once the ice-sheets had melted away. However, they persisted until more recently than further south; indeed many of the Scottish Highlands, such as the Cairngorms, still sometimes experience intensely cold winters that are reminiscent of those in the Ice Age. Many of the impressive screes in these mountainous areas were substantially formed in the relatively short interlude between glacier retreat and the onset of milder temperate conditions. Take, for example, the spectacular scree slopes at Wastwater[1] in the Lake District (Plate 4.3). The eastern valley side is mantled with loose rock

*PLATE 4.3 Huge fans of boulders liberated by the pressure of water freezing in cracks in the rock cliffs above, mantle the valley side, and continue down into the lake at Wastwater in the Lake District.*

fragments and boulders (scree) banked one on top of the other almost to the skyline – a dramatic backcloth to one of the deepest lakes in Britain, and a testimony to the efficiency of frost action in levering blocks of rock apart. In this case the blocks are of volcanic rocks that were formed over 400 million years ago. A clue to the action of frost in prizing the rocks away from the cliff face comes from their angular shapes; if chemical disintegration had been responsible, the boulders would tend to have more rounded edges. Once broken away by ice forming in joints, the boulders tumble downslope. Typically the larger ones travel farthest before coming to rest towards the base of the slope or even plunging into the lake. This gives a grading in the size of boulders down the scree slope.

When one looks at scree slopes there are two other features that often stand out, namely the steep, uniform angle of slope and the concentration of the scree into distinct cones of debris each falling away from one point on the cliff face (Plate 4.3). It is hard to believe that the slope angle is only 30 to 35 degrees, for it looks much steeper, but this is the steepest slope angle at which loose sands and boulders remain stable. The debris cones, which look as though the slope has put on an apron of scree, are easily explained by the fact that some parts of the cliff face will be 'weaker' than others probably due to the closer spacing of joints, to patterns of folding, or to higher porosities. Here more water will penetrate into the rocks, creating more stress when the water freezes, and this more effective frost attack will result in greater amounts of debris being prized off. Thus, from each of these locations the downward tumble of boulders gives rise to a cone-shaped heap falling away from the area of production. In time neighbouring scree cones grow large enough to join sideways, as well as extending upwards, and so the whole valley side becomes mantled in a curtain of scree.

Wastwater has some way to go before this stage is reached, as on average the top 100m (330ft) of the rock cliff is still exposed and supplying material onto the screes below. As more and more of the valley side is covered, the exposure of cliff face decreases and the rate of scree production slows. Scree production today is also limited by the climate, and only occurs in any amount on the higher, cold north and east-facing slopes in the highlands of Britain. Compared with production rates at the end of the last glacial period, the present supply is a mere trickle. The inactivity on many scree slopes today is shown in their colonisation by lichens, grasses and even low shrubs and trees, as in the famous Eglwyseg Screes[1] near Llangollen in north Wales.

One question that remains to be [illegible] climate is significantly warmer than in, for example, Scotland. This aids chemical disintegration and helps to create a protective mantle of soil over rock surfaces.

## PINGOS

In contrast to the scree slopes formed in the tougher rocks of highland Britain, the softer rocks and sediments of the south and east record much more the effects of water freezing to great depths within the ground, of seasonal thawing in the uppermost – active – layer, and of wind. If you were to encounter a heathland containing numerous small, near-circular ponds or marshy hollows, each surrounded by a rampart of soil and soft sediment about 1 to 2m (3 to 6ft) high, would you believe that they had formed naturally under arctic conditions, or would you be tempted to think they were bomb-craters or the result of small-scale mining activity? A bird's eye view from the air (Plate 4.4) does little to resolve the problem, but shows the beautiful hollows and the intricacy of the ramparts – some complete, others superimposed and interlocking.

These particular features are found on East Walton[2] common near King's Lynn, Norfolk, and it is true that they were created in the arctic environment that existed in this area during most of the last glacial phase (70,000 to 10,000 years ago). The ice-sheet at that time only just reached the north Norfolk coast; desolate, barren and windswept conditions extended across Norfolk and Suffolk; the landscape shivered and froze. The growth of ice in the ground was responsible for these peculiar shapes. But scientists are still not sure whether the creation of these hollows and ramparts was a direct consequence of the growth of ice lenses in the ground, or the indirect result of ice growth which ponded up the natural flow of water. It is not immediately clear how the former presence of either ice lenses or water in the ground under pressure can result in rounded hollows tens of metres wide and only a few metres deep, such as these.

The answers are really surprisingly simple. In the case of ice lenses, the ice accumulated at shallow depths in the soft soil and sediments. This led to the doming upwards of the frozen material above the ice lenses, giving the landscape a pimpled appearance rather than its present pock marks (Fig 4.2). On the domed surface the soil and rock debris was unstable during the warmer summer months when thawing of the surface took

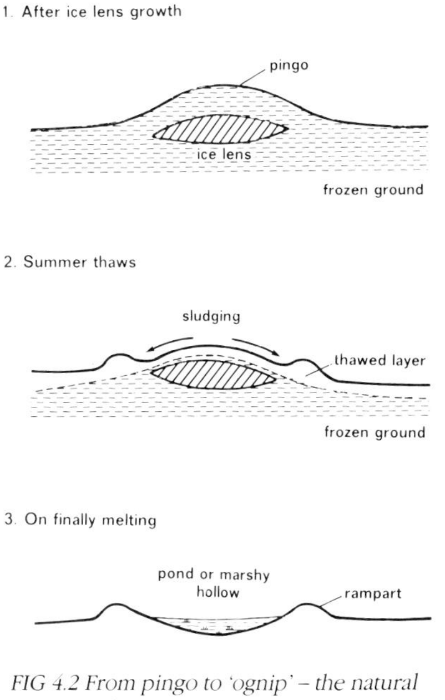


*FIG 4.2 From pingo to 'ognip' – the natural creation of ponds surrounded by ramparts of sediment.*

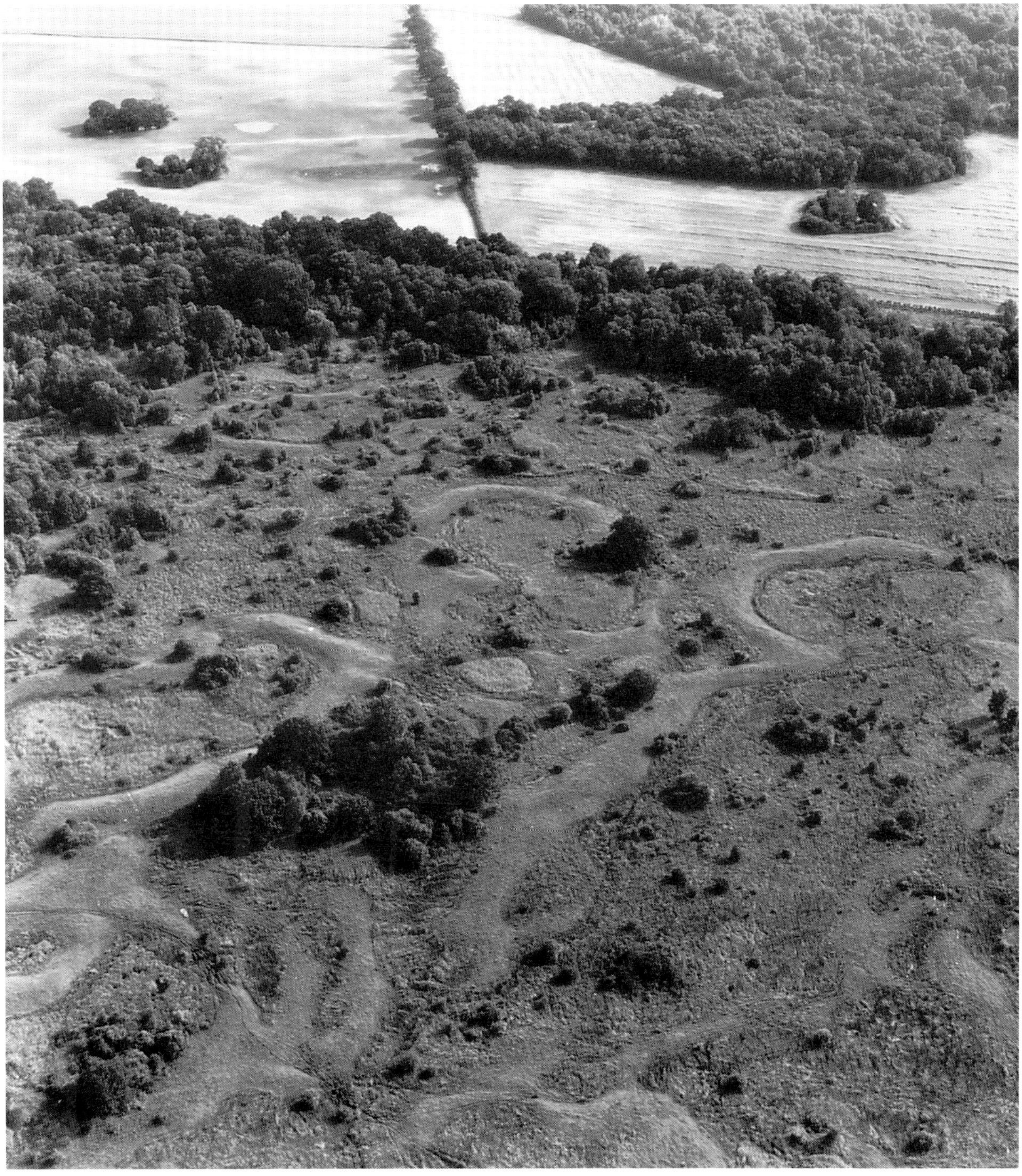

*PLATE 4.4 Nature's patchwork of small ponds and marshes enclosed by wavy ramparts of soft sediments. These are beautiful and intricate reminders of the landscape's arctic past.*

place. Thus, some of the material slid off the mound and accumulated around its margins. Then when the climate warmed sufficiently to melt the ice lenses, the land settled back down, almost as if it had been deflated. But because some of the soil and sediment had slid off the domed surface there was less available to fill the void left when the ice turned to liquid, and so a small hollow was created. The ramparts are the remains of the material that accumulated around the margins of the mound.

The alternative mechanism, like the first one, has been observed in the Arctic today. The pressure created by the confined water can also be enough to dome up the land surface. This has the same effect as a dome created above an ice lens. Release of the water pressure by bursting through the surface ice, or upon thawing, will similarly create small depressions.

We can see that, in the case of East Walton, the ice-lens or water-pressure domes were only small features, often less than 50m (165ft) in diameter. In addition the superimposition [illegible] In the British Isles traces of their former existence can be seen in places as far apart as East Anglia, south Ireland, and Cardiganshire, Wales. But their relative scarcity and patchy distribution probably relates to the particular conditions needed for their formation. Both of the suggested mechanisms require a relatively abundant source of water near the surface, or even waterlogged ground. Furthermore, the formation of ice lenses is favoured by fine silty or clay-type sediments. At Walton the pingos are formed close to where the boundary between the permeable Chalk and the impermeable clay below reaches the surface. As a result there are many springs, seepages and boggy areas of ground.

Features similar in appearance to the pingos at Walton, but several times larger, are found in the Brecklands[1] of East Anglia. Known as meres, they are a surprising set of small lakes, all occupying depressions in the land, and set for the most part amid conifer plantations. The most appealing, and the deepest – the Devils's Punchbowl – is almost perfectly circular in plan, and up to 7m (23ft) deep; it looks too perfect to be natural (Plate 4.5). But they are certainly natural in origin, and one suggestion is that they are the hollows left by the collapse of large pingos, comparable in size to the larger ones present in the Arctic now.

[illegible] of ice.

ICE WEDGES

In marked contrast to the peculiar hollows and ramparts characteristic of an area once dotted with pingos, fossil ice wedges (Plate 4.6) are easily missed in the landscape. They are, however, a very important indicator of the former existence of arctic conditions. To spot them you need to be keen on looking at cliff faces, freshly excavated road cuttings, foundation trenches or sand and gravel pits. They are all that remains of the past accumulation of massive wedges of ice, penetrating deeply into the ground. Wedges present today in the Arctic are usually more or less vertical, and may extend in excess of 10m (33ft) below ground; at the ground surface they can be more than 1m (3ft) wide, and the ice tapers downwards in a wedge form. Those formed in Britain and Ireland never attained this size, 2m (6ft) being about their limit.

The theory of their origin dates back to 1915 when it was discovered that they were directly linked to the refreezing of the surface layers of the ground – the active layer – that had melted during the summer. In

*PLATE 4.6 A deep wedge of ice once occupied this crack in the ground that is now filled with loose gravels. As the wedge of ice finally melted, it left a void which was filled by gravels from above tumbling down into it. The soft sand and gravel layers either side of the wedge are contorted.*

autumn, as this layer cooled and froze it contracted, creating a pattern of cracks that penetrated through the 'active layer' and into the permanently frozen ground below. Typically the cracks map out polygonal shapes several metres in diameter. This pattern is similar in shape (but much larger in size) to that formed when a small muddy pond dries out and cracks in a hot dry summer. The cracks in the permafrost then fill with ice crystals, giving rise to a vein of ice.

Imagine this happening year after year for hundreds of years, the ground always cracking in the same place because, once formed, the cracks and veins are points of weakness. Gradually the vein grows in size, with each annual addition of ice crystals filling the slightly enlarged crack. Layer upon layer of vertical ice represents year upon year of cracking. In this way an ice wedge develops, for the crack is wider at the surface and tapers downwards.

Ice wedges are most readily formed in fairly soft, fine sediments that are capable of retaining water and so will shrink and crack readily on drying. Often the layers of sediments immediately around the upper part of the wedge are contorted and deformed. This happens because during the summer thaw the ground around the wedge warms up and expands, so pushing against the still-frozen wedge of rigid ice.

Obviously the wedges we see in Britain today are fossil remnants. They contain no ice, for it is too warm, but their shape and former existence has been preserved in ghost-like form by a fill of sediment that collapsed into, and filled, the void left when the ice finally melted. They are especially common in the Midlands and southern Britain (Fig 4.3), ie in areas experiencing the necessary cold and relatively humid conditions, but not covered by ice-sheets during the last glacial phase. Given that active ice wedges in the Arctic are found where the temperatures consistently fall well below -6°C (20°F) for much of the year, it implies that when the wedges were formed in Britain the average temperatures were at least 10°C (18°F) lower than at present.

Fragile and fascinating reminders of the past, fossil ice wedges and veins can be seen in cliff exposures at Baggy Point[1] in north Devon; in former quarries at Long Hanborough[2], Oxfordshire; in numerous quarries in south and east Suffolk, and at many other locations.

PATTERNS IN THE GROUND

Should you be flying at low level over parts of the Midlands and southern England you may see a strange patterning in the ground. It is often shown up by variations in the type of vegetation, as in the Brecklands of East Anglia, or by the density of crop plant-growth. On flat ground the patterns appear as circles or polygons, often more than 10m (33ft) in diameter; on sloping land the more common form is stripes (Plate 4.7). If this is not spectacular enough, where two sets of stripes intersect, as in some Breckland valley floors, a herringbone pattern may result. This is England's arctic patchwork that predates, by thousands of years, the old field boundaries and land-use patterns superimposed by early farming upon the polygons or stripes.

Their creation can be linked, in some cases, to the growth of ice wedges. When the ground contracts on freezing, the pattern of the cracks is usually roughly polygonal if viewed from above – a lacework pattern. Ice wedges form in the cracks, giving rise to a polygon of frozen land surrounded by ice wedges. When the ice melts the cracks are filled in with sediment, but where the infilling material is different to that all around, the outline of the polygons is preserved. If the 'filler' has different chemical properties or drainage characteristics, the pattern of plant growth may be affected. Good examples can be seen around Wolverhampton[3] where the polygons are formed in boulder clays (mixtures of sands, clays and gravels) dumped from ice-sheets that covered the area earlier in the Ice Age. But the former cracks are very distinct as they were filled by better sorted and coarser sands and

*PLATE 4.7 This zebra-like landscape can be seen in several places in south-east England. Here, near Thetford in Norfolk, the stripes and polygon patterns are picked out by the different plants, but the patterns reflect subtle and regular variations in the material beneath the ground surface.*

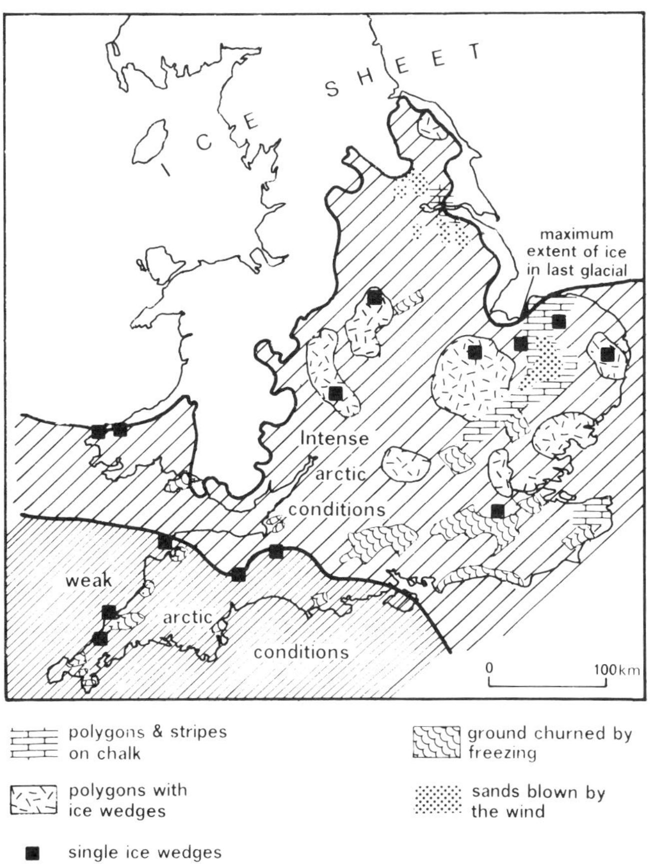


*FIG 4.3 The location of the main areas in southern England with patterns in the ground, 'fossil' ice wedges, inland sand dunes, and ground churned up by freezing.*

gravels washed into them from overlying material. This clear distinction between the core areas and the edges of the polygons is a fossil record of arctic conditions. The polygons range in diameter from 50cm (20in) to over 19m (62ft), and sometimes the smaller ones are found inside the larger.

Unfortunately this mechanism does not form stripes, even on quite steep slopes. In addition, it does not explain the different types of polygons (and stripes) that are found on the chalklands of southern England. Take Thetford Chase[1] (Plate 4.7) as a classic example. Here, the polygons merge into stripes on all slopes, even the very shallow ones of 3 degrees. The patterns are large, polygons of 10m (33ft) diameter are common, and the stripes are extensive. It is the vegetation of alternating grass and heather that first gives a clue to the patterns that exist below the ground surface.

The ground here is made up of chalky boulder clay, dumped by an ice-sheet, and it is covered by a veneer of wind-blown sand of varying thickness. Where the sand is thin, and the boulder clay near the surface, the soil conditions are quite alkaline, and grass covers the area. This is the case in the centres of the polygons and between the stripes. On the other hand, deep sand fills the shallow troughs that form the edges of the polygons and stripes. The deeper sand gives more acidic growing conditions, and heather flourishes. The troughs themselves are not like the fossil ice wedges found at the edges of polygons in the Midlands and elsewhere. Instead, they are wide and shallow (Fig 4.4). As yet we have little idea of the precise ways in which these particular polygons and stripes form, although they closely resemble landscapes present in the Arctic today.

Somewhat surprisingly, a visit to the higher parts of Snowdonia[2], the Lake District[3] or the Cairngorms[4], will reveal similar polygonal patterns, but on a miniature scale – often less than 50cm (20in) diameter. These patterns are formed in the bare earth; the edges of the polygons have concentrations of coarser rock fragments and small boulders, whereas much finer material is present in the central parts of the polygons. The

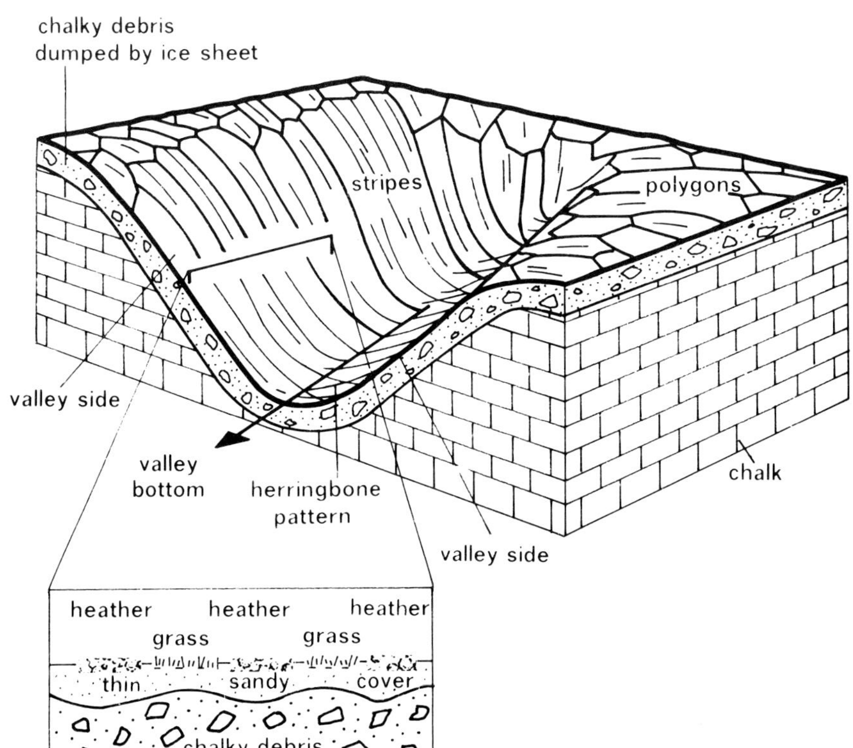


*FIG 4.4 The patterns of polygons and stripes that can be found on the chalklands of eastern England. Alternations of heather and grass reflect the differences, below the surface, in the thickness of sands over the chalky debris.*

SGG UNIT TITLE: WEATHER CLIMATE, ENVIRONMENT AND HUMAN ACTIVITIES. E105I1

KEY IDEA 12: FARMING SYSTEMS PROVIDE FOOD SUPPLIES AND RAW MATERIALS

STUDY THEME: Theory, case studies

## SCHEME OF WORK DETAILS.

LEARNING OUTCOMES in terms of EGRC:

K/U a: factual work; K/U c: representing data in graphic and numerical forms; Ev a : interpreting information, both text and data; Ev c : expressing point of view; Ev d : identifying points of view.

TYPE OF ACTIVITY:

Exposition and individual pupil work in co-operation with adjacent pupils will be assumed to be the norm. Additional or different activities are :-
answering questions based on text and illustrations
use of maps; completions/analysis of Wss; drawing map/diagram; study of . . slices..VHS..audio tape; group activity; discussion.

## [illegible]N PLAN DETAILS.

[illegible]

[illegible]n f. Classification of f. F. as a system. [illegible]ttern. Case studies in Europe. Current changes [illegible] France. EC food policy.

[illegible]ERCISES (EGRC):

[illegible]rs in f. R 87 elaborates this theme. Reading!

[illegible]t' should illustrate the factors in f (Ulster [illegible]).

[illegible] to be read; Q1 orally; read R 89 for another [illegible]

[illegible]rally. R 91 simple explanation of the farm as [illegible]

R [illegible] pattern; Q3 as written answer.

S[illegible]ences here >>> A separate instruction s[illegible] work involved in this unit.

limestone pavement 72

ice sheet troughs 67

roches m. and crag/tail 69

deposition mechanism 73

drumlin mechanism 73-4

tor mechanism 84-5

sorting process that separates the fine from the coarse material holds the key to their origin. The really fascinating part is that they are forming in these areas today. This has been shown experimentally by destroying all trace of them and then monitoring their regrowth over a period of years.

The sorting occurs when the ground freezes, but in this case the freezing only extends down to a few centimetres even in harsh winters. It is known that coarser material freezes more rapidly than finer, and that the finer particles move away from the points at which freezing is taking place. Gradual movement over many seasons gives rise to the patterns – the finer particles move away leaving the coarser ones concentrated at the edges and boundaries of adjoining polygons. The polygon patterns are 'elongated' into stripes on steep slopes (greater than 25 degrees). This is because of the additional downhill component of movement on the slopes due to the force of gravity (see Chapter 7).

*PLATE 4.8 Even on a misty day at Welcombe Mouth, North Devon, the solid rocks reveal the shape of an ancient valley, eroded down to approximately the present level of the beach. This valley was filled during the Ice Age with angular debris that sludged down from the sides of the valley. Today the small stream is slowly eroding the debris fill.*

## DRY VALLEYS

Until now we have paid little attention to the effects of summer thaw on the landscape. As stated earlier, nearly every hillslope will have been smoothed by the sludging of soil, rock debris and water across it during such brief milder periods. The slurries slid and flowed over the permanently frozen ground beneath and dumped vast quantities of material in the valley floors. Sometimes the dumped masses show up as lobes in the landscape; but the filling and smoothing effects are often most easily seen on the cliffed coastlines of the south and west of England. For example, where the cliffs slice through a valley in the brilliant white Chalk, you may see a thick layer of reddish-brown soil and rock debris lining the bottom of the valley. In north Devon many of the sheltered coastal valleys record

the effects of sludging on a massive scale, some valleys being filled with more than 15m (50ft) of debris. Stand on the beach at Welcombe Mouth[1] and look up towards the cliff. You will be able to trace the outline of the former valley carved into the solid rocks down to roughly present sea-level. But the present valley floor is up at the top of the cliffs (Plate 4.8).

What does this valley and the dry valleys found on the limestone rocks of the Cotswolds[2] and Pennines[3], and Chalk landscapes such as the Chilterns[4] and the Downs[5] of southern England, have in common? The answer is that they all have experienced the same set of processes, and what led to the infilling at Welcombe Mouth also led, many believe, to the creation of steep dry valleys nestled into the limestone escarpments. Normally limestones have little water running on their surface, and so the valleys in them appear dry. This is because limestones are permeable and any water falling on them soaks in until it reaches the top of the saturated layer in the rock – the water table. But without concentrated surface flow of water it is impossible to carve valleys; so how did these valleys form?

To answer this we have to return again to the arctic times, when the limestones were made impermeable by water freezing to ice within the pores and joints, thereby sealing them. In the permafrost layer they remained permanently frozen, but in the active layer there was seasonal thawing and sludging, as described earlier. This surface water, and any debris carried in it, flowed over the ground and was funnelled into depressions and then into small channels. Where there was enough flow, the channels amalgamated and valleys began to be carved. Erosion was helped by the repeated cycle of freezing and thawing in the active layer. This prized apart fragments of rock, so that they could be removed later by meltwater and sludging. Gradually, over tens and hundreds of years, the valley deepened. But this meant that the north and east facing slopes were increasingly in the shadow, whereas the sunnier west and south facing ones were more likely to thaw and freeze more often. This is the main reason why the valleys are often asymmetrical, with gentle west and south facing slopes and steep north and east facing ones.

Proof that at least some of the dry valleys were formed in such a way comes from careful excavations in the Devil's Kneadingtrough[1]. This is a small dry valley hiding in the North Downs escarpment near Brook, Kent. Here the sludged debris was found to extend as lobes or fans onto the clay vale at the foot of the escarpment (Fig 4.5). By dating the former soil buried by the sludge of debris, it was found that the last phase of excavation took place in the short, intensely cold and humid interlude between 10,800 and 10,300 years ago. Estimates of the amount of debris spread out in front of the valley suggest that as much as one-third of the volume of the valley was carved out by this combination of freezing, thawing and sludging in that short time – a mere 500 years. If we allow for the fact that some of the chalky debris will have been dissolved since then, it is likely that over half of the dry valley was excavated at this time. What a dramatic change the landscape must have seen.

*PLATE 4.9 The Manger of the White Horse at Uffington in Oxfordshire is a striking dry valley carved into the scarp face of the Marlborough Downs. The valley was carved when the conditions were arctic, and the ridges on the far slope were probably formed by avalanches of snow. Lynchets (see Chapter 8) can be seen in the valley floor in the foreground.* (Full-size illustration on pp82-3.)

Presently the Devil's Kneadingtrough is trough shaped; a few hundred metres long and well over 50m (165ft) deep, with steep valley sides and a more or less flat valley floor partially filled with sludged debris. Not all escarpment dry valleys are like this. In fact, the variety in shape and size is almost infinite. The poorly developed ones are little more than surface depressions, whereas the classic shapes take the form of large embayments, or linear valleys running back at right angles into the scarp. The valleys can be straight, curved or zigzag, but they usually have steep sides, a steep and abrupt back wall eating into the scarp, and a flat, gently sloping floor. From space they would look at though the Devil had taken one huge bite out of the scarp. The dry valley pictured here (Plate 4.9) is the Manger of the White Horse near Uffington[2], Oxfordshire. It is a short valley cut into the scarp slope, and it nestles beneath the Ridgeway and Iron Age fort on the crest of the scarp. A great fan of chalky soil and debris spews out onto the clay vale in front of the valley, and huge furrows, possibly caused by snow avalanches, give the western side of the valley an unusual, and beautiful, serrated appearance.

The variation in shape and size of dry valleys is probably due in part to differences in the hardness of the rock, the rock structure and the age of the valley. But it may also be because some of the valleys have formed in another way. This alternative explanation sees the valleys not as arctic fossils, but as a result of 'normal' river erosion. The question is, where did the rivers come from? The suggestion is that the valleys were formed when the level of the ground water was higher than at present. If the level of water in the ground – the water table – is high enough it will intersect with the land surface, giving rise to surface-water flow and streams, which in turn will carve valleys. If the water table should then fall to below the [illegible]

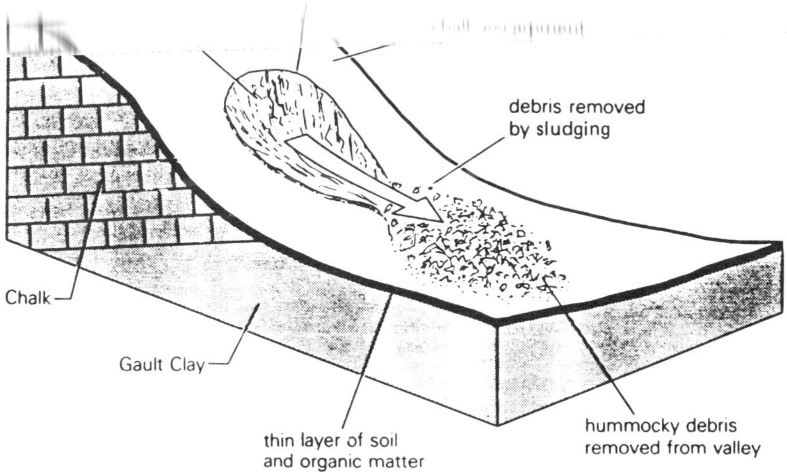


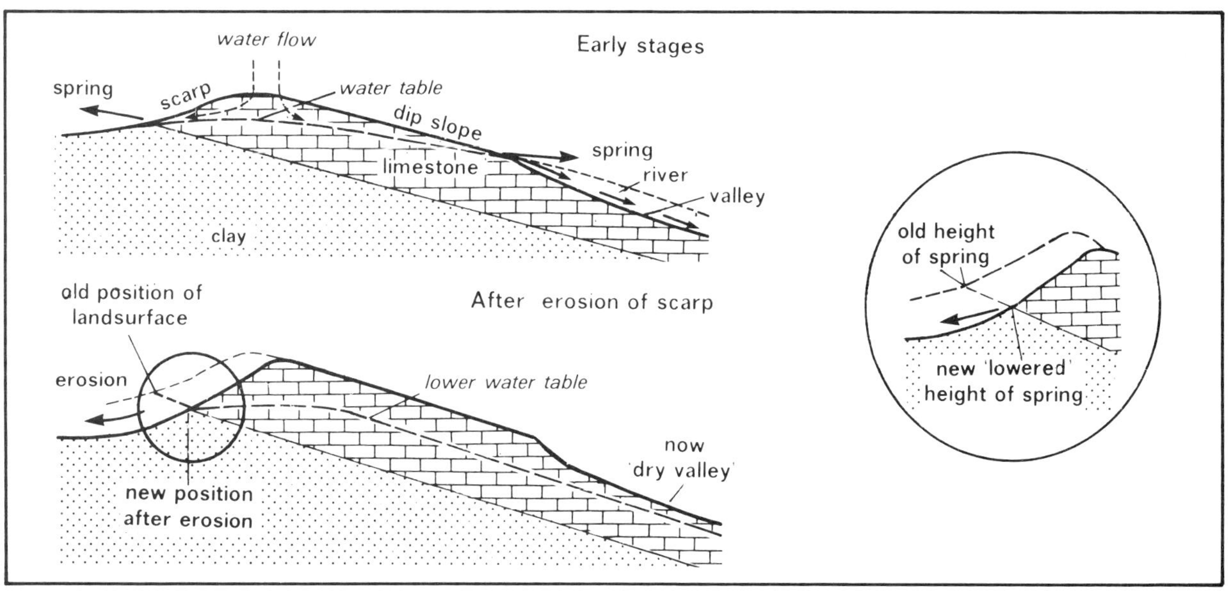


*FIG 4.6 Valleys in limestone can be left dry as the level of the water table falls. The diagram illustrates how a fall in the water table can result from the erosion and retreat of a scarp and the associated lowering of the springs.*

*PLATE 4.10 Dune remnants in the Breckland, north Suffolk, near Lakenheath. They were first fashioned as the wind whistled across a barren arctic landscape. In our present, warmer climate they have been stabilised by a thin cover of soil and the vegetation.*

changes of sufficient scale. More plausible is the idea that its level is controlled fundamentally by the height of the junction between the base of the permeable limestone and impermeable rocks beneath. At this point water cannot sink any further and is forced to flow sideways and emerge as springs (Fig 4.6). The position of the springs controls the height of the water table beneath the limestones; lowering of the level of the junction between the two rock types, and hence of the emergence of the springs, will lead to a lowering of the water table. This happens when the weaker impermeable rocks in front of a scarp are eroded. This causes the limestones to be undermined with the result that the scarp 'retreats' backwards. Support for this argument comes particularly from the dry valleys cut into the gentler dip-slopes of the limestones (see Chapter 2). Here the dry valley systems are generally much longer than those on the scarp, and have many more branches. The dry valley networks thus resemble very closely the patterns of modern rivers.

In fact it is likely that both factors have helped to shape most dry valleys. They probably began life as ordinary valleys, carved by 'normal' rivers when the water tables were higher. At this time the landscape as a whole would have been flatter, with far less variation in height between the scarps and vales. This early river erosion may well have started several million years ago. Gradual excavation of the weaker rocks in the vales would have then slowly lowered the water table, thus leaving the valleys progressively drier and fossilised. During the arctic conditions of the Ice

Age the valleys undoubtedly experienced a new lease of life. The rocks were sealed up by ice in their pores and water once again flowed over the ground surface and down the valleys, but this time carrying loads of frost-shattered debris. Erosion of the surface at these times was particularly easy as there was little vegetation to bind or stabilise it. Some of the scarp-face valleys may have been entirely created by such arctic events.

Who would think that such a simple and common feature, the dry valley, could have had such a complex history, spanning in some cases millions of years and repeated changes in climate.

WIND ACTIVITY

In 1668 the village of Santon Downham[1] near Brandon, in the heart of East Anglia, was overwhelmed by loose, moving sand. Whilst you might [illegible] slowly accumulated into layers (loess deposits) no more than a few metres thick in undisturbed areas to the south. The sands were just the right size to be bounced along the ground by the wind and refashioned into sand dunes.

One such area of sand originally washed out of ice-sheets and then refashioned by the wind, is around Thetford. This is The Breckland – for many a sandy wasteland best suited to conifer plantations or the growing of carrots, but the widespread existence of sand attests, in this instance, to its arctic past. Unfortunately today the dune forms have been much subdued by gradual erosion and the invasion of builders, or covered by dense conifer forests. However, they can still be seen in a few locations, such as Wangford and Lakenheath Warrens (Plate 4.10).

Undisturbed dunes already have a thin cover of soil, for they became stabilised as the climate warmed and vegetation developed on them some 10,000 years ago. Before then the area would have resembled a minature cold desert. Even today occasional reactivation of the dunes occurs following the degeneration or destruction of the vegetation cover. Then the wind soon gets to work on the vulnerable loose sand beneath, scooping out a hollow and carrying the sand off downwind. This probably happened at Wangford in 1668 and in turn led to the swamping of Santon Downham, 9km (5.6 miles) north-east of the reactivated area. Indeed, around this time (1667) the area was compared with the 'Desarts of Libya' by John Evelyn. Whilst inland dunes are not common, other examples can be seen near Sandringham[2], Newark[3] and Scunthorpe[4].

## CONCLUSION

Far from being an inactive landscape beyond the margins of the ice-sheets, we have seen how ice in the ground, sludging and the wind have combined together to bring about change in the landscape. The features that they formed may not be so impressive as great troughs carved by glaciers, or gorges excavated by rivers, but they are often intriguing, unusual, and unexpected – valleys that have no rivers, patterns in the ground, the bouldery heaps of tors, and sand dunes in the middle of the countryside. The great freeze has certainly left its mark on our landshapes.

5

# THE POWER OF RUNNING WATER

Denys Brunsden and David Jones

# THE POWER OF RUNNING WATER

Water is an amazing substance. It can be an invisible gas which we inhale with every breath, a liquid which is calming and soothing when warmed and placed within the confines of a bath, and a hard solid when cooled below its freezing point. But even the water in the bath has something of a Jekyll and Hyde character, for in different circumstances it is capable of acts of awesome violence. This is mainly because it is such a heavy substance. One large bathful weighs between half and three-quarters of a tonne. However, it is not weight alone that accounts for its destructive power but the combination of amount of water and speed of movement.

Imagine a million tonnes of water held as a reservoir behind a dam high up in some mountain valley. The water is not reshaping the land because it is at rest. But it has the potential to create change should the dam fail. If this happens, then the potential energy that the water contains due to its elevation will be converted into kinetic energy, or energy of movement, and this increases alarmingly with the increase in speed. Indeed, each doubling of speed results in a fourfold increase of energy. Thus the water that was placid and tranquil behind the dam becomes a raging torrent, smashing objects in its path and tearing open the floor of the valley.

The same transformation happens in nature. Streams and rivers that for most of the time wind peacefully through their valleys occasionally become swollen, muddy torrents in flood. Once the floodwaters have subsided it is possible to see the changes that have occurred: trees toppled, banks and walls undermined and spreads of recently moved material, often sand and gravel but sometimes boulders weighing several tonnes, as is described at the end of the chapter. Here we see clearly displayed evidence testifying to the potency of moving water in shaping the ground.

Despite the evidence of floods, it has taken humans a long time to recognise that running water is responsible for much of the shape of the surface of the Earth and for the essential nature of many landscapes. For example, in the medieval period our views of natural science were fostered by the church and by a literal belief in the Bible. Most scientists thought that valleys had been shaped by the retreating waters of the Flood and believed that the features of the Earth's surface could only be understood in terms of great catastrophes, for was it not written that

> The Flood continued forty days upon the earth; and the waters increased, and bore up the ark, and it rose high above the earth and the waters prevailed so mightily upon the earth that all the high mountains under the whole heaven were covered.

This was not merely a Biblical view. Nearly every culture had similar legends in which the Earth was ravaged by cataclysmic flood events. Usually the theories invoked powerful forces in the past that were no longer present in the modern world. They claimed that only such forces could have created the mountains and valleys because the Earth was thought to have been formed in 4004BC and was, therefore, very young. Clearly there was no time for slower processes to have carried out all the work required to create the landscape visible today.

Slowly, however, under the influence of scientists such as James Hutton, John Playfair and Charles Lyell, it was demonstrated that the Earth must be very old; that landforms were created by the everyday action of almost imperceptibly slow processes and that streams have indeed eroded the valleys they flow in. They showed that although the processes of change associated with running water were slow, they nevertheless came into operation with every rainfall and that, given sufficient time, even mountains could be worn away and great gorges, valleys and plains created. Soon engineers and geomorphologists were able to demonstrate and calculate how these processes worked. Later they developed sophisticated measuring devices to understand river behaviour and worked out complex equations which allowed the construction of devices to control the rivers' more extreme moods.

## THE CHANGING MOODS OF RIVERS

Today most river systems in the British Isles are managed to provide drinking water, industrial water, waste disposal facilities and recreational areas. Many stretches of water are also controlled to prevent floods and the hazards they pose to life and property. In order to achieve these various aims as efficiently as possible, it is necessary to know exactly how much water passes along the channel of a river and to calculate the velocity as well as the quality of the flow. There are expensive installations on most of the larger rivers which measure river flow on a continuous basis (Fig 5.1). A typical installation, or gauging station, consists of an irregularly shaped concrete barrier (weir or flume) with a measuring board for the visual estimation of water depth and a float which is linked to a continuous recorder so that the level of the water surface is marked on a rotating drum.

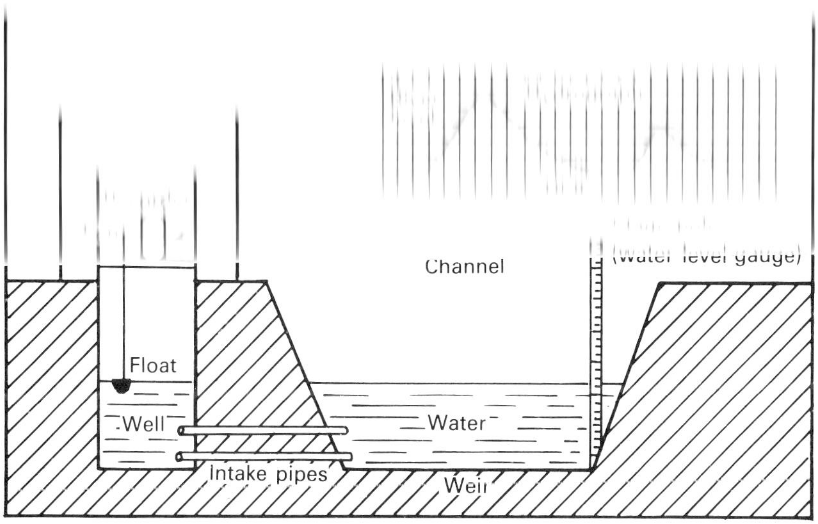


This description reveals that the water level in a channel is not static but rises and falls according to the amount of water flowing along the channel. This rise and fall is recorded on the rotating drum with the ink mark rising as the flow increases towards a peak and then subsiding, usually more gently than on the rise, towards a relatively low level again. We call this record a hydrograph. The low level is made by the water that is slowly draining out of the ground long after rainfall has ceased and it is known as 'baseflow'. It is supplied from deep within the rock and soil of the area drained by the river (the river basin; Fig 5.3). The bulge on the hydrograph represents water which runs off the hillslopes relatively quickly, either over the surface of the ground or as subsurface flow down the slopes but within the shallow soil. In very simple terms it is the effect of that part of the rainfall which quickly passes into the channel and away toward the sea, and this accounts for the name 'quickflow'.

On many occasions the quickflow bulge on the hydrograph never rises high enough for the water to overspill from the channel. Sometimes, however, so much water attempts to pass downstream that the channel cannot cope with it all and the excess water spills over the adjacent ground to form a flood. The bigger the quickflow bulge the higher the flood. Where flooding could pose a major hazard to villages or towns downstream of the measuring station, automatic warning systems are often installed. In these instances, the float arms are often connected by a trip switch to an alarm system in the relevant central police station. The alarm is then raised automatically when the water level rises above a critical level in the gauging station.

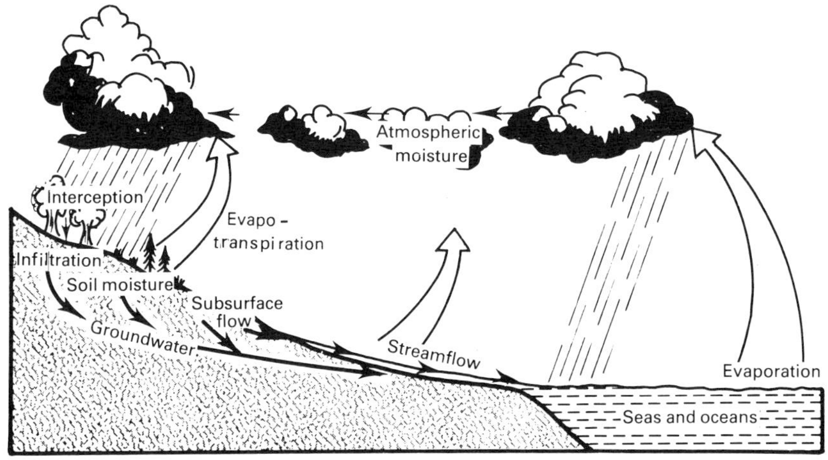


*FIG 5.2 The main components of the hydrological cycle.*

Of course, the rise of the water level in the river or stream does not begin immediately there is rainfall, because there must be time for the water to collect, run across the surface and through the soil toward the freely flowing water in the channel. This is called the 'lag' time of the basin. Some rivers, such as the Taff in south Wales[1] and many short mountain streams, respond very quickly. In these cases, the water level suddenly rises and falls and the hydrograph shows a very sharp peak. Such streams are called 'flashy' and are notorious for their sudden, very destructive floods. Others appear more docile and respond slowly to rainfalls. These characteristics have for a long time intrigued water scientists. One of them, Bernard Palissey (1510-90), described how river flow was just one part of a most important scientific phenomenon called the hydrological cycle (Fig 5.2).

The hydrological cycle is the most fundamental of all natural cycles, affecting the well-being of the human species. The whole process is driven by the heat of the sun which evaporates water from both the land and the sea. The evaporated water is in the form of a gas known as water vapour. If the air containing water vapour should be forced to rise, it cools, and some of the water vapour condenses out to form clouds which, in turn, often deposit the moisture back to the land and sea as snow, ice, hail, sleet or rain. Some of this moisture evaporates straight back to the atmosphere. A proportion is trapped or 'intercepted' by the vegetation cover and again

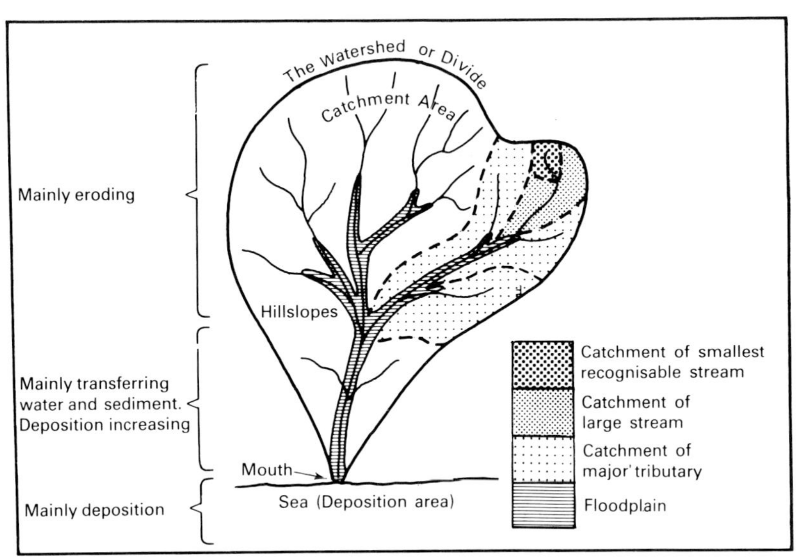


*FIG 5.3 The main features of a drainage basin showing how a number of small catchments combine to form larger catchments.*

is evaporated directly from the leaves back to the air. If the rainfall that reaches the ground is unable to filter into the soil or rock, it runs directly across the surface in rills and gullies to the rivers. Often, however, most of the moisture is able to penetrate downwards into the soil. This either seeps downslope within the soil as subsurface flow, or penetrates much deeper into the permanently saturated zone known as groundwater. Both, however, eventually emerge as springs and seeps to feed the streams, or at least this is what happens to what remains after trees and plants have sucked up moisture through their roots and transpired the water into the air through their leaves. Together all the water in the streams then returns to the sea, with some further evaporation from the flowing water surface, and the cycle is completed.

The network of rivers with their feeder streams, rivulets, gullies and seeps may therefore be likened to the gutter system of the landscape. [illegible] All things being equal, the larger the catchment the larger the river created within it.

But all things are not equal in nature, and this is the reason why some rivers are flashy and others docile. The behaviour of rivers reflects both the pattern of rainfall that is 'caught' by the catchment and what happens to the water when it arrives at the Earth's surface (Fig 5.4). Flashy rivers tend to drain short, steep catchments underlain by impermeable or 'waterproof' rocks which do not allow much of the rainwater to sink downwards into the ground. The incoming rainwater therefore collects on the surface and rapidly runs off to the streams and rivers to quickly create a quickflow bulge. The rapidity of this transfer and the size of the bulge can both be increased if there is little vegetation to intercept the incoming rainfall, or if the rainfall is very heavy.

The more docile rivers tend to be fed by catchments which may have gentle slopes covered with deep loose soils, or be underlain by rocks which are permeable. They may also have an extensive cover of forest which intercepts a significant proportion of the incoming rain. The end result is that less rainwater reaches the ground surface and most of that sinks straight downwards into the soil and rock where it may stay for weeks or months before emerging in springs and seeps. It takes very prolonged or heavy rains to create enough surface water for a quickflow bulge to develop. Just compare the phlegmatic streams of the Chalk hills of southern England with the flashy flood-prone streams on the adjacent lowlands cut in impermeable clays.

The proportion of incoming rainwater that follows these various routes can be changed by human actions so that rivers become more flashy (Fig 5.4). The cutting down of forests in the past, and the continuing clearance of woodlands, has the effect of reducing interception so that more water arrives at the ground surface. The use of heavy farm machinery on fields compacts the soil so that less of the water can sink downwards. This means that more remains at the surface to run off quickly, at the same time removing some soil to form rills and gullies. The creation of towns represents the greatest change, for the roofs and roads with their efficient drains quickly transport water to the rivers.

The broad details of these movements were first established by a string of famous scientists: Claude Perrault who compared the volume of the rainfall

*FIG 5.4 What happens to the rain when it arrives at the Earth's surface is very important with regard to river flows. The change in land use from forest through agriculture to urbanisation alters the balance and results in increased 'quickflow' run-off. This in turn causes rivers to flood more often and to become more 'flashy'.*

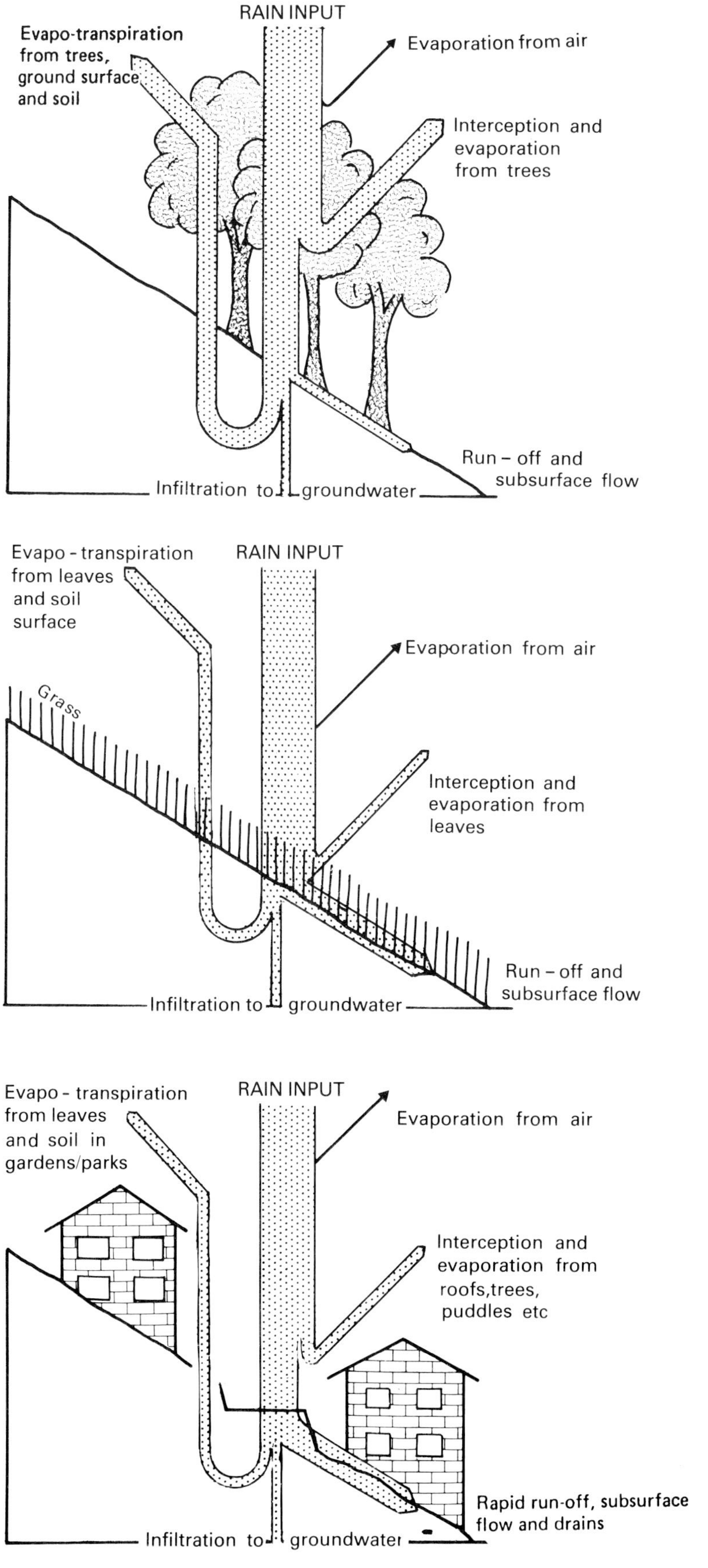

which fell on the Paris Basin with the volume which eventually formed the River Seine; Edmé Mariotte who concluded that rainfall fed springs by sinking into the ground (infiltration) and Edmund Halley (1656-1742) who first measured evaporation. Despite their eminence, however, they had a hard time replacing the ideas of the ancient Greek and Roman scientists who thought that the water in surface rivers came from huge underground rivers and lakes – a sort of vast subterranean plumbing system! Things have since changed, and we are now able to demonstrate that the planet Earth contains some 1,359 million km$^3$ (326 million cu miles) of water. Of this perhaps 97 per cent fills the ocean basins; 2 per cent is locked up in glaciers and ice-caps; 0.017 per cent resides in lakes; 0.28 per cent is in the atmosphere and only 0.0001 per cent (1,359km$^3$, 326 cu miles) of the Earth's water is in the rivers at any one time.

[illegible]

[illegible] but soon becomes organised into channels which join downslope to form even larger conduits. Thus the smaller finger-tip channels merge to form streams which combine to create rivers that may continue to grow so as to attain the size of the Thames, Severn, Trent or Shannon.

These streams and rivers carry out the basic functions of landscape change. Upstream the rivers are mainly cutting into (eroding) the land to form hillslopes. The eroded material is transported downstream in many ways. Some is carried in solution, especially if the river drains an area underlain by limestone. Very small fragments float downstream (suspension), larger fragments (sand-size) bounce along and big pieces roll along the bottom. The very large boulders often visible in the beds of streams move only at times of flood and the bigger they are the larger the flood that is needed to move them. Some of this transported material is deposited in the channel as sandbanks and gravel bars. A proportion of the finer material may be deposited in estuaries (see Chapter 6) or in deltas. What remains is redistributed by the sea to form beaches or taken offshore where it may accumulate and ultimately form new sedimentary rocks. This is the second great cycle of land shaping – the rock cycle – a never-ending succession of rock creation, destruction, transport and deposition which is nearly as old as the Earth itself (see Chapter 2).

## CREATING THE PATTERNS

As we have already seen, the size of a river is controlled by the area of the catchment, the extent to which the underlying ground materials allow water to move downwards, the amount and type of vegetation cover, the elevation and slope of the land, as well as the type of climate, whether 'wet' or 'dry'. Within the British Isles the combination of all these factors, but particularly the area drained, means that the rivers are small. Only twenty rivers have lengths of 100km (62 miles) or more and none drain areas in excess of 10,000km$^2$ (3,860 sq miles). Only the River Tay carries more water than 100m$^3$ (1,076 cu ft) in one second. The comparison given in Table 5.1 puts these figures into global perspective.

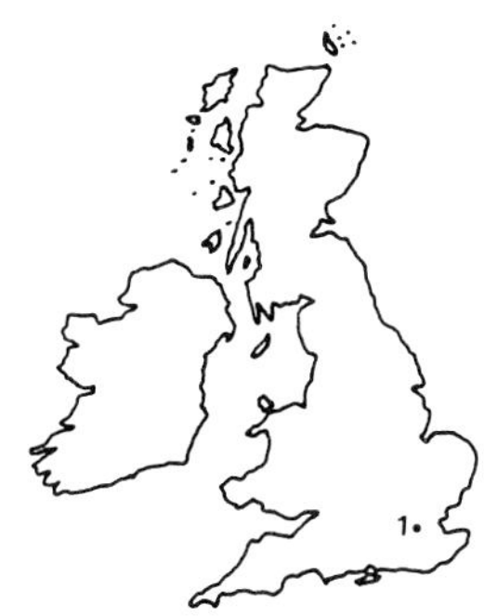


It is, in fact, very difficult to answer the question, 'What is the biggest river in the British Isles?' In terms of length it is the Thames[1], in area

drained it is also the Thames, but in terms of the actual amount of water carried to the sea it is the Tay[1]. Here the Thames[2] lags behind the Tay[1], Trent[3], Ness[4], Tweed[5] and Wye[6], all of which, drain wetter parts of Highland Britain. Yet, how small they all really are. You could take all the water in all the British rivers listed in Table 5.1 and pour it onto South America 175 times before you would make the Amazon!

The British Isles has a climate that ranges from 'wet' in the west and north to 'dry' in East Anglia and London. Estimating from maps, it has been shown that the main island has 1,445 major river systems and this does not include the tiny streams. In other words, the density of rivers in the British Isles is high. There is over 0.33km (361yd) of stream channel for every square kilometre (sq mile) of north-west Scotland, declining to 0.15 km (164yd) in the east and south-east of England. It is not surprising that river action follows human activity as the dominant processes presently shaping the inland landscape.

TABLE 5.1
COMPARISON OF BRITISH AND MAJOR WORLD RIVERS
(from J.Lewin, British Rivers, 1981)

| *River* | *Length* | | *Area* | | *Volume/sec* | |
|---|---|---|---|---|---|---|
| | *km(miles)* | | *$km^2$(sq miles)* | | *$m^3$/sec ($ft^3$/sec)* | |
| Thames | 239 | 148 | 9,950 | 3,842 | 67.40 | 2,380 |
| Trent | 149 | 92 | 7,490 | 2,892 | 82.21 | 2,903 |
| Tay | 110 | 68 | 4,590 | 1,772 | 152.21 | 5,375 |
| Tweed | 140 | 87 | 4,390 | 1,695 | 73.85 | 2,608 |
| Severn | 206 | 128 | 4,330 | 1,672 | 62.70 | 2,214 |
| Wye | 225 | 140 | 4,040 | 1,560 | 74.41 | 2,522 |
| Ouse | 117 | 73 | 3,320 | 1,282 | 40.45 | 1,429 |
| Great Ouse | 184 | 114 | 3,030 | 1,170 | 14.16 | 500 |
| Spey | 137 | 85 | 2,650 | 1,023 | 55.86 | 1,973 |
| Avon | 125 | 78 | 2,210 | 853 | 14.43 | 509 |
| Tyne | 89 | 55 | 2,180 | 842 | 43.45 | 1,534 |
| Aire | 114 | 71 | 1,930 | 745 | 36.89 | 1,303 |
| Ness | 107 | 66 | 1,840 | 710 | 76.60 | 2,705 |
| Tummel | 90 | 56 | 1,720 | 664 | 54.89 | 1,939 |
| Clyde | 105 | 65 | 1,700 | 656 | 34.40 | 1,215 |
| Dee | 116 | 72 | 1,370 | 529 | 35.70 | 1,261 |
| Eden | 102 | 63 | 1,370 | 529 | 31.02 | 1,095 |
| Tees | 103 | 64 | 1,260 | 486 | 19.46 | 687 |
| Ribble | 94 | 58 | 1,140 | 440 | 31.72 | 1,120 |
| Tywi | 82 | 51 | 1,090 | 421 | 38.34 | 1,354 |

| *River* | *Length* | | *Area* | | *Volume/sec* | |
|---|---|---|---|---|---|---|
| | *km(miles)* | | *$km^2$(sq miles)* | | *$m^3$/sec ($ft^3$/sec)* | |
| Amazon | 6,437 | 4,000 | 7,050,000 | 2,722,000 | 180,000 | 6,345,000 |
| Congo | 4,700 | 2,920 | 3,457,000 | 1,335,000 | 41,000 | 1,458,000 |
| Ob-Irtysh | 5,410 | 3,360 | 2,975,000 | 1,149,000 | 15,000 | 54,000 |
| Mackenzie | 4,241 | 2,635 | 1,841,000 | 711,000 | 11,000 | 378,000 |
| Ganges-Brahmaputra | 2,897 | 1,800 | 1,621,000 | 626,000 | 38,000 | 1,350,000 |
| Zambezi | 3,540 | 2,200 | 1,330,000 | 514,000 | 7,000 | 243,000 |
| Tigris-Euphrates | 2,740 | 1,703 | 1,114,000 | 430,000 | 1,000 | 35,100 |
| Danube | 2,850 | 1,770 | 816,000 | 315,000 | 7,000 | 243,000 |
| Columbia | 1,950 | 1,212 | 668,000 | 258,000 | 7,000 | 243,000 |
| Rhine | 1,320 | 820 | 160,000 | 62,000 | 2,000 | 70,200 |

We must never forget that these figures refer only to the *present* drainage pattern. If we admit to 'the immense geological time' over which the landscape has evolved, then there must have been many periods in the past when the ground surface of these islands was affected by much greater volumes of water than occur today. Not the retreating waters of the Flood but the meltwater generated by the great ice-sheets which once covered the British Isles (see Chapters 1, 3 and 4). Often we can only understand the great size and shape of the 'river' valleys that we see today if we postulate that at some time in the past they were excavated by huge flows of meltwater released by the ice-sheets. Sometimes very extensive lakes were created between the ice-sheets and ridges or escarpments, the water draining via enormous overflows which often cut major valleys where none had existed before. One example was Lake Harrison[1], an immense lake originally dammed up between the ice sheet margin in the vicinity of [illegible] estuary rather than continuing eastwards to the Wash.

One of the major ice-sheets of the Ice Age (the Anglian, see Chapter 1) even deflected the River Thames. The Thames originally flowed well to the north of London via a route that took it north-eastwards along the Vale of St Albans to Hertford[5], Harlow and the sea in Essex (Fig 5.6). The Anglian ice-sheet, advancing southwards from East Anglia about 270,000 years ago, effectively blocked this course and forced the Thames south to its present

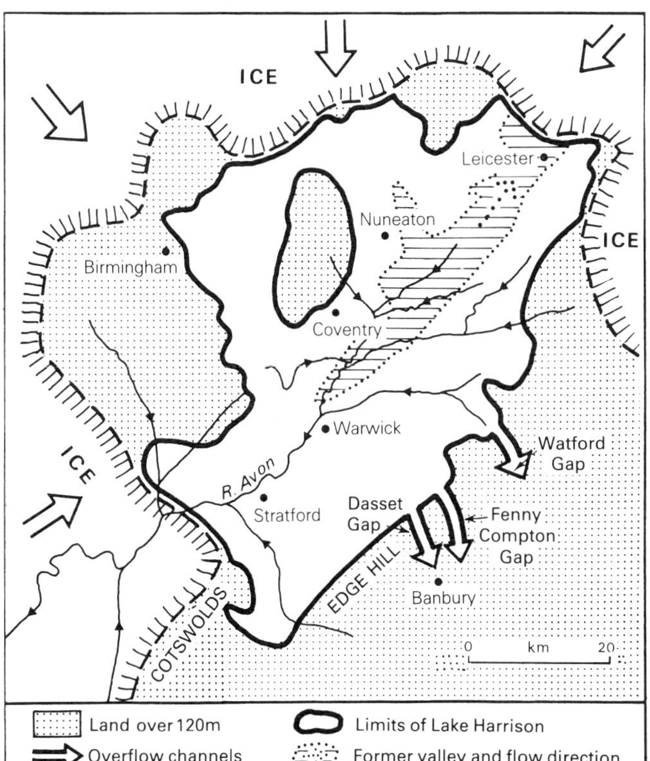


*FIG 5.5 A reconstruction of Lake Harrison ponded up between the Wolstonian ice-sheet and the North Oxfordshire Heights. This lake not only excavated large overflow paths along its southern margin, but also caused the original drainage to the north-east to be abandoned and the Warwickshire Avon to be born.*

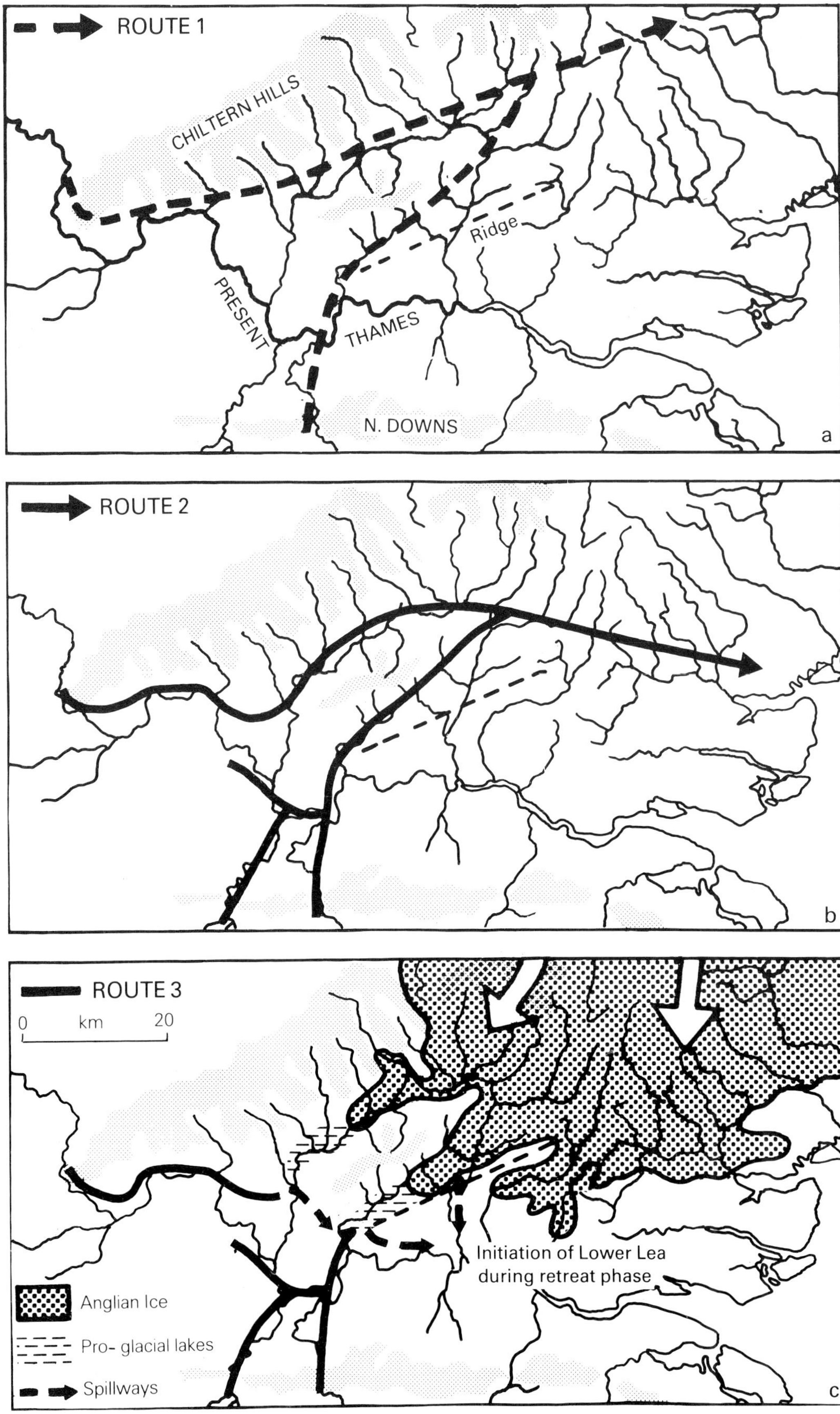
ROUTE 1
CHILTERN HILLS
Ridge
PRESENT
THAMES
N. DOWNS
a
ROUTE 2
b
ROUTE 3
0 km 20
Initiation of Lower Lea
during retreat phase
Anglian Ice
Pro- glacial lakes
Spillways
c

position. This was a truly remarkable event. Rivers, once established within their valleys, are not easily moved elsewhere. Only a massive ice-sheet or widespread land movement is capable of doing this. Nor was the Thames very stable in its new route, for it changed its course many times as it enlarged its newly occupied valley. Even during the last 20,000 years the Thames has occupied many positions between the present north bank joining Chelsea and the City[1] and the terrace edge between Wandsworth and Clapham in the south. The development of London's river is one of the true detective stories of geomorphology.

Sometimes the patterns of water flow were more complex. Series of small and short-lived lakes were dammed by the ice which drained from one to another via networks of channels, some of which ran under the ice, some against the edge of the ice, as well as numerous examples that drained away from the ice across the frozen ground. The hillsides of Eskdale[2] in [illegible] extensive sheets. As the water levels changed with time, these sheets of 'outwash gravels' were cut into by the river to form low terraces composed of much coarser material than that carried by the rivers today. Rivers like the Feshie[4] in the Cairngorms are still in places quite braided and their valley floors often reveal the irregular patterns of the low terraces, islands and branching channels of the recently abandoned cold-climate condition (Plates 5.1 and 5.2). When these swollen rivers met the sea or the heads of fjords or lakes, the abundant loads were deposited as alluvial fans or deltas. Today the rivers are cut into these deposits so as to leave the old sediments as elevated terraces. Classic examples of these features can be found on the Isle of Arran and many other of the islands along the west coast of Scotland.

Beyond the ice-sheets, in the areas underlain by frozen ground, the land surface often became saturated during the summer thaw (see Chapter 4). Since the water was unable to escape downward through the frozen subsoil, the surface became sopping wet. Abundant small streams, lakes, bogs and marshes developed so that the drainage would have appeared highly disorganised. However, when each of the ice-sheets wasted away and the climate ameliorated to a more temperate condition, the rivers as we know them re-established themselves in their old valleys. Within overdeepened ice-gouged troughs, such as occur in the Lake District valleys, lakes were created in the hollows (eg, Crummock Water[1] and Buttermere[2]). Then began the long process of filling in at the points where rivers entered the lake, were checked, and deposited their loads as deltas and fans. The old braided valley floors were replaced by rivers which were smaller and wound (meandered) within the valley in a single channel. The present rivers often have meanders that are of much smaller scale than the bends of the valleys (valley meanders) that confine them and are called 'misfits' or 'underfits' (see Plate 1.4). As the size of meanders is thought to reflect the magnitude of the flow of water that creates them, this difference in scale is believed by many to indicate that the valleys were excavated in the past by much larger flows of water than at present pass through the river channel. Most of the Cotswold rivers are of this type.

Where old glacial deposits and cold-climate sludge deposits (head) existed in the floors of the valleys, these were eroded as small streams began the laborious task of clearing their path. Today terraces of gravel

*FIG 5.6 The diversion of the ancestral River Thames to the south in the London area as a result of the arrival of the Anglian ice-sheet.*

PLATE 5.1 (left) *Photograph of the River Feshie, Scotland, taken from the air which clearly shows the two main characteristics of rivers in the British Isles. In the section in the middle distance the river displays what is known as a 'braided habit' with several channels or threads of water separated by gravel bars. During the cold periods of the Ice Age all rivers in the British Isles had this appearance. Nearer the camera the river utilises a single channel and the patterns of sediment indicate that it will soon begin to bend so as to form meanders. The irregular ground flanking the stretches of single channel are evidence of the braided character of the river in the past. Former courses of the river are clearly visible on either side of the present river.*

PLATE 5.2 (inset left) *Another view of the River Feshie showing the multiple channels, rapids and gravel islands (bars) that are characteristic of braided rivers.*

PLATE 5.3 (above) *Many river valleys in the British Isles contain complex sequences of sediments often arranged in terraced form. The river below Alport Castle in Derbyshire possesses bars within its shallowly cut meanders as well as low alluvial terraces.*

and the preservation of complicated sequences of gravel, mud and peat in valley floors provide clues that allow us to reconstruct what happened in the past (Plate 5.3). However, the fact that the debris laid down by the ice-sheets is still found over much of the British Isles tells us that the processes of landshaping today are indeed slow, despite the ever-flowing rivers.

Rivers are clearly dynamic features in the landscape. They change their character not only with the mood of the weather but also as the environmental conditions vary. Similar rivers to those that exist today may have been created during each of the warmer interludes between the arctic phases of the Ice Age. But during the cold phases they both looked and behaved very differently, braided in summer and frozen solid in winter. They are schizophrenic. It is little wonder, therefore, that the valleys that contain the gently flowing rivers of today between their lines of willows should also contain shapes and deposits that reflect their differing character through time. Even the level surface of the floodplain built by a river conceals hidden varieties of materials that testify to what the river was like at some point in the past (Fig 1.2). Next time you walk by a river just think that there is history beneath your feet.

## THE EVOLVING LANDSCAPE

Nearly a century ago a famous geomorphologist, William Morris Davis, published a scientific paper called the 'The Geographical Cycle'(*Geographical Journal*, 1899) in which he laid the foundations for the whole section of geomorphology which is concerned with landform description and evolution. Davis proposed that the shape of the ground (the landforms) could be regarded as the result of processes of erosion and deposition acting on the materials of the Earth's fabric over time. He discussed the way in which river patterns evolved, how valleys were formed and how hillslopes changed their shape over time, and summarised all of these themes in a simple model. This stated that when an area of land was uplifted above the sea, the rivers that became established on the new surface began to excavate, creating a landscape of steep-sided valleys which he called the Stage of Youth. In time the maximum relief between the original landsurface and the valley floors was established and the rivers, now flowing close to the level of the sea, would begin to meander and widen their valleys. This was Maturity. As still more time passed, the ridges themselves would be lowered, and after a very long time a low-lying plain would be produced, covered in weathered debris and with only a few remnant hills telling of the huge volume of rock that had been consumed over many millions of years. This was the Stage of Old Age, and the plain he called a peneplain.

There is still much merit in using this generalized descriptive approach although our knowledge has increased and we are aware that this is only one way of many to understand or study the landscape. In fact, nature is much too complicated to be summarised in any one simple model and no single region in the British Isles exactly fits the Davisean idea. Therefore, most geomorphologists today are concentrating far more on understanding the processes at work in the landscape in the belief that only when we fully understand how the landscape machine works, can we ever hope to build general models of the history of landshape change. The lesson for the more casual observer or someone new to the subject is clear. Concentrate on observing what is there. Progress to a description of the shapes and what they are made of. Speculate on how it all happened. In these three simple operations there is endless fascination for rivers and landshapes themselves are capable of infinite variety and beauty.

Let us consider the simple fact that rivers create the valleys they flow in. They achieve this by employing three important mechanisms. First the mere hydraulic action of flowing water corrodes the bed and banks of their channels and causes pressure-cavitation effects to leave typical fluted marks and pot-holes on the rocks over which they flow. Secondly they carry rock fragments of varying size; silt, sand, gravel and even boulders, through their channels which steadily wear away (abrade) anything which lies in their path to cut gorges, rapids and waterfalls such as Cheddar[1] (Plate 5.4), Lydford Gorge[2] and High Force[3] (Plate 5.5). Thirdly, they possess a potent chemical action dissolving cements, or soluble materials such as limestone, to create the spectacular variety of features ranging from fluted boulders on the Burren[4] (Plate 1.11) or Ingleborough[5], to disappearing rivers such as Fell Beck at Gaping Ghyll[6], and extensive cave systems like Eastwater Cavern[7], Wookey Hole[8] or Dovedale[9] (Plate 5.6). The effects are most noticeable in limestone, but all rock types, even granite or basalt, are affected by water in a complex series of chemical reactions which decompose the rock, create soil and prepare the solid hills for transport [illegible] then at last seeps of water and the first open conduits occur. Where the water and soil are able to flow directly off the surface, such as on colliery spoil tips, china-clay tips in Cornwall[10], or even on steep, rocky hillslopes in the Highlands, rills and small gullies replace the subsurface pipes (Plate 5.7). Each, however, in turn feed the first true finger-tip channels of the emerging river pattern.

For Plates 5.4, 5.5 and 5.6 see pages 118-119

This pattern extends by headward erosion into the potential catchment area in competition with neighbouring streams. This is achieved both by the development of rills and gullies by overland flow and by the evolution of further subsurface percolines and pipes which carry subsurface flow water. The streams eventually extend to their maximum length and the divide between neighbouring catchments becomes firmly established. The network continues to develop by the processes of elaboration. There is further development of finger-tip channels but these processes result in internal competition between the small tributaries that now try to take each other's water. The divides show continued slow movement away from the steepest and most aggressive or successful streams towards those less successful. As a consequence, the catchments of the aggressive streams expand at the expense of intervening, less capable streams. This internal competition begins to have an effect on the pattern which simplifies in two ways. Some of the larger streams manage to divert water from lesser streams through a process known as river capture, which results in the creation of more powerful streams. Secondly, the small rills in the headwater areas steadily become fewer in number since valley widening will eventually absorb and completely erode away the original small channels.

If we were to follow a stream downstream as it developed we would find that it endeavours always to join other rivers at the same level by means of a smooth junction. The gradient of the river bed also tends to form a smooth curve, or long profile, when traced down-river toward the sea. Always a river tries to follow any geological weakness it encounters and to adjust beautifully to the hard and soft rocks in its path. Should there be well developed patterns of joints or faults in the rock, the river network will be sure to etch them out. Should there be an uplift of the land or a lowering of sea-level, the river will respond by cutting down to the new level, thereby steepening and deepening its valley. Sometimes this results in the creation of a deep gorge. The spectacular incised meanders of the River Wye[1] are of this type.

PLATE 5.4 (above) Cheddar Gorge in the Mendip Hills of Somerset is deeply cut through Carboniferous Limestone. The valley is assymetrical and also of 'youthful' form with interlocking spurs. Many suggestions have been made for its origins including the collapse of the roof of an extensive cave system and the effect of torrential glacial meltwater. The 1968 storm, however, suggests that its origin may also lie partly in the effects of rare, catastrophic floods (Plate 5.9).

PLATE 5.5 (far right) The magnificent High Force waterfall on the River Tees shows many of the typical features of waterfalls: resistant rock, a deep gorge downstream, clear evidence of river incision and a well-developed plunge pool. The waterfall has been created here as a result of the river cutting downwards so as to encounter the sheet of hard intrusive igneous rock which forms the Whin Sill (Plate 2.4).

PLATE 5.6 (right) Cave systems underlie most of the upland limestone massifs in the British Isles. In Dovedale, Derbyshire, some of the caves have been exposed by river down-cutting to reveal typical arched forms produced mainly by the subterranean solution of the limestone.

When the reverse happens and sea-level rises relative to the land, the river, though drowned at its mouth, is not beaten. It now begins the task of infilling the estuary by dumping its sediment within its drowned channel to form bars and banks. These features grow steadily and eventually become vegetated to form solid land across which the river once more winds its peaceful way. The drowned valleys or rias of the Dart[1], Kingsbridge[2], Plym[3] or Fal[4] in south-west England are typical of this never ending process of adjustment to the vagaries of mother nature. The lower parts of the Cuckmere[5] and Ouse[6] valleys in Sussex are examples of formerly drowned valleys now, once more, filled with so much sediment that the rivers have great difficulty in finding a route to the sea, winding about on the surface like serpents (Plate 5.8) until constrained by the man-made dykes.

One of the great delights of the countryside is to be beside the gentle waters of a stream, to paddle, picnic or fish the day away. But look more closely, beside you is one of the most varied and complex forms in nature. Beneath the water the bed of the channel has a multitude of colour and form. At the smallest scale the bed may be rough or smooth depending on whether the sediment is clay, silt, sand or even gravel, cobbles, boulders and bedrock. The sediments are not merely dumped but are often arranged in beautifully patterned shapes, especially sands which have rippled surfaces. The materials also tend to be regularly arranged in a downstream direction, with zones of accumulation forming riffles or rapids, separated by pools of deeper water. All these sediments occur within an equal complexity of channel shapes which range from square in section to semi-circular and may be deep and narrow or shallow and wide. Much of the variety in shape depends on the nature of the materials in which the channel is cut.

The patterning of the landscape by streams is also extremely variable. Anyone who studies the arrangement of streams shown on a map cannot help but be fascinated by the variety. The patterns differ so much, one from another, that geomorphologists are forced to employ a formidable armoury of descriptive terms: 'dendritic' for the tree-like patterns of streams on the clay vales of lowland Britain, 'trellised' for streams on the highly jointed rocks of the Pennines, 'radial' for the Lake District[1], 'annular' for the semi-circular arrangement of the Woolhope Dome[2] and 'deranged' for the apparently random patterns on recently laid down glacial deposits. Within valleys themselves the patterns may be meandering such as the Cuckmere[3] (Plate 5.8) in Sussex or the Tees[4] in Yorkshire, braided with many islands such as the Feshie[5] in Scotland, straight like the Dart[6] at Bellever on Dartmoor, incised like the River Wye[7], or engorged like the Avon[8] at Bristol.

Nothing is more mysterious than why a river meanders. Normally we would expect it to follow the shortest possible course downhill toward the sea. Why does it persist in adopting such a convoluted and lengthy course? At the simplest level it has been said that a river is easily deflected by a hard rock outcrop, a fallen tree or even another river, and that once diverted the flow of water will continue to bounce from one side of the channel to the other, eroding its banks at regular intervals so as to give rise to meanders. Yet experiments have shown that if we build our artificial stream in uniform materials that cannot create a force for deflection, the steam will still develop meanders.

The answer seems to lie in the nature of the water flow itself. One common explanation is that water actually follows a spiral path as it moves downstream so that if we were to follow just one molecule of water it would move like a helix. It would move across the surface but in a downstream direction, then down and across the bed, still always going downstream, then up again to the surface but now much further downstream than when it began. Of course where the water impinges against a bank, it may erode sediment. These particles are transported across the bed and downstream and, when the water rises, the sediment is deposited to form a bar. So one side of the channel is eroded while the other grows inwards and so a meander is born. Once created, the features continue to grow so that the bends become greater and eventually the size of the bend becomes so great that the river cuts through the neck, thereby creating a straight reach of the river and an arc-shaped lake known as an 'ox bow' lake, in the now abandoned channel. Next time you walk along a floodplain, look at the surface and you will see marshy depressions and small ponds that represent the remains of former meanders.

One of the most striking features of river valleys in the British Isles is that they often contain terraces. Close inspection of the terrace edges in cuttings or excavations reveals that they are of two main forms. Where cut in rock, the flat surface of the terrace can be seen to be underlain by [illegible]

In plan, river terraces may be paired or unpaired. That is, they either match each other in height on either side of the valley or they alternate in elevation. The reason for this difference lies in their origin. If an area is uplifted or if the sea-level falls, the river will try to adjust itself to the new relative sea-level. It cuts down into its former valley floor – a process known as rejuvenation – to leave the remnants of the old valley floor as terraces. The terraces will be the same height, paired, on either side of the valley but inclined gently downstream toward the old sea-level. Unpaired terraces are produced without a change in the height of the river or sea-level at its mouth. As a river meanders across its floodplain it may alternately cut a surface into first one side, then the other side, of the valley. At the same time it is slowly lowering the valley floor so that next time the river returns to an old meander position, it is at a lower elevation and a terrace is formed as the old valley floor is abandoned.

These changes are also recorded on the long profile of the river as it descends to the sea. The gentle concave slope may be interrupted by irregularities causing waterfalls, rapids or very steep sections, such as High Force on the Tees, which represent points on the river where down-cutting has yet to be completed, possibly due to the presence of bands of hard rock. This point is given a curious name, the 'knickpoint'.

None of these features are permanent. Just as the water itself is never still, so the landshapes themselves are neither fixed nor immutable. Ripples move steadily downstream, channel sediments are eroded and deposited, banks are undermined, channels widen and narrow, patterns evolve, headwaters erode into the hills or dry up in times of drought – and in times of flood everything may be carried away.

## FLOODS – THE FORCE FOR CHANGE

Floods show rivers in their most terrifying mood. Even normally placid streams can become raging torrents. During the night of 15 August 1952 at Lynmouth[1] in north Devon, the little River Lyn rose 9m (29.5ft) in level; 200,000 tonnes (tons) of boulders, cobbles and gravel buried part of the village and shoreline. The biggest boulders weighed over 15 tonnes, 93 houses were destroyed, 132 vehicles were washed into the sea, and 34



(pp122-3)
*PLATE 5.7 As water falls onto the Earth's surface it begins to organise itself into faint underground channels, rills, gullies and river channels. Here, in the headwaters of a catchment in the Black Mountains, rills are present on the steep valley sides. They drain down into the small river which is eroding vigorously, as shown by the undermining and collapse of the river banks in many places, and the small river cliffs.*

*PLATE 5.8 When sea-level rises, the mouths of river valleys are drowned to form rias or fjords. The river then attempts to infill this arm of the sea with sediment to form new land. The River Cuckmere in Sussex has achieved this objective by dumping up to 30m (98ft) of material in the valley floor. However, the seaward slope on this alluvial carpet is so shallow that the river has been forced to make huge meanders. These have subsequently been straightened by humans so as to shorten the journey for sailing craft and to assist in flood control.* (Full-size illustration on pp102-3)

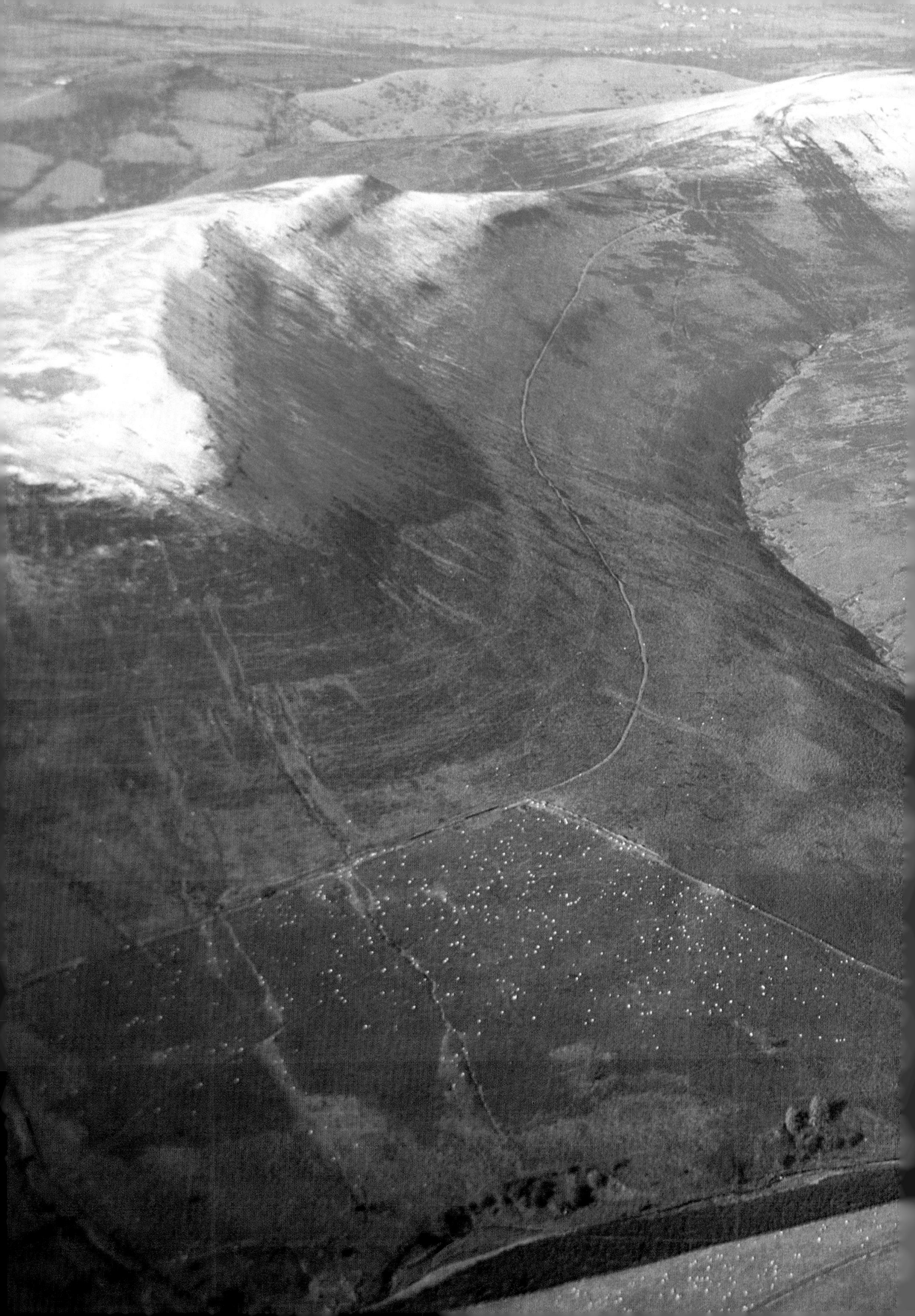

*PLATE 5.9 Cheddar Gorge looking downstream during the 1968 flood and looking upstream after the flood. The debris is mainly eroded from the road and banks within the gorge. Today little sign of the flood can be found.*

people died. The total rainfall in 24 hours was 22cm (9in), of which 15cm (6in) fell between 6.30pm and 11.30pm. Yet the River Lyn is a very small river with two main branches, the West and East Lyn, which drain only 100km$^2$ (38 sq miles) of Exmoor. How could this happen?

Catastrophic events require the combination of several favourable factors before they can occur. At Lynmouth it was the coincidence of a very steep catchment, shallow soils saturated by two weeks of August rain so that they could absorb no more water, the occurrence of a rare very heavy storm, and the location of the town at the confluence of the two streams, both of which carried floodwater. The result was an event so rare that it is estimated to occur on average only once in 50,000 years. It could, of course, occur again tomorrow, but the chances of this happening are low.

To geomorphologists such events are regarded as formative landshaping occurrences. So much debris is moved that the valley form is irrevocably altered and the scars of the flood normally remain visible for a very long

time. Normal processes cannot move the huge boulders, nor the volume of debris, in order to restore the previous valley form and thus we have to take into account the fact that many of our landforms may have originated in big events. Yet is is not always easy to identify the forms today because humans are very effective in removing the effects of disaster. At Lynmouth the river was bulldozed clear of debris and the channel widened to cope with any re-occurrence of the flood in the future. An equally big event on the Mendip Hills in 1968 ripped out the road in the floor of Cheddar Gorge[1], filled many of the famous tourist caves with sediment, infilled the fish ponds and damaged many houses and shops (Plate 5.9). Today only those who can remember the event are able to point to the small changes in the landscape that it created, because the debris was quickly cleared away by emergency teams. Vegetation has since covered the scars on the hillsides, the caves are clear and the road repaired. But do not be deceived. Nature is wayward and the Earth is a fragile place to live on.

6

# THE MEETING OF LAND AND SEA

Rita Gardner

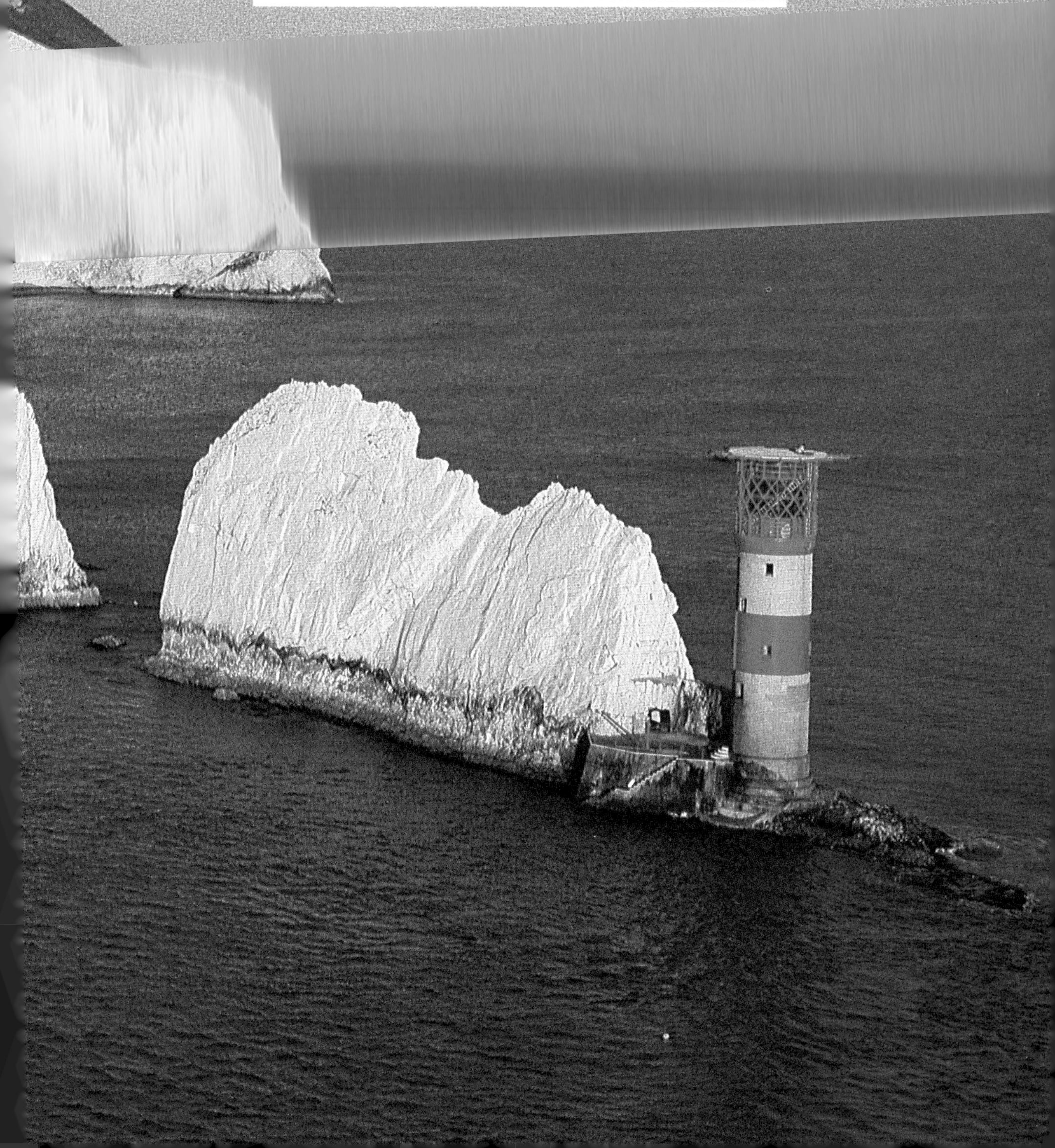

Cliffs in some parts of the British coastline, most notably near Holderness[1] and in East Anglia, retreat over 2m (6.5ft) per year (Plate 6.1). It is thought that in Roman times the Holderness cliffline was up to 4km (2.5 miles) further out to sea in places, so that more than 200 km$^2$ (77 sq miles) of land has been lost. With such spectacular rates of erosion it is hardly surprising that the plight of those with cliff-top homes has been highlighted in the press. A similar tale can be told of Dunwich in Suffolk, a flourishing port and town in the thirteenth century, but now largely swallowed up by the waves. For a seafaring nation we seem, at times, to have been acutely unaware of the power of the sea to consume our coastline – not by occasional nibbles but in bite-sized chunks year after year. We have persisted in building homes and services in places vulnerable to coastal erosion and have then been forced to defend these areas against the natural action of the sea, often at great expense and inconvenience, and not always very effectively (see Plate 6.1).

Yet at the same time other parts of the coastline have been growing seawards. At Harlech[2] the magnificent castle that dominates the town was originally built (AD 1290) with a water-gate, indicating direct access to the Glaslyn estuary or the coast. That access is now blocked by sand dunes and a salt marsh; the estuary is more than 4km (2.5 miles) distant, and the coast 0.5km (550yd) away. Many other estuaries require periodic dredging to keep a navigable channel open. The wind too does its best to build up the coastline. At Studland[3], near Poole in Dorset, four large ridges of sand dunes have developed since 1607. The third of these blocked off a tidal inlet around 1900, leaving the 'Little Sea' as a freshwater inland lake. The last ridge, just behind the beach, has developed since 1930.

There can be no doubt that our coastline is changing, in places somewhat unnervingly before our eyes, but elsewhere much more slowly. Although the numerous cases of rapid erosion are more dramatic, on balance the coastline as a whole is gaining a little land each year; more material is being deposited than eroded. But of course, erosion and deposition tend to occur at different locations, and in general the erosion causes far greater havoc. The important question to answer therefore is, what controls whether erosion or deposition will occur? To answer we need to consider how the sea succeeds in eroding, carrying and depositing materials, and how the land tries to resist its persistent attacks.

One key element in whether the coast is eroding is the energy of the waves reaching the coastline. This is determined by the strength of the winds that whip up the waves, and by the distances over the sea that the wind has been blowing. The west coast of Britain receives the largest and highest energy waves, often exceeding 5m (16ft) in height close to the shore. The reason for this is that the prevailing south-westerly winds can blow unimpeded across the Atlantic for thousands of kilometres (miles), and thus generate huge waves. In contrast, an easterly wind at best blows across a few hundred kilometres of North Sea before reaching the east coast of Scotland.

The second important consideration is the degree to which the coast is exposed to the full force of wave attack. In sheltered areas, such as in coves, behind islands or spits, or in an estuary, the force of the waves is much diminished, and so the capacity for erosion is limited. This is either because the waves are deflected away, or because the wave energy is absorbed by the intervening barrier. The energy to erode will be concentrated on exposed coasts such as at Holderness or north Devon and deposition will take place in sheltered areas.

Most of the vast amount of energy reaching the coasts is either absorbed by a beach, or dissipated by friction between the water molecules themselves or between the sea and the sea bed. Where the shore is shallow for some way out to sea, much energy is lost by friction as water movement in the base of the waves rubs against the sea bed. This slows the waves down,

PLATE 6.1 *Rapid erosion of cliffs in soft sands and gravels has succeeded in destroying these homes at Hornsea on the Lowestoft coastline.*

particularly towards their base, and leads to an increase in the height of the waves. Moreover, the tops of the waves, travelling faster, curl over and break a long way offshore. On steeper shores, the waves generally break much closer to the beach because it is not until the waves are in the shallow water close to the shore that the base of the wave interacts with the sea bed, and is slowed down. In deep water, negligible wave motion is felt near the sea bed, as explained later.

If you stand on Chesil Beach[1], for example, you can see this, for here the shore slopes very steeply, and makes this a particularly dangerous place for swimming. Where less wave energy is lost by friction with the sea bed, the beach is left to absorb more of the energy. Beaches are the best defence, natural or manmade, against wave attack. The tremendous energy constantly being hurled against Chesil Beach on a windy day is absorbed in a few rattling movements of the pebbles and as the water trickles down the large pore spaces between the pebbles. Excess energy not absorbed in these ways is available for erosion. Thus, coasts that are not sheltered, and where the shore slopes steeply, are more prone to erosion, particularly if there is no protective beach.

The character of the rocks also plays a role in determining how susceptible the coast will be to the power of the waves. Obviously, the softer the rock the more easily it is eroded. This is one of the main problems at Holderness where the cliffs consist of weak layers of gravel, sand and clay dumped by ice-sheets during the Ice Age (see Chapter 3). Such materials offer minimal resistance to wave attack. In contrast, the tougher rocks of the Pembrokeshire coastline for example, offer more resistance to the huge waves that come crashing onshsore here in winter. As a result they form towering cliffs – bastions against the attack of the sea. However,

*PLATE 6.2 The rugged coastline near Hartland, north Devon, is not immune from erosion. The retreating cliffs have left behind a rocky shore platfrom, being covered here by the rising tide, and they have cut off a valley, leaving it hanging on the cliff top.*

even the toughest rocks are not without points of structural weakness. In cracks, such as joints and faults (see Chapter 2), the compression of air by the bombarding waves can cause blocks of rock to loosen, and slowly the cliff will retreat. As it retreats it leaves behind a planed-off, and gently seaward-sloping, rock surface at about the level of high tide. This is the shore platform (Plate 6.2).

The other mechanisms by which the sea demolishes rocky shorelines includes the quarrying of loose rock by the waves themselves, and the scouring action of sand and shingle carried in the waves against the rock face – the sea's own Brillo pad. But erosion is not only by mechanical means. Chemical dissolution of some rocks, particularly limestones, takes place in the sea and often creates a fantastic landscape of jagged pinnacles and pitted rock surfaces. Additional erosion can result from rainwater chemically breaking down the rocks exposed in the cliff face above the level of the sea and salt spray. In a few cases even biological activity can be important. Some molluscs bore holes in the rock face, and browsing fish, and shellfish such as limpets, can smooth the rocks on the shore platform.

Several very characteristic landscapes are created by the erosion of cliffs, in addition to shore platforms. In north Devon[1] the fairly rapid retreat of the coast has left valleys hanging on the top of the cliffs, high above the sea (Plate 6.2). Often the areas of rock more resistant to the attack of the waves are left as forlorn and eye-catching pillars and pinnacles (stacks) surrounded by sea. The best known stacks are probably the Old Man of Hoy[2] in Orkney, and the Needles[3] (Plate 6.3). Even more stunning are the cases where the sea has hollowed out a passage through a rock headland, creating a natural arch of rock such as the famous Green Bridge of Wales[4] in Pembrokeshire.

Given all this activity, it is surprising to learn that in many areas only about one-sixth of the sediment on the coast is supplied by erosion of cliffs. By far the most important source is material carried down by the rivers in their continual quest to flatten the land masses. On average over 75 per cent of the sediment is supplied in this way. The remaining one-twelfth comes from erosion of the sea bed offshore, and from accumulation of skeletal remains (shells) of marine organisms. The result is a vast amount of material of many sizes – pebbles, sands, silts and even the very finest, the clays – and of many compositions, being carried into the coast. The size of the material depends upon how it was supplied, the distance it has travelled before reaching the coast, and the type of rock that it is made of. But where does all this material go to?

Although the waves are the most obvious and often noisiest part of the coastal environment, particularly as they swash up the beach, they are in fact [illegible] pathways. That is, the currents are not random, but form a well-organised pattern in the nearshore area.

[illegible]

Most of the currents are generated by the waves that are whipped up by, and travel in the same direction as, the wind. But how can waves create currents? Most of us think of a wave as a moving wall of water, but this is very far from true. If it were, then all the ocean waters would pile up at the coastlines. In fact waves are the deformed *shape* of the water surface, and it is the *wave form* only (crests separated by troughs) that moves across the surface of the water. There is some movement of the water within a wave, but this movement is quite small and follows a very different pattern.

What happens beneath the deformed surface (the wave) is that each water molecule moves in an orbit, as shown in the diagram (Fig 6.1). This orbital movement decreases with depth below the surface until, in deep water, it ceases altogether. This is why there is little friction between the sea and its bed in deep water. In shallow water, however, the molecules are still in orbit close to the sea bed, and the orbits are quite elongated in shape. A most important fact is that by the end of each orbit in shallow water the molecules have moved a *very small* distance forward in the same onshore direction as the wave is moving. Taking the millions of water molecules that are in motion, together they create a net onshore movement (a current) that is capable of moving loose sediments such as sand grains. The greater the current the larger the sizes of grains, and the more of them that can be moved. The current flows in the same direction as the waves, so that when the waves approach the shore at right-angles, the current flows onshore also at right-angles to the beach.

If you take a careful look at most coastlines, say from a cliff top or headland, you will see that the waves often approach obliquely to the shore. In this case they will set up currents in the same way, and the currents will also flow obliquely and not at right-angles to the beach. We can think of this oblique current as having two components – one that is onshore and the other of movement along the shore. The longshore component increases as the angle of wave approach becomes more oblique and as wave height rises. The resulting movement of sediment along the shore (longshore drift) is concentrated in the shallow water landwards of

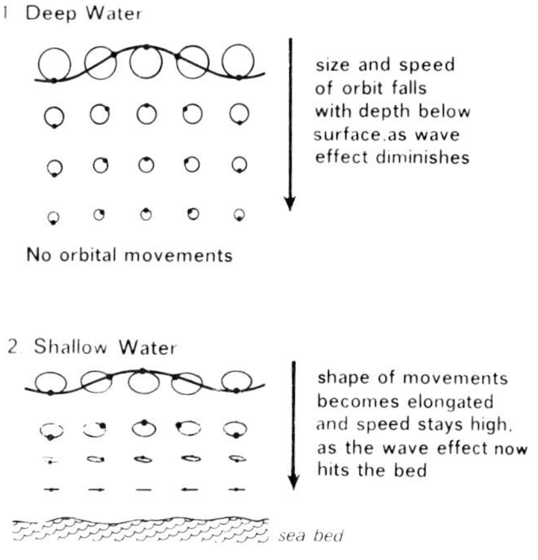


*FIG 6.1 The movement of water molecules beneath a wave. As the water surface is deformed into a wave shape, the water molecules beneath the surface move in orbital pathways in deep water but in more elongated pathways in shallow water. In shallow water the molecules are also still moving close to the sea bed. These movements create steady onshore currents, in shallow water, because with each orbit the molecules move a small distance onshore.*

the breakers. On most shores there is a preferred direction of longshore drift that relates directly to the prevailing wind direction, for it is this that controls the direction, and hence angle, of wave approach. This is clearly shown where groynes have been built in the beach. You will usually see sediment piled up against one side of the groyne, while on the other side there is little accumulation. The groyne is doing precisely what it was designed for – preventing the removal of sediment from the beach by longshore drift. Piers and breakwaters can have the same effect (Plate 6.4).

To balance up the small but steady net movement of water onshore and alongshore, we need an offshore flow. This occurs most dramatically as so-called 'rip currents'. These are narrow, often strong, seaward flows and are typically spaced at intervals along the shore. They complete the on-, along- and off-shore circulation pattern (Fig 6.2).

Not all currents are generated by the wind and the waves, others are linked to tidal flows. High and low tide are merely the crest and trough of an enormous, low wave. Unlike wind-generated waves, this (tide) wave is stationary. Is this possible you ask, as we all know that the tide flows in and out – or does it?

Most people know that the tide wave is generated by the gravitational pull of the moon (and far less so of the sun) that is felt on Earth, but how does it actually work? In general terms the gravitational pull towards the moon and sun is balanced by the force pulling the Earth away – the centrifugal force generated by the Earth's orbit round the sun. But whereas the centrifugal force is the same for each particle on Earth, the gravitational pull experienced varies slightly according to distance from the moon. This creates local imbalances between the two forces. Any point on the Earth that happens to lie directly under the moon experiences a stronger than average gravitational pull. Water particles in the sea are pulled upwards by it and a huge bulge is formed in the ocean surface. The opposite effect occurs on the other side of the Earth, farthest away from the moon. Here the gravitational pull is weakest and it fails to balance the outward push of centrifugal force. This imbalance leads to a second bulge on the ocean surface. The positions of both of these bulges are fixed in relation to the moon, one centred immediately beneath it and the other on the opposite side of the Earth.

Why, if we have two fixed bulges of ocean water does the tide appear as a wave, forever going in and out? The answer is that the Earth is rotating. This means that no point on Earth stays directly below the moon for long. So, one rotation of the Earth every 24 hours means that every point passes beneath the two bulges (or at least nearer to and further from them). The

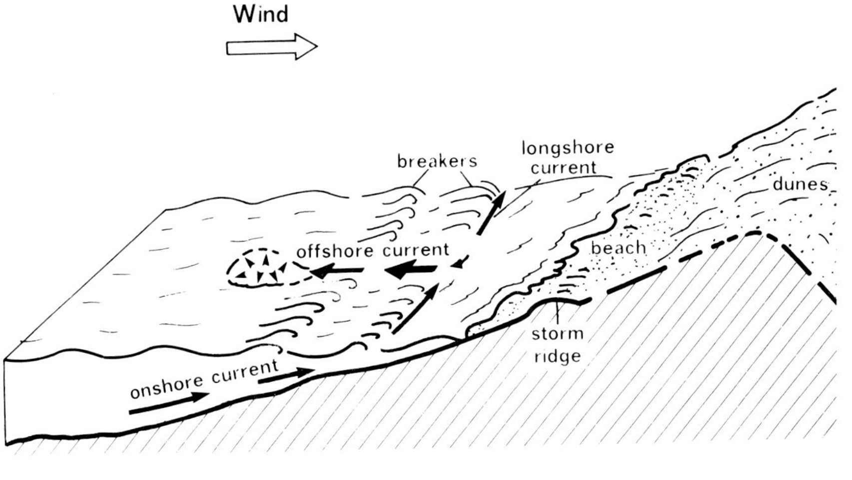


*FIG 6.2 The onshore currents have to be compensated by offshore movement of water, otherwise water would just pile up at the shore. The nearshore circulation of water typically involves onshore, longshore and offshore currents.*

sea surface rises and falls, and we have our two daily tides. But, of course, the moon is in orbit round the Earth; one orbit every 28 days. And so every day the moon itself has moved on a short distance. This explains the daily difference in timing of the tides.

The effect of the tide wave in the open ocean is a mere 50cm (20in) or so rise in level, but the effect is amplified in shallow water and by the particular shapes of the coastline. The tides in small sheltered areas, such as bays, estuaries and seas like the North Sea, are the result of the beat of the ocean tides against their mouths. This sends a shock wave echoing down the bay. Once the shock wave reaches the other end it will be reflected back and if the shape of the bay, and so the timing, is right, it will meet and reinforce the next 'tide' shock wave. This is capable of generating the large tidal ranges seen in parts of Britain, and events such as the Severn Bore. It also helps to explain the variation in tidal [illegible] [illegible] the tidal range exceeds 4m (13ft) tidal-related landscapes dominate, such as salt marshes and mudflats. For tidal ranges between 2m (6.5ft) and 4m (13ft), the landscape has elements of both regimes.

All the material that is brought to the coast, by one means or another, is affected by these currents. They sort it into different size classes, like a giant sieve. The coarser material can only be transported by very high energy wave-driven currents. Thus it is often stranded, for long periods between storms, in storm ridges on open beaches facing the direction of the strongest winds. In contrast, the finest material can be transported by even the slowest of currents, but it is only deposited in the quietest of sheltered areas, giving rise to mudflats and salt marshes. In higher energy areas the fine particles are generally carried off out to sea. The intermediate sizes, such as sands, are the most common along British coastlines. Before being dumped most have withstood the hardships of being eroded from the land, carried to the shore in rivers, winnowed and moved by the currents, and moved on again and again. It is no wonder that much of the sand on beaches is composed of resistant grains of the mineral quartz.

We have seen that the coast can be viewed as a constant merry-go-round of activity – erosion in exposed areas with high wave energy, transport of materials on to and along shore by the currents, then its deposition and accumulation especially in areas of lower energy where the sea can no longer carry its load. All this activity relating to the energy of the sea is merely the way the coast has of trying, in the long term, to adjust its shape to match the energy levels being thrown at it. In other words the coast is fashioned into a shape that will absorb the energy without the need for erosion or deposition. In the process it takes into account the natural resistance of the land. So, here it shrinks, and there it grows, until there is a balance between shape and energy. Most places have not reached this, and so the coastline continues to change. Above all, no area of coastline can be treated in isolation from a neighbouring area, they are inextricably linked by the movement of currents and of sediments. What happens in one place will inevitably affect what happens further down the coast.

If we think about this complex system operating over thousands of years, we have to build in ideas of changing sea-levels. Some of the causes of sea-level change were mentioned earlier (see Chapter 4), but their effect on the coastal landscape will be discussed here. In essence our beautiful

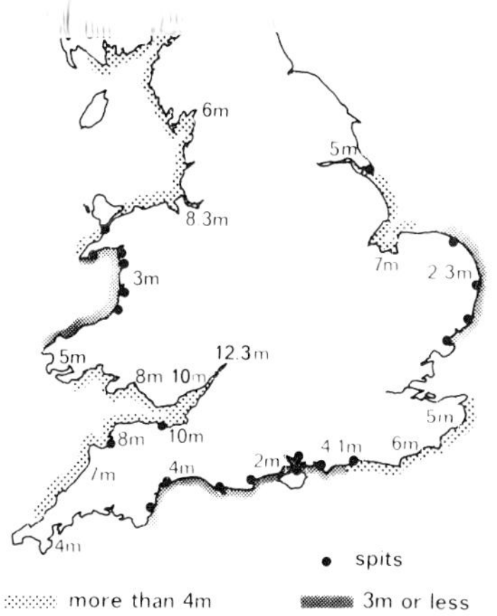


*FIG 6.3 Zones of different tidal range along the coast of Britain. Spits mostly form in areas of relatively low tidal range.*

*PLATE 6.4 The breakwater at West Bay, Dorset, has been in existence as a solid structure for less than 100 years, but even in that short time it has had a dramatic effect on the shape of the coastline. It has interrupted the longshore currents flowing from east to west. The result is a great accumulation of sediments on the eastern side, and starvation of the beach and erosion on the western side.*

and varied coastline is so because it encompasses a mixture of features that are both ancient and newly formed, of landscapes devastated by erosion intermixed with those built up over the centuries by deposition. Let's look at these in more detail.

RAISED BEACHES

In places as diverse as Islay[1] off the west coast of Scotland, Portland Bill[2] in Dorset, and Westward Ho![3] in Devon, there is evidence that sea-level around the British Isles was significantly higher than present, even quite recently. The evidence is in the form of 'fossilised' beach sands and pebbles, often seen exposed in cliff faces several metres above present sea-level – hence the name 'raised beaches'. Often these sands and pebbles sit upon a bench or platform cut into the rock by the sea. The platforms are quite distinctive; they are usually smooth and slope gently seawards, and have the remains of an old, now degraded, cliffline carved into the rock behind them. Plate 6.5 shows such a platform and old cliffline on Islay.

Not all examples are as well preserved as this. Where the shoreline is formed in soft rocks the chances of preservation are small. And not all platforms have old beaches on them. Either the sands may not have been dumped there in the first place, or they may have been removed since by wind or rainwater. In other cases the beach materials have been covered by the downhill sludging of soil and rock debris from the land behind during periods of the past when arctic conditions prevailed (see Chapter 4). At Westward Ho!, for example, the old, rounded beach pebbles exposed some 5m (16ft) above present sea-level are covered by 'sludged' angular debris dating back to the last glacial phase of the Ice Age. The two layers are quite distinct. The beach itself probably formed between 120,000 and 80,000 years ago – the last warm, interglacial, phase – when sea-level reached up to 10m (33ft) higher than present. It was higher then mainly because more of the water stored in ice-sheets melted. Eventually, if sea-level stays at its present height for long enough, most traces of these fossil 'raised' beaches will be removed by marine erosion.

Some raised beaches are much older, for sea-levels have been yo-yoing around between the glacial and interglacial phases for the past 2 million years. But some confusion arises because raised beaches of the same age are not always of the same height, and those of the same height are not necessarily of the same age. The answer to this puzzle lies in the fact that a change in the level of the sea relative to the land can be brought about either by an absolute change in the amount of water in the world's oceans, which would cause the ocean level to rise or fall, or by a more localised change in the vertical position of the land itself. Whilst the raised beaches in south and south-west Britain tend to reflect the changing amount of water, those in the north are formed by a combination of the two factors. The rising of the land was caused, somewhat perversely, by the weight of ice in the huge and thick ice-sheets that covered the land during the glacial phases. This weight pushed down the Earth's crust, by up to one-third of the thickness of the ice. But when the ice melted the crust bounced back, slowly of course, like a ship being unloaded and the land rose vertically.

For the land to recover fully takes several thousand years. In Scandinavia the recovery since the ice melted, about 10,000 years ago, exceeds 300m (980ft) in places. In Scotland, where the ice was nowhere near as thick, the land has risen by up to 100m (330ft), and is still rising in places. This explains why a raised beach some 14,000 years old, formed when the level of the world's oceans was tens of metres below present, is now found 30m (98ft) above present sea-level in eastern Scotland. Thus a combination of the effects of changing water volumes in the oceans and of land subsidence and rebound, can give a complex picture of local sea-level change. In some instances a whole staircase of fossil shorelines can result, like the fourteen separate shorelines on the margins of the Firth of Forth[1].

*PLATE 6.5 The gently sloping platform on the coast of Islay is now several metres (yards) above sea-level, but it was cut by the sea, and it shows that there have been changes in the level of the sea relative to the land. The old cliffs, now also covered with grass, can be seen at the back of the platform.*

## THE RISING SEAS: CHESIL, DROWNED FORESTS AND RIAS

The effects of changing sea-levels are not solely restricted to the creation of raised beaches. It is thought that the impressive ridge of pebbles, 29km (18 miles) long and known as Chesil Beach[2] (Plate 6.6, page 138), is also a

'fossil' landscape. It owes its origin to the most recent major rise in sea-level brought about by the melting of the last great ice-sheets between 15,000 and 5,000 years ago. As the sea rose, it sorted out and combed up pebbles from the debris that had been dumped by rivers in the then 'dry' English Channel.

The pebbles were sorted from the finer sands under the influence of the high-energy waves coming from the south-west. Winds blowing from this direction could have travelled thousands of kilometres across the Atlantic Ocean, whipping up the seas, for Chesil is one of the most exposed locations in Great Britain; it is not quite protected by the South West Peninsula. The pebble ridge was gradually pushed shorewards by the rising seas, not en masse but by individual pebbles being washed from the seaward edge over to the landward side of the ridge during storms. Thus, this giant ridge, well over 20m (65ft) high in places (with up to 13m (43ft) of it above sea-level), 'rolled' landwards until sea-level ceased to rise some 5,000 years ago and it was beached against the cliffs of West Bay at one end and Portland Bill at the other. For some distance in between these two points the ridge was not quite pushed onshore, and is separated from the land of Dorset by the Fleet – a shallow tidal lagoon.

Chesil is by far the largest shingle ridge of its kind in Britain. Unlike nearly all other shingle features it is a single, straight ridge with a regular crest. It has no sideways pointing (lateral) ridges associated with it, as compared with Orford Ness[1] or any other spits, or with Scolt Head Island[2]. It is a truly remarkable feature with an unusual origin. But there is one very important implication, namely that it does not appear to be forming today. Thus it is not able to repair any gaps created, for example, by the mining of shingle from it. Studies of the Chesil coastline have indeed shown that there is very little shingle on the floor of Lyme Bay offshore. Moreover, no shingle is at present being supplied from the west along the shore by longshore drift. In short, there is no supply with which the ridge could be replenished naturally. Thus it does seem to be a fossil feature, resembling an ancient whale beached by a giant high tide.

Occasionally high seas generated by storms overtop the ridge and throw shingle over to the landward side. This happened at Chesilton as recently as 1979. The resulting devastation – flooding and damage to properties – and the threat of further breaches, was enough to convince the County Council that protection was necessary for this, most exposed, part of the ridge. As a result the sea wall was raised and wire baskets of pebbles implanted in and on the beach to reinforce it.

One of the most intriguing aspects of Chesil beach is the increase in the height of the ridge, the steepness of the ridge and the size of the pebbles, from west to east. In the west the pebbles are of varying size but predominantly small, pea-sized. In the east they are less variable in size but all well over 5cm (2in) in diameter. Even now no one is quite clear how this happened. One idea is that the sorting has come about as the result of longshore currents. The strong south-westerly winds drum up waves that hit Chesil obliquely, and that creates a strong longshore current flowing from west to east. This current, it is argued, can move all sizes of pebbles along the shore (Fig 6.4). But the weaker waves that are generated by less frequent and lighter winds from the south and south-east, and which produce currents flowing in the opposite direction, from east to west, are only capable of moving the smaller pebbles. This moves the smaller pebbles to the west and leaves the larger ones in the east, and the beach is sorted.

There is a more recent view that the sorting on the surface of the ridge relates to different wave powers reaching different parts of the beach. The western end is somewhat protected and the wave energy therefore lower. Thus only the finer pebbles can be moved by these waves and they are sorted to the surface, so covering up any larger pebbles. Compare this with the

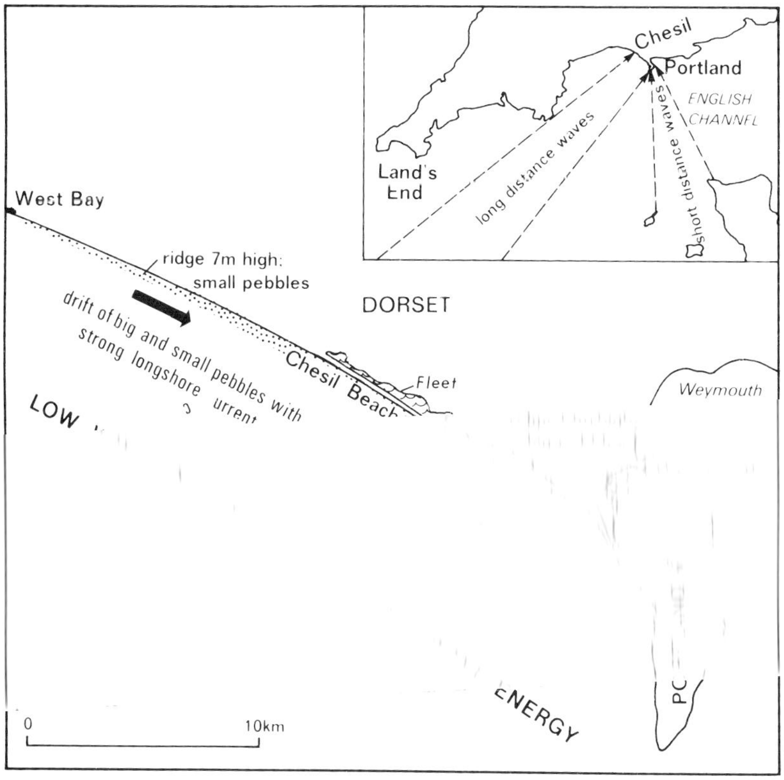


*FIG 6.4 The location of Chesil Beach, and the two ideas to explain the peculiar sorting of pebbles upon it; small pebbles in the west and large pebbles in the east may be the result of different strengths of longshore currents, or caused by variations in wave energy received at different points along the beach.*

east where the higher powered waves winnow out the small pebbles and dump them offshore below low-tide level. In this way the larger pebbles are brought to the surface and remain there.

A less dramatic indication of recently rising sea-level, are the remnants of forests submerged by the sea. A superb example is seen in Plate 6.7, photographed near Bexhill[1], Sussex. The trunks of former trees, some still in their original position of growth, emerge forlornly from the floor of the sandy bay. Eventually they will rot away. Similar weird and unexpected remains are sometimes visible near Westward Ho![2]. All were created by the last stages in the rise in sea-level following the melting of the ice. This flooded the lower lying former forests, killing the trees.

On many of our rocky coastlines can be found small, narrow inlets that provide excellent natural harbours – the Dart[3] in Devon, the Fowey[4] in Cornwall, at Solva[5] in Pembrokeshire, and numerous others. Typically the hillslopes rise steeply up from the inlets, which are usually winding (meandering) in shape when viewed from the air. The Solva inlet, or ria as it is called, is a good example of the meandering shape (Plate 6.8, page 140). You can also see that the inlet further inland gives way to a steep river valley carved into the surrounding landscape. It is this that holds the key to the origin of rias.

By tracing the contours of the land beneath the sea it can be shown that the shape of the river valley extends under the sea. But when were the valleys formed because obviously they cannot be created whilst flooded by the sea? For an answer to this question we have to imagine the effects of past low sea-levels on the landscape. For most of the past 2 million years sea-level was lower than at present, by over 100m (330ft) at times. The shorelines would have been located many kilometres (miles) 'offshore'. The rivers would have extended across this exposed area of land, carving out valleys and flowing down to the lowered sea-levels. As the depth to which rivers can erode their valleys is ultimately limited by

PLATE 6.7 *Remains of tree trunks emerge unexpectedly from the beach at Little Galley Hill, Bexhill, Sussex.*

sea-level, it follows that lowered sea-levels encouraged the rivers to erode and deepen their valleys. The effects of this down-cutting was most felt near the shorelines. It was also aided by the changed climatic conditions at the time. Under the prevailing arctic conditions there would have been an increase in the amount of water running off the surface of the land, as explained in Chapter 4.

The subsequent rise in sea-level, when the glaciers melted, flooded the deepened river valleys, so forming the rias – drowned river valleys. The most recent phase of flooding took place about 6,000 to 5,000 years ago as the seas reached more or less their present level. Some rias have been filled since with sediment dumped by the rivers flowing into them. This has created alluvial lowlands, such as those near the mouth of the Cuckmere valley in Sussex (Plate 5.8). The beautiful fjords on the west coast of Scotland, such as Loch Fyne[1], look very similar to rias, but their valleys have been deepened by glaciers rather than by rivers, as explained in Chapter 3.

Submerged river channels extend beneath the sea from most of the main rivers in the British Isles. These old, deep channels also continue inland beneath the present river valleys. One of the largest is associated with the Thames[2], where a former channel at a depth of 47m (155ft) below present sea-level near the mouth of the estuary can be traced upstream, beneath London, to Brentford[3]. This channel is filled with gravels dotted with the occasional remains of mammoths – huge woolly mammals that roamed the area in the colder periods of the Ice Age. The bones have been dated to 28,000 years old.

PLATE 6.6 *Chesil Beach, the longest single ridge of shingle in Britain and Ireland, sweeps between Portland in the foreground and West Bay in the far distance. Chesilton, the town last hit by flooding in 1979, lies just behind the ridge where it joins onto the Isle of Portland.*

## COVES

Who would think that the origin of rias applies equally as well to some of our most beautiful bays and coves fringing the coastline? But it

*PLATE 6.8 Solva ria is a small flooded inlet, typical of many on the coasts of the South West Peninsula and Wales. It is a river valley flooded as the sea-level rose between 12,000 and 6,000 years ago. The continual accumulation of debris brought into it by the river at one end and the sea at the other means that the inlet will eventually silt up completely, as indeed its neighbouring inlet, right foreground, already has.*

is true, and Lulworth[1], the cove of coves in Dorset, is probably the best example (Plate 6.9). The near circular cove is backed by majestic Chalk cliffs; its sides are carved from much weaker sandstones and clays, whilst the narrow entrance is guarded by relatively tough Portland and Purbeck limestones, famous as building stones.

For a long time it was believed that the cove was the result of modern erosion by the sea, which succeeded in carving a narrow breach at a weak point in the limestone barrier. The bay was then eroded out of the weaker clays and sandstones, which are very prone to undercutting by the sea and to landslips. Once, the story continues, the bay was eroded sufficiently for the sea to come into contact with the tougher Chalk, the rate of erosion slowed right down. The result was a classic fisherman's cove. The underlying idea is that the sea attacks and erodes weaker, softer rocks more easily than tough, hard rocks. So, in areas of alternating hard and soft rock at the coastline, the sea will hollow out the soft rocks into coves and bays, and leave the hard rocks as headlands. This is indeed the way that many of our bays have been created over the centuries, often with a little additional help from landslides and the weakening (weathering) of rocks above sea-level by rainwater.

But it is now believed that other factors were also important at Lulworth, and this is where we come back to rias. A careful look at Plate 6.9 shows two small valleys extending across the lower ground developed on clays and sandstones and into the cove. These are too big to have formed after the cove, but for a long time they were considered unimportant. Then soundings in the narrow mouth of the cove revealed a channel some 16m (52ft) deep. This changed the scientific view, and it is now thought that the streams once joined together and flowed across the exposed continental shelf at times of low sea-level. They flowed through the breach in the limestone ridge that they, and not the sea, had cut.

Like rias, Lulworth Cove was created by the flooding of the river valleys as the sea-level rose at the end of the last glacial phase. Thus, the perfect circular shape of the cove partly reflects the presence of the two valleys joining into one by chance at this particular point, in contrast to the long narrow ria formed by the flooding of one major valley. So now Lulworth Cove is seen as a partly drowned river valley system, the precise outline of the cove having been trimmed by subsequent erosion by the sea.

Such coves provide ideal, sheltered places for the accumulation of sands washed in by the sea or eroded from the cliffs. If you stand on the cliffs you will [illegible]

EXPOSED BEACHES

In sheltered coves the slope of the beach, from the cliff foot to the point only briefly exposed by the lowest of tides (Low Water Mark Spring Tides), often changes little with the seasons. Where the beach is less protected, its slope typically flattens in the winter or after bad storms. This is because the high and steep storm waves – the high-energy waves – tend to erode the beach. Some of the eroded material may be thrown by the waves to the back of the beach, to accumulate as a storm ridge, but the majority is carried down the beach to form a bank or bar just below low-water mark. In contrast, the low, flatter 'swell' waves of hot summer days – the low-energy waves – build up and steepen the beach.

In reality, the changing slope of the beach is a very complex matter. It is also related to the sizes of particles present; steeper beaches usually exist in shingle and shallower ones are formed in sand. This is thought to occur because the sea-water running up the beach (the swash) drains away more readily into a pebbly beach owing to the large gaps between the pebbles, than it does into a densely packed sandy beach. This leaves far less water to flow back down the beach, as the so-called 'backwash', on pebble beaches. With less backwash the sea is less able to erode and to carry material back down the beach. This in turn results in a steeper beach angle; the sea has more power to push material up than to comb it back.

Whatever the precise mechanism, it seems to be true that beaches develop a slope that is a response to the wave energy that they receive. The beach has to absorb all the energy that is thrown at it, and to do so most efficiently it adjusts its steepness to the sea's energy levels, whilst taking into account the sizes of particles present on the beach. For example, high wave energy tends to create wide and flat beaches, if the beach is sandy (Plate 6.11), as this is the most efficient shape for absorbing by friction all the incoming energy. But if it is shingle, the beach need not be so wide and flat because energy is absorbed very rapidly by percolation of the water between the pebbles. On the other hand lower energy waves tend to create narrower and steeper beaches. So we have seen that the slope of the beach will change seasonally or even more frequently depending on the strength of the wind and the waves it drives. The slope will also vary from place

PLATE 6.9 *The classic cove, Lulworth in Dorset, was etched out by the combined action of rivers and the sea. Its shape reflects the differing resistance to erosion of the rocks all around it.*

PLATE 6.10 *The never ending spit at Orford, in Suffolk, that hijacks the River Alde and forces it to travel many extra miles before finally allowing it to reach the sea. Each of the intricate curves in sand and shingle marks a former end of the spit as it grew, inexorably, southwards, feeding on debris carried south in longshore currents from the eroding cliffs of north Suffolk and Norfolk.*

to place according to the average levels of wave energy received and the character of the beach materials.

## SPITS

As yet we have not looked at the landscapes formed by longshore drift, ie the movement of particles in currents along the shore. Some of our most spectacular coastal landscapes have been created in this way. Take, for example, the great accumulations of sands and gravels that leave the land and extend outwards into the sea or across an estuary. We are talking here about 'spits' such as at Blakeney[1] in Norfolk, Orford[2] in Suffolk, Harlech[3] in north Wales and Spurn Head[4] poking across the Humber estuary. These features vie in visual impact with huge triangular-shaped outgrowths such as at Dungeness[5] in Kent, or with totally detached 'beach islands' as at Scolt Head Island[6], Norfolk. All these examples are in areas of low tidal range, and are formed on open coastlines.

Normally on such coastlines the beach develops until the angle formed between it and the prevailing waves generates a strong enough longshore current to carry out from the beach the same amount of sediment that is coming in from longshore drift at the other end. So the net result is no deposition or erosion, just stability. And the sands carried in the longshore current are moved further along the shoreline. But what happens when the coastline turns abruptly inland, such as the entrance to an estuary or bay? First there is a rapid drop in wave energy reaching the shoreline as it turns inland. This forces sediments carried in the longshore current to be deposited, leading to the growth of a beach, continuing its previous orientation. This takes it outwards into the sea and away from the land – a spit is born. The spit grows as long as the supply of particles from along the shore continues. Eventually it reaches a point where the estuary

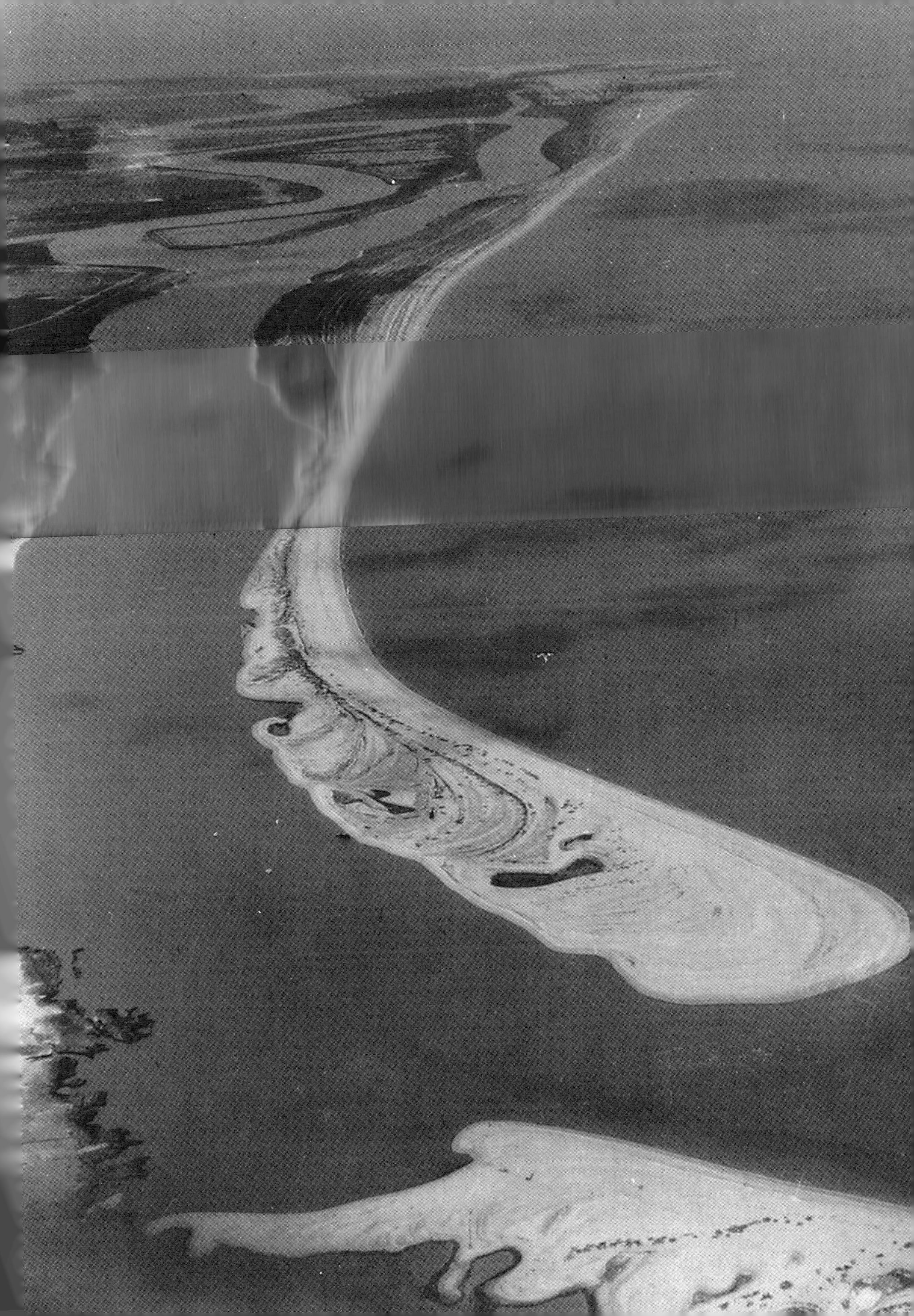

entrance is so confined that the tidal currents in the narrow remaining channel become strong enough to prevent any further dumping, so keeping the channel clear.

One fascinating aspect of spits is the frequent presence of an inward curved end, bent in towards the estuary or bay. A nice example is at Spurn Head[1] across the Humber estuary. It results from the bending (refraction) of waves and currents around the end of the spit. Dumping of sediment by these recurved currents in the sheltered waters just in the lee of the main spit forms the curved end. As the spit grows, each successive position may be marked by a recurved end. They are best seen on Orford Ness[1] in Suffolk – an uninspiring little bit of land to look at from the ground, you may think, but from the air (Plate 6.10) it is wonderful. Here numerous former positions of the spit are recorded in great detail by the recurved ends, one close upon the heels of the last, all along the length of the spit. And to think that the last 6km(3.7 miles) of the 13km(8.1 miles) spit has grown since AD 1500.

Waves whipped up by north-easterly and easterly winds generate a southwards-moving longshore current. This carries an ample supply of particles down from the rapidly eroding soft cliffs formed in glacial and marine deposits in north Suffolk and Norfolk. Then the current meets the Alde estuary and it starts dumping its load. Out across the mouth of the estuary has grown Orford Ness. The growth has been so prolific that the spit has deflected the mouth of the estuary 13km (8.1 miles) southwards of its original position. Tidal and river currents flowing through the present narrow entrance to the estuary serve to stop the spit from completely blocking the entrance.

Not all spits are as long-lived as that at Orford. On coasts suffering very rapid erosion close to the spit, as in Humberside[2], the link between the spit and the land is periodically eroded away, and the spit disintegrates into islands and eventually disappears. While this is happening, a new spit forms and grows for about 250 years until it, too, is destroyed by erosion of the cliffline. It is amazing to think that a feature as large as Spurn Head 5.6km (3.48 miles) long and 100-200m (110-240yds) wide can form in less than 250 years. The present one started to grow in about 1860 and is due to disappear in about 125 years time.

The quiet sheltered water found in the lee of spits is often the site of dumping of silts and clays brought down into the estuary by the river. It is not uncommon, therefore, to find large expanses of mudflats and salt marsh in such areas. The dumping of fine materials is also helped by the mixing of the fresh river-water and the salty sea. This rise in salinity causes the clays to coagulate into larger, heavier lumps, which settle out from suspension in the sheltered areas. But there is more about this on page 148.

SAND DUNES

Before we leave beaches and spits behind, it is worth noting that sand dunes are very often associated with them. Unlike all other coastal features, they are formed by the wind, which carries sand off the exposed beaches and dumps it a short way inland. If you have ever walked along a beach on a very windy day, you may have felt the stinging of sand grains being blown against your legs. This is because the wind is usually only capable of lifting the relatively heavy sand grains a small distance off the ground. But even if the wind is strong enough, it can only move sand under certain circumstances.

First, there needs to be an available supply such as on a broad, gently sloping beach exposed at low tide, as at Braunton Burrows[1] in Devon (Plate 6.11). This is the sort of beach where you have to trek metres (yards) out to sea before the water is even knee-deep. The beach needs to be sandy and it helps if the tidal range is moderate, thus exposing an

even greater area of beach. (One of the reasons why there are so few dunes in the Mediterranean is because the beaches are narrow and the tidal range small.) The reason the beach has to be sandy is that the wind cannot move grains larger than about 2mm (0.8in) in diameter. Also particles smaller than 0.1mm (.04in) tend to be carried up and away as dust in the atmosphere, and so they hardly ever form dunes. The wind is very efficient at sorting out larger and finer particles from the sands.

Secondly, the material must be dry before it can be moved. When it is wet there are thin films of water between the sand grains. This increases the cohesion between the grains, making the force required to lift them off the ground too great for the wind to manage. Drying is helped by a good tidal range, and the wind itself in evaporating the water. Wet, tropical coasts rarely have dunes because of the small tidal ranges and the frequent rainfalls.

Thirdly, the onshore wind has to be sufficiently strong to pick up and carry the grains along; this usually means a speed greater than 5m (16ft) per second (18km (11 miles) per hour). The rate of sand transport increases

*PLATE 6.11 Braunton Burrows is rightly famed for its spectacular chains of sand hills. The broad flat beach supplies vast quantities of sand, and the prevailing westerly winds carry the dry sand up into the dunefield. Much of the sand in Barnstaple Bay is brought down by the rivers Taw and Torridge.*

rapidly with wind speeds above this. A wind of 60 km (37 miles) per hour can shift well over 1 tonne (ton) of sand per hour for every metre (yard) width of beach.

Lastly, there needs to be an area of low-lying land behind the beach on which the sand can be dumped. But how does the wind carry the sand?

Wind can move sand along in two ways. First, there is a 'hopping' motion whereby a grain is picked up and carried a short distance (a few metres (yards) at most) before it falls back to the ground owing to its weight under the influence of gravity. When it hits the ground it often rebounds from the impact to start the next 'hop'. Second, there is a rolling or creeping motion along the ground, often helped by the impact of falling 'hopping' grains (Fig 6.5). The finer sands are more often carried the first way, and the larger sands the second way. The mechanisms are called saltation and creep, respectively, and they are responsible for the growth of both wind ripples a few centimetres wide and the much larger forms – the sand dunes.

The wind carries the sand until its speed falls, whereupon it is forced to deposit some of its load. This can happen where the wind is deflected around obstacles. One of the earliest theories of sand-dune formation in deserts, saw dead camels as the initial obstacles in the wind. A drop in speed also occurs when the wind encounters a rougher surface. Debris left by a high tide, for example, can lead to the growth of small sand mounds. Once these mounds are colonised by plants, they too roughen the surface and slow down the wind near the ground. This encourages further deposition and the mound grows upwards.

Fortunately, the plants suited to this sandy, alkaline environment are also capable of growing upwards with the dune. In fact the vegetation is so efficient at trapping sand that the dunes can grow upwards at the impressive rate of 1m (3.3ft) per year. The most common plants are sand twitch (*Agropyron junceiforme*) and marram grass (*Ammophila arenaria*). So, in a surprisingly short time the dune can grow from a baby feature less than 1m (3.3ft) high into a proper sand dune up to 30m (100ft) in height (in the British Isles). As sand dunes go this is not particularly big; those in desert areas can exceed 150m (500ft). The ultimate height reached probably depends on how fast the wind speed increases with height above the ground, and on the patterns of eddies in the wind. As the dune grows up into areas of higher wind speed, its upward growth ceases. This is because the stronger winds carry more sand off the top of the dune.

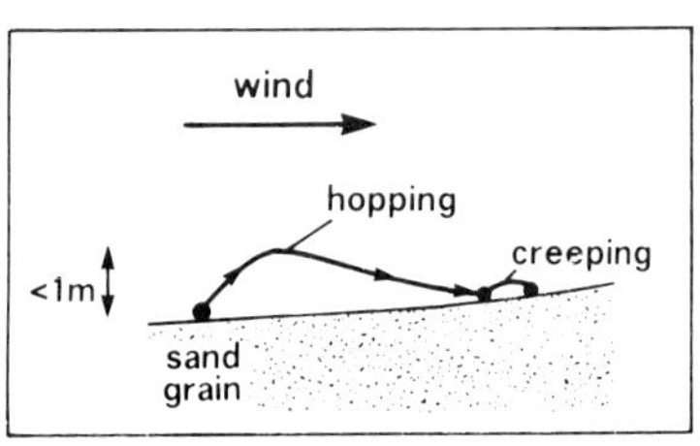


*FIG 6.5 The role played by the wind in moving sand from the beach and piling it up into sand dunes at the back of the beach and on flat ground beyond.*

Often dunes coalesce along the beach to form long ridges roughly at right-angles to the prevailing wind direction (Plate 6.11). Several sets of such ridges may exist in a coastal area, the ridges usually becoming progressively older away from the shoreline. At Studland[1], near Poole, for example, four ridges have developed since 1607. As one ridge is formed it either moves slowly inland under the influence of the wind, or the coastline is pushed slightly further out to sea. Either way, space is made for a new baby ridge to form at the back of the beach. The older ridges are usually better colonised by vegetation, and because of leaching by rainwater the sands are less alkaline.

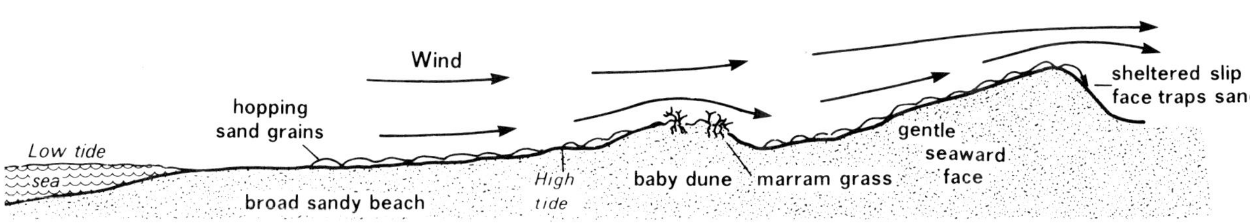

PLATE 6.12 An intricate lacework pattern of creeks drains the Mersea salt marshes. Originally mudflats, the marshes have grown sufficiently high, by the gradual accumulation of thin layers of silts and muds, to sustain a cover of salt-tolerant vegetation, and to have thus become salt marshes.

One characteristic you may notice about dunes is their asymmetrical shape. Where well preserved, they have a steep landward side and a much gentler seaward face. This can be explained if we consider the movement of sand grains hopping and creeping up over the dune (Fig 6.5). The wind blows them up the gentle seaward face until they fall over the crest or top of the dune. Beyond the crest the wind cannot follow the shape of the dune and streams out behind it, much as it would when passing over the back of a car. This leaves the upper part of the landward face very sheltered indeed. So as the grains are pushed over the crest by the wind they fall into the doldrums on the landward face, and are deposited.

Gradually this landward face builds up and becomes steeper and steeper. Once dry sand is at an angle of about 35 degrees it becomes unstable, and it avalanches downwards to lower the angle back to a stable one of 32 to 35 degrees. This is what happens on the landward face, which even though it may look mountainous on large dunes, never exceeds 35 degrees, and is aptly called the 'slip-face'. In windy areas, the constant movement of sand grains from the seaward face and over onto the landward face causes the dune as a whole to move downwind. It rolls slowly landwards like a giant lumbering slug, until its path is obstructed.

MUDFLATS AND SALT MARSH

On more sheltered parts of the coastline, and particularly those with a larger tidal range, the sandy beaches, spits and sand dunes give way to tidal mudflats and salt marshes. These oozing, sticky and potentially dangerous areas are a fascinating sight from the air as in the Blackwater estuary[1] in Essex (Plate 6.12). At low tide a filigree of meandering creeks separates glistening mudflats and vegetated salt marsh. In these environments, activity is linked with the continual inward and outward movement of tidal currents, and the loads of predominantly fine materials – silts and clays – that they carry and dump. Interestingly, once deposited these muds (each particle less than 0.06mm (.002in) diameter) are difficult to erode. This is because chemical bonding of the grains and the high water content gives the material great cohesion.

The way in which a mudflat grows is fascinating. The tide wave carries in suspension a mixture of fine sands, silts and clays. The tide washes up through the narrow creeks quite rapidly, particularly at the time midway between high and low tide when the velocity is greatest. At high tide, two things have changed. First the velocity of the tide wave has slowed right down, and secondly the water is no longer confined to the creeks but has spread out over the mudflat, further reducing its velocity. Under these conditions the very sluggish water is only capable of carrying the very small particles, the clays, which are then dumped as a thin film over the mudflat at the slack high water. On the falling tide, the maximum velocity is again reached at a time midway between high and low tide, when the water is probably little more than half filling the creeks. The scour at this time helps to prevent the creeks from silting up.

Tide upon tide, the mudflat grows imperceptibly upwards until it reaches a height at which it is only inundated by the highest spring tides. At this point its supply of mud is more or less cut off, and its growth virtually ceases. Plants play a key role in speeding up the growth process. When the mudflat has grown high enough for plants to be able to survive in its salty, periodically inundated environment, colonisation begins. This is long before the mudflat finally stops growing. Algae are often the first inhabitants, and are followed by three early colonisers, namely marsh samphire (*Salicornia sp.*), marsh cord (*Spartina sp.*) and eel grass (*Zostera sp.*). These plants make the land surface appear rougher to the sea-water and they impede its movement. This means that the water velocity is very low for a longer period than just at slack high tide and more of the particle load is dumped. The plants also trap the particles within their crevices, and so prevent the particles from being eroded. Under very favourable conditions the mudflat can grow upwards by up to 10cm (4in) per year.

Unfortunately for these particular plants this causes a change in the environment – less frequent inundation and therefore less salty.The colonisers are not so happy in these conditions and thus, having made themselves redundant, new species take over. These include sea aster (*Aster tripolium*), sea poa (*Glyceria maritima*) and sea blite (*Suaeda maritima*). These in turn are followed by others; a veritable succession of species that eventually often ends with sea lavender (*Limonium vulgare*) and sea pink (*Armeria maritima*) and possibly sea rushes. On Scolt Head Island[1] in Norfolk the full sequence from earliest colonisation to sea rush takes 200 years.

[illegible]

[illegible] onshore, the resistance of the rocks repelling the attack, and the supply of debris that is continually being dumped at the shoreline by rivers. This interplay has already given us a wealth of beautiful, dramatic, and often surprisingly intricate coastal landshapes.

7

# THE FORCE OF GRAVITY

Denys Brunsden

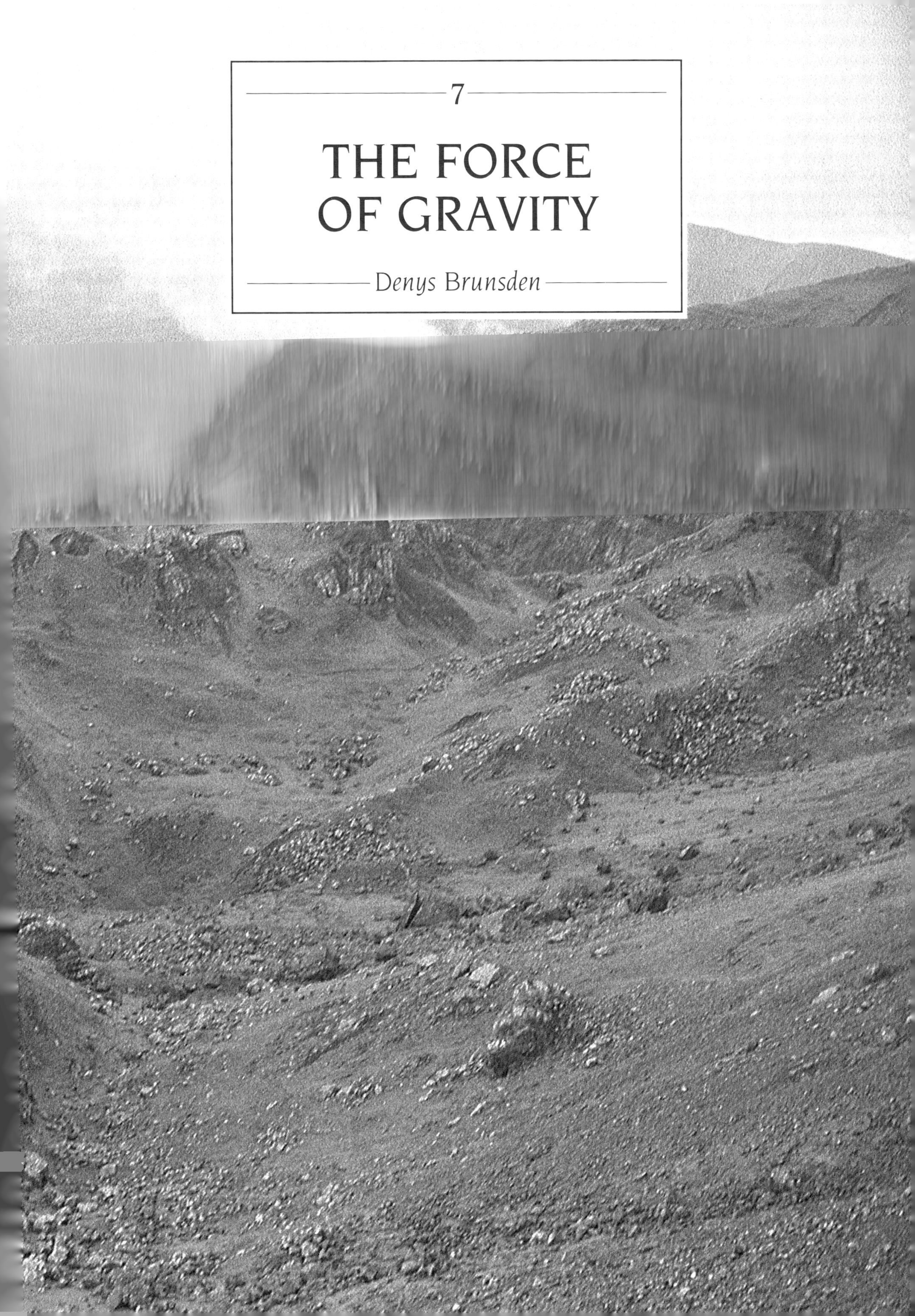

PLATE 7.1 *The famous landslide at Bindon, east Devon, that occurred on Christmas morning 1839. Many of the most impressive features of this landslide are clearly visible including, from left to right, the rear scarp (the cliffs at the edge of the fields), the chasm and the displaced block, called Goat Island, which moved seawards by up to 92m (300 ft). This is the first geomorphological event since the Mosaic Deluge to be celebrated in a piece of music.*

In the early hours of Christmas morning 1839 fissures opened up in the cliff top at Bindon, in east Devon[1]. By the evening a chasm 92m (300ft) broad, 46m (150ft) deep and 1,200m (3,940ft) long had appeared and 'a pyramid of rock of great size and remarkable outline sank in the order of 150 feet [46m]' (plate 7.1). Offshore a reef was thrown up enclosing a large body of water. This 'most extraordinary and terrific explosion of nature' was accompanied by a sound 'like the rending of cloth' and 'flashes of fire and a strong smell of sulphur' all of which promoted strong rumours that the Devil was near. Thus began the most dramatic event ever to hit this coast. Today it is known as the Landslide Nature Reserve though not because the National Trust feels that this landslide is especially interesting. The site was designated as being of scientific interest because of the vegetation that has grown within the chasm since the event.

In 1839, however, the scientific interest in the site was directed at [illegible] further massive movement at Whitlands, Lyme Regis, on 3 February 1840 (Plate 7.4). The occupants of a cottage at this site were only 'with difficulty rescued'.

The manuscripts that describe these events can be seen in the Lyme Regis Museum. They not only depict the geomorphological features but also show how farmers harvested their crops using ladders and tell the story of tourists who visited the site on paddle steamers from Weymouth, took afternoon tea, and then danced on their way back across Lyme Bay to the strains of the quadrille. In Parliament questions were asked whether the water enclosed by the reef, which was in reality the front or toe of the landslide, could be converted into a much needed haven for ships. For a brief moment geomorphology was famous. Today how may have heard of it? Certainly few have visited the site which is of difficult access without a long cliff walk from Lyme Regis or Axmouth.

*Have you seen this piece of music?*

[illegible] famous Victorian events. All his music is known except this piece. We offer a free copy of this book for the first reply that leads to the discovery of the music.

*PLATE 7.2 View of the Great Chasm of the Bindon landslide, east Devon, drawn by an artist shortly after the event. The rapidly collapsing rear scarp and the back-tilted blocks behind Goat Island are beautifully portrayed.*

*PLATE 7.4 Shortly after the Bindon slide, further movements occurred in what is now the landslide reserve. The Whitlands slide occurred 1.6km (1 mile) to the east of the Great Chasm on 3 February 1840 and the inhabitants of this cottage were 'with difficulty rescued'.*

(pp154–5)
*PLATE 7.3 Black Ven in 1987. The most striking features are the two lobes of debris (mudslides) which extend into the sea. These mudslides are like great conveyor belts feeding materials from the cliffs down into the water. They can operate throughout the year if there is enough water, but are usually most active in the winter months when they look and behave like porridge. Also clearly visible are the various cliffs made of Lias limestone and shale, and the steep and rapidly eroding rear scarp formed in Upper Greensand.*

Easier to visit, but no less dramatic, is the Black Ven mudslide[1] between Lyme Regis and Charmouth. Here there have been many periods of movement. In the late summer of 1957 and again on 9-10 February 1958, two huge lobes of mud extended nearly 100m (330ft) across the beach, trapping a walker between them so that he had to be rescued by rowing boat. Again in the periods 1969-73 and 1985-7 there was rapid erosional activity. In the winter of 1986-7 a wholly new movement began and there are now three huge lobes across the beach and extensive damage to fields and a golf course at the top of the slope (Plate 7.3). These latest movements were accompanied by severe movements to the cliff, chalets and beach huts just to the west of the Cobb at Lyme Regis. During each of the active periods between 5 and 30m (16-100ft) of cliff top were lost. A recent survey of the landslide hazards in this area has revealed that the cliffs have been eaten back this century at an average rate of 0.75m (2.5ft) per annum, representing the loss of over 80,000 tonnes (tons) of material to the sea each year. Black Ven is certainly the most active and dangerous site in Britain. In 1958 an eye-witness wrote:

> I saw a great mass of Upper Greensand [the yellow sand layer that forms the upper part of the landslide] densely covered with bushes and trees slowly crawling downward from the highest terrace, while below a river of liquid mud was slipping over the low cliff above the beach...the main movement in the night must have been very rapid, as by daylight a huge fan of debris, crested with uprooted trees had pushed out across the beach to beyond low water neap tides.

Charmouth must be the mecca for all landslide enthusiasts. Just the other side of the River Char from Black Ven is the spectacular bowl of Stonebarrow Hill[1], sometimes called Cain's Folly or Fairy Dell. Here permeable Upper Greensand overlies clays and silts of the Liassic period (Table 2.1). This is the geological situation that most favours the creation of landslides, for

*PLATE 7.5 Photograph of the rear scarp of Stonebarrow showing the radar station which slipped downhill 30m (98ft) at 8.00am on 14 May 1942 (for location see Plate 1.2). The back tilting of the building caused by the rotational movement is obvious.*

[illegible] *Warren is crossed by the main railway line between Folkestone and Dover and was a potential source of great danger. The last major movement in 1915 caused the railway to be displaced seawards by 50m (164ft) and derailed a train.*

*PLATE 7.7 The Storr on Skye is probably the most massive and dramatic of landslides in the British Isles. It has an almost mystical quality because of the jumble of towers, hollows, pinnacles and hidden dells. It is caused by the characteristic association of permeable coherent rocks overlying impermeable clay.* (Full-size illustration on pp150-1.)

the rainwater which percolates downward through the sands reaches the impermeable clay and cannot sink any further. The result is a saturated layer on top of the clay with high (extreme) water pressures. Such cliffs and hills are characteristic of west Dorset which accounts for the widespread occurrence of slope movements. Indeed, the Upper Greensand is so vulnerable that it is called 'running sand' by workmen who take very great care to shore-up their excavations. The cliffs at Stonebarrow consist of a mixture of huge, intact landslides (blocks) above small but active gullies and mudslides (see Plate 1.2). At the foot of the upper cliff there are two small buildings (Plate 7.5). These are the remains of a radio-location (radar) station which slipped at 8.00am on 14 May 1942 just after the men had gone on shift! The slope of the roof of one of the buildings shows just how the mass moved, for it is tilted back towards the land suggesting that the mass slipped toward the sea on a failure surface that was curved. A belt of land up to 28m (92ft) wide covering an area of 7,500m$^2$ (9,000sq yd) was lost in this one event.

These are, of course, dramatic examples, but they are by no means unique. In some areas, such as Ventnor, Isle of Wight,[1] whole towns are built on landslipped ground. At Folkestone, Kent,[2] a railway runs across the disturbed ground of the Warren where the movements were once sufficient to derail a train (Plate 7.6). Fortunately expensive remedial works have now rendered this site safe. Many other large examples could be listed but it is probably true to say that the accolade 'most impressive landslide' should be awarded to the Storr on Skye[3] (Plate 7.7) where repeated movements have created a mysterious landscape of towers and pinnacles.

Examples can be found throughout Britain of hillslopes which have been formed or affected by such movements, although on a much smaller scale. In addition to currently unstable slopes, which are recognisble by their irregular appearance, fresh scars and presence of surface fissures (tension cracks), there are many areas composed of hummocky and wet ground which were formed by earlier but now quiescent conditions. For example, the lower slopes of many escarpments are mantled by lobes and sheets of debris from upslope. Almost the entire length of the Cotswold edge[4] and the Lower Greensand escarpment[5] of the Weald (eg Leith Hill and Hindhead) are mantled by ancient landslides. The same is true of a great many of the deep Pennine valleys, where the widespread occurrence of old landslides includes some splendid large examples such as the prominent cliff of Mam Tor[6] (Plate 7.8) and the towers of Alport Castle[7] (Plate 7.9). Many of the South Wales valleys, like the Taff and Rhondda[8], also contain good examples of such features. Indeed, almost everywhere that permeable rocks, such as sandstones and limestones, overlie impermeable clays there is a likelihood that landsliding may have occurred at some time in the past. In the Cotswolds[9] it is the Oolitic limestone over Jurassic clays, in the Weald[10] the Lower Greensand over the Atherfield and Weald clays, in the Pennines[11] it is the sandstones and shales of the Millstone Grit, and in South Wales[12] the Pennant sandstone over Coal Measures. There are, in fact, almost innumerable combinations. In fact, a recent survey carried out for the Department of the Environment has recorded over 10,000 landslide sites in England, Wales and Scotland; but this total only includes those slides mentioned in the scientific literature. There must be many more.

Sometimes movements may occur which are disastrous in terms of loss of life, damage to houses, engineering structures, roads, railways or dams. Well-known recent examples include the Aberfan[13] coal-tip disaster of 1966, the collapse of part of the Sevenoaks bypass[14] during construction in the early 1960s, and the repeated dislocation of the A625 in the Pennines where it attempts to cross the broken ground beneath the 'shivering mountain' of Mam Tor[15] (Plate 7.8).

*PLATE 7.8 Mam Tor in the Pennines is a massive ancient landslide that still moves sufficiently to have caused the permanent closure of a main trans-Pennine road from Sheffield to Manchester. The scar intersects a hill-top fort and the main mass is crossed twice by the now much broken road.*

*PLATE 7.9 Alport Castle in the Pennines is one of the biggest landslides in the British Isles. Several blocks are detached or partially detached from the hill with wide open tension cracks and chasms. The landslide once dammed the valley below to form a lake.*

In many coastal locations, erosion by the sea undermines the cliffs and causes rock to fall, slide, sludge and collapse onto the shore. The occurrence of these processes is betrayed by the presence of pinnacles of rock detached from the cliff, open cracks and chasms, tumbled boulders and lobes of debris across the beach. Typical sites include Daddyhole Plain, Torquay[1]; the steep cliffs of Portland Bill, Dorset[2]; the undercliff of the Isle of Wight[3]; Barton-on-Sea in Hampshire[4]; the Lover's Seat at Fairlight near Hastings[5]; the north Kent coast at Herne Bay[6] or Warden Point on the Isle of Sheppey[7]; Cromer[8]; Holderness[9]; Robin Hood's Bay[10]; the Wirral coast[11]; north-west Isle of Man[12], and the coast of South Glamorgan[13]. The examples are so numerous that it is almost possible to believe that [illegible]

in such a way as to favour the creation of landslides. A wetter climate, or a cooler one in which the evaporation of water was low, or one in which the ground was seasonally frozen but thawed in summer, all promoted the accumulation of water within the ground and the build-up of water pressures. Under these conditions, hillslopes frequently failed to resist the erosional forces and collapsed. Sheets of debris and lobes of mud accumulated at the bottom of the hills and sometimes even dammed or choked up the valleys.

Several periods of climate are now recognised to have produced conditions favouring widespread landsliding (Fig 7.1), with the Lateglacial phase of cold climates between 13,000 and 10,000 years ago being especially important in the generation of slope instability. Over the centuries the deposits created by these movements have been weathered, cultivated, become vegetated and have generally settled toward a position of relative stability. Often only discontinuous patches of wet ground and irregular, rippled topography enable us to recognise the dramatic events which once took place. Yet these features may represent a considerable hazard to constructional activity or road building, because they may start to move again if disturbed. The reason for this is that they contain within themselves slippery discontinuities called 'shear surfaces' on which they once moved. The materials of which they are made have been weakened

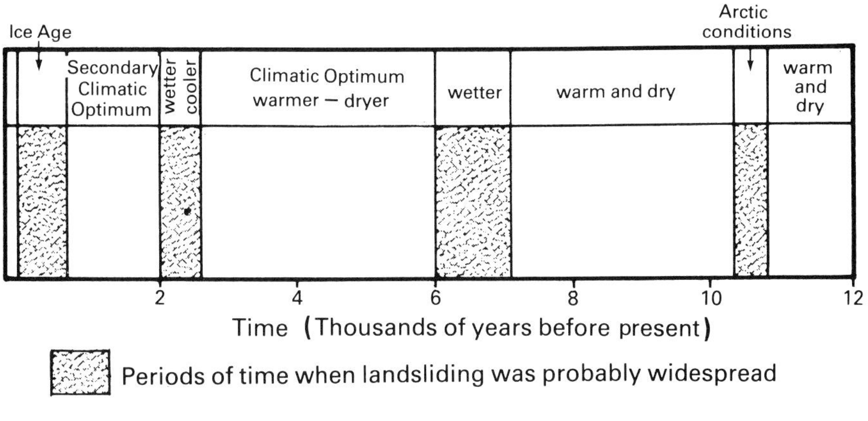


*Fig 7.1 Periods of time during the last 12,000 years when landsliding was probably widespread in the British Isles.*

by the original movements and very little additional stress is needed to set them in motion again.

If, for example, the front part of an old landslide is cut away by a bulldozer, or a river, it is very probable that the remaining mass of material will start slipping again over the ancient slip surfaces (shear planes). This is precisely what happened at the Sevenoaks bypass[1] in Kent, when a motorway was being excavated through the apron of debris near Riverhill (Fig 7.2). The northern side of the road began to move inwards and eventually the road had to be realigned, which proved very expensive. Similarly, at the Taren landslide in the Taff valley, South Wales,[2] great care had to be taken to select the correct alignment for the new Taff Vale trunk road in order to avoid reactivating the very large slide that extends over the full height of the valley. Problems of this type occur throughout the British Isles from the coastal road of Antrim[3] to the Cullompton bypass[4] in Devon or the M25 south of Croydon[5].

In addition to changes of climate, a well-known cause of ancient landslide activity was the removal of vegetation cover during periods of forest clearance. The loss of the binding effects of roots, in combination with the changes in the water regime within the ground due to reduced rainfall interception and reduced evapo-transpiration, have been known to cause both removement and disastrous new activity or soil erosion. The shallow slides on the northern slopes of Bredon Hill[1], Worcestershire, the slow ground distortions at Toy's Hill in Kent[2] and 'The Landslip' at Leith Hill[3] in Surrey, can all be related to historical records which show that landslide activity was related to land-use changes.

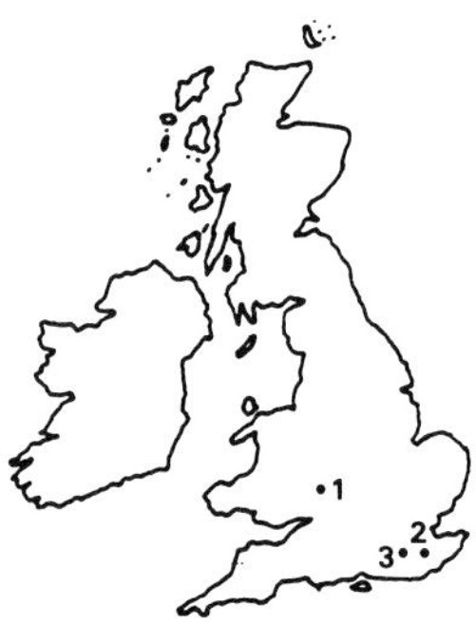


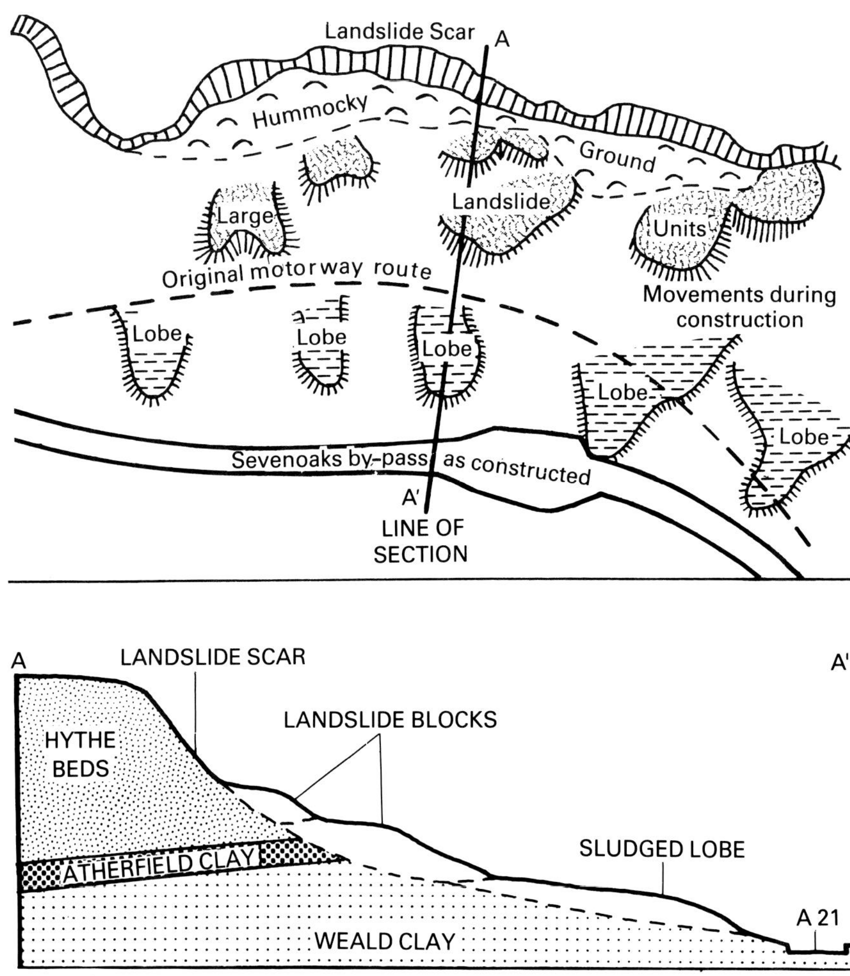


*FIG 7.2 A simplified version of the detailed map produced of part of the Sevenoaks bypass in Kent (A21) showing the landslide features crossed by the originally planned route, the location of the new slope movements created during the construction programme, and the eventually built roadline to the south of the landslides.*

*PLATE 7.10 Terracettes betray the slow but steady movement of a thin cover of soil downhill under the influence of gravity. Where the slope is not too steep, however, the soil moves so imperceptibly that it does not actually fracture the vegetation cover to cause these miniature steps.*

Not all the movement of material on hillslopes under the influence of gravity is quite so noticeable. A useful way to think about a hillslope is to imagine it as a surface made of various components such as soil, mineral particles, vegetation, rock and water. Onto this mixture the atmosphere pours water, evaporates the surface moisture, and heats or cools the surface when the temperature changes. It is easy to envisage such a surface swelling, shrinking, expanding or contracting every time the conditions change. All the time the materials are being tugged downward by gravity, pushed bodily downward by treading animals, the weight of trees, houses or the passage of vehicles. Rivers erode the foot of the hill, explosions shake it, percolating water washes little bits away, earthworms and animals burrow into it.

The soil behaves very sensibly in response to these forces – it steadily but surely moves downhill towards the rivers and streams. This process is called soil creep. Normally the rate of movement is imperceptibly slow, with near-surface particles perhaps moving 1cm (.4in) downslope every year. Of course the steeper the slope the more effective is the force of gravity (Fig 7.3), so that the rate may rise until the process becomes visible.

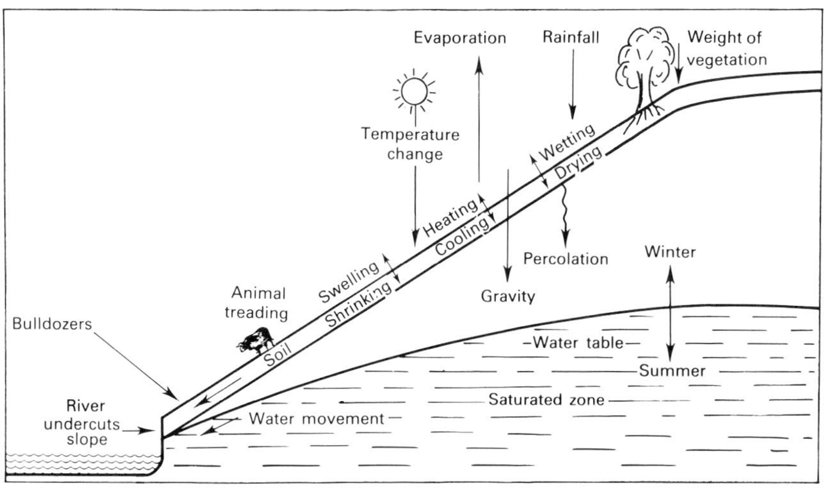


*FIG 7.3 Some of the forces acting on a hillslope and the 'magic carpet' of soil that moves slowly downhill.*

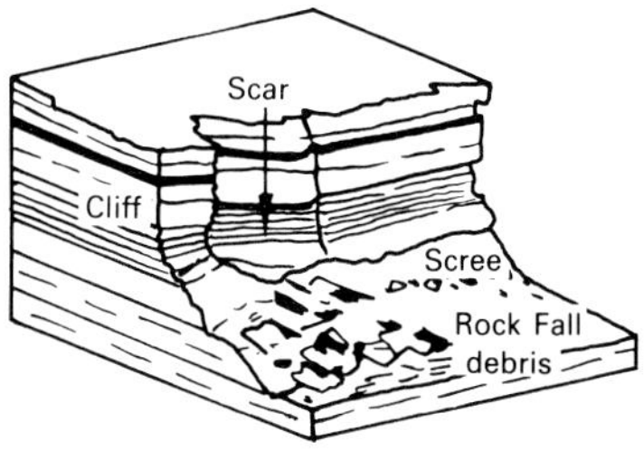


*FIG 7.4 A rock fall.*

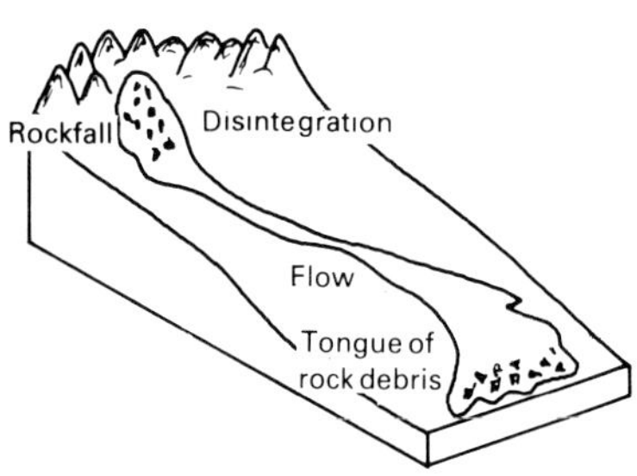


*FIG 7.5 A rock avalanche.*

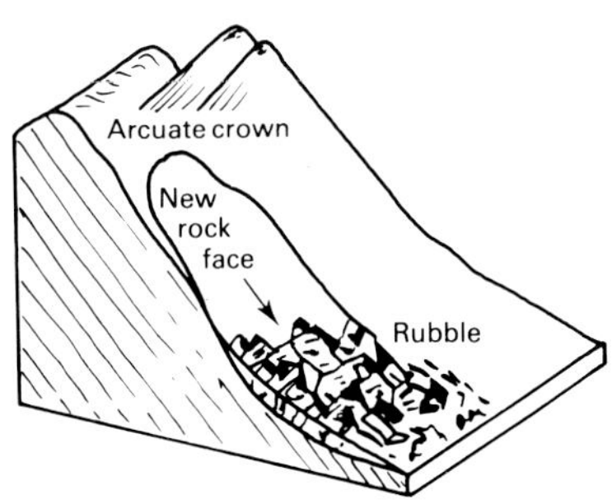


*FIG 7.6 A planar slide.*

The surface then appears torn and the movement creates small vegetated steps known as terracettes or 'sheep tracks' (Plate 7.10).

There are, in fact, many causes of slope movement (Table 7.1). In the British Isles the most common is the undercutting of a slope by rivers, ice, sea or man so that the slope eventually becomes too high or steep for the strength of the rock or superficial deposits to support. Build a sand castle on the beach; as the tide comes in so the sea washes away the base of the structure then, suddenly, down tumbles the tower! This process is called unloading. Almost as common a cause is the effect of water within the hill. Normally, when a landslide occurs, local newspapers attribute it to the effect of heavy rain which, according to one reporter 'lubricated the hill so that it fell down'. This explanation is too simple. During such times what really happens is that the water table in the hill rises (ie the surface of the saturated zone) as more of the hill becomes saturated. This increases the weight of the hill pressing downward under gravity. The pressure of water within the hill also rises, which has the effect of lifting and separating the individual particles of material, thereby reducing friction and enabling the material to move.

Changes in undercutting and the water content of the ground probably account for 70 per cent of all landslides in the British Isles. Others are caused by slow weathering of the rocks so that the physical and chemical resistances of the materials within the slope are changed. The addition of a sudden weight to the top of a slope tends to push the mass downward. Sudden shocks such as earthquakes, vibration of traffic or explosions, subsidence due to erosion of underlying rock, mining or solution to form caves and pipes, have all been recorded as landslide 'causes'.

TABLE 7.1
CLASSIFICATION OF LANDSLIDE CAUSES

| *Process* | *Change to Hillslope* |
|---|---|
| Weathering of hillslope materials | Changes in size, strength and chemistry of materials; opening up of joints; development of thick soil layer that could move. |
| Erosion of the slope by rivers, sea, ice or man | Change in geometry, height and angle; removal of lateral support; expansion of slope; fissuring. |
| Subsidence | Undermining; removal of fine material and cements; backsapping. |
| Deposition or tipping | Addition of weight to a slope. |
| Shocks | Earthquake shaking; explosions; vibrations from traffic. |
| Water-regime change | Heavy rain, rainy periods, saturation; rise in water table; high water pressures. |
| Vegetation removal | Loss of root strength; less water extracted from within slope by plants; more water arrives on slope because of reduced interception. |

Weathering is particularly important in clays, such as the London Clay, where many landslides have occurred due to progressive softening of the material. The collapse of some railway cuttings on the Southern Railway system as much as a hundred years after they were constructed is well known to anyone who travels south on the lines from Charing Cross. Today such cuttings are held up by sheet piling. The addition of material to a slope is a common cause of failure both inland and along the coast. At West Bay, Dorset, there was even a case where material was taken from a cliff in one place in order to stabilise it against erosion, and placed on the top of a nearby cliff which then slipped into the sea because it was overloaded and made of very weak materials! Earthquakes are not a common cause of slope failure in the British Isles because these islands lie within a relatively stable seismic zone of Europe. Shocks do occur, however, and the biggest can shake down loose rocks, but they rarely [illegible]

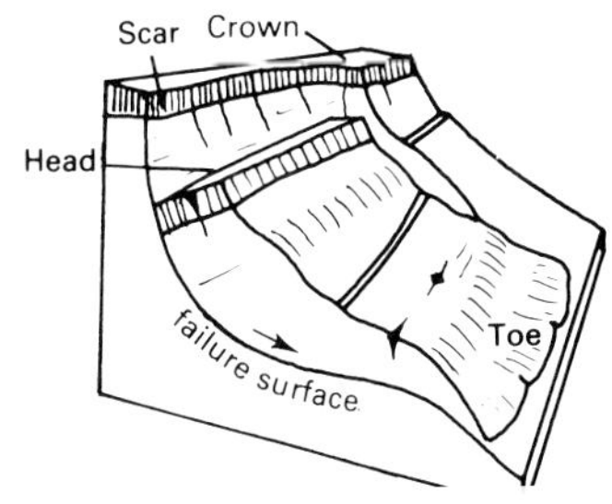


## [illegible]

Once a landslide has been started, from whatever cause, there are many ways it can move and many shapes that it can adopt. The simplest subdivision of the possible mechanisms of movement is into the three basic categories of fall, slide and flow.

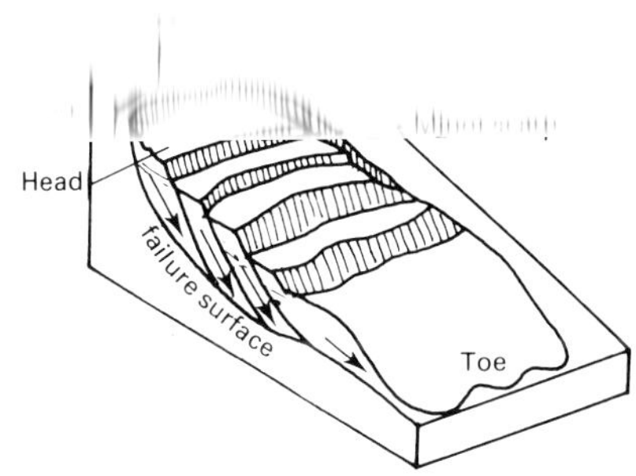


*FIG 7.8 A multiple rotational slide.*

### FALLS

A fall of soil, debris or rock is a vertical downward movement of material, usually by free fall through the air, although on the lower slopes the debris may break up, roll, bounce or slide downhill (Fig 7.4). The material becomes detached from steep scars and cliffs either through the collapse of an overhang or as a consequence of initial sliding on lubricated joint surfaces or steeply tilting bedding planes (see Chapter 2). In some cases it may even be prised loose by frost or the growing roots of trees. Whatever the cause, material descends to form a jumbled heap of debris at the base of the slope.

If the cliff is high enough, the material may accelerate to high velocity and run out across the low ground as a catastrophic avalanche. Fortunately, this rarely occurs in the British Isles though the remains of ancient avalanches (Fig 7.5) are quite common in the Highlands and glaciated valleys of the North and Wales. Since falls require the presence of very steep slopes, they are especially common along coastal cliffs, particularly those developed in the relatively soft sedimentary rocks of Lowland Britain (see Chapter 2) such as the Seven Sisters of Sussex[1].

### SLIDING

Sliding may take place in all material types and in several ways. The simplest form is a long, narrow planar slip (Fig 7.6) which is quite shallow but rapid. Steep cliffs, river banks and mountainsides throughout Highland Britain bear the scars of such failures which have developed in both rock (rock slides) and superficial deposits (debris slides). Slides are a typical form of failure after intense rain storms or following forest clearance, but fortunately their scars do eventually heal and the excavated hollows disappear. It is, for example, still just possible to recognise the debris slides on Exmoor[2] that were created by the Lynton and Lynmouth flood disaster of 1952 (see Chapter 5), but not for much longer.

The most common form of sliding is where movement has occurred on a curved failure surface. This results in the material tilting or rotating as it moves downhill, thereby accounting for the name 'rotational slides' (Fig 7.7). These may be single units, or multiple with one unit following another in a giant staircase down the slope (Fig 7.8). Folkestone Warren[1] (Plate 7.6), the Storr[2] (Plate 7.7), Mam Tor[3] (Plate 7.8), Alport Castle[4] (Plate 7.9) and Stonebarrow[5] (Plate 1.2), are famous, large examples. Similar, but smaller landslides can be identified on river banks, sea-cliffs and eroding locations throughout the British Isles and in virtually all materials. They therefore range in size from tiny slumps on river banks to huge complexes of moving units such as the Storr (Plate 7.7). Signs to look for include arcuate (curved) cliffs and scars, back-tilted ground, broken strata, ponds trapped by hummocky ground and sometimes an upraised ridge at the base of the slope, known as the toe (Figs 7.7 and 7.8).

Where geological structures are strongly developed (see Chapter 2) the normally curved slip-surface may be modified so that a horizontal component is introduced into the movement. Such slides are called block slides or slab slides (Fig 7.9). Typically they possess a chasm at the back of the moving block formed by the subsidence of relatively intact masses of rock into the void left at the base of the cliff. Such a chasm is termed a 'graben' – the German word for a sunken block of land. The most famous example is at Bindon[6], and was described at the start of this chapter (Plates 7.1 and 7.2). Smaller examples can be seen on the north Kent coast at Warden Point, Sheppey[7] – the Miramar landslips – and at Llanhilleth in Ebbw Vale in Wales[8]. All these different kinds of slide are produced by varying combinations of slope steepening and water-regime changes as outlined earlier.

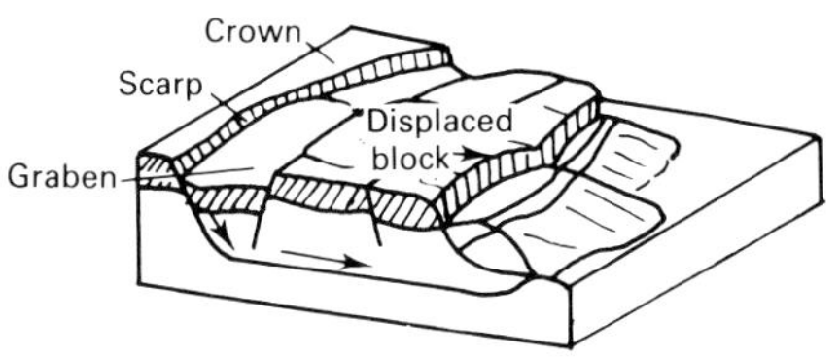


*FIG 7.9 A block slide.*

FLOWS

Flows are among the most exciting of all landslide phenomena. Try an experiment – next time you are mixing concrete on the garage floor add a little more water than is recommended. Keep mixing. Suddenly the heap of aggregate, sand and cement will collapse and flow toward the door. There is a critical point of moisture content, actually not very much extra water at all, at which the very coarse mixture begins to rapidly deform and to change its state from a plastic to a liquid condition. Imagine such a material, on a hillside of perhaps 30-40 degrees steepness, moving downslope in a debris slide. As it falls into the little channels of small streams, it is churned about in what is, in effect, a linear concrete mixer. It takes off and descends with considerable velocity to overwhelm everything in its path. Typical forms include debris flows of cobbles, sand and silt and mudflows of fine material. The names merely describe the size of material particles included. In some instances, air substitutes for water in generating flowage, resulting in the creation of rock avalanches (coarse debris) and powder flows (fine materials), but these are relatively unusual in the British Isles.

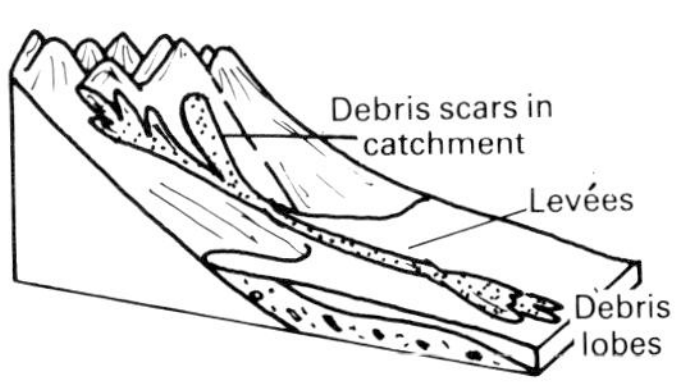


*FIG 7.10 A debris flow.*

The mountains of Britain have hundreds of flows. They can be recognised by small bare patches of ground at their head, shallow sinuous courses between raised edges called levées, and multiple overspilling lobes of debris and low-angle fans at their base (Fig 7.10). Classic sites are the scree slopes of north Wales[1], Borrowdale in the Lake District[2] or, in perfection, the Llarig Gru in the Cairngorm[3].

Often confused with debris flows are the type of planar slide called mudslides (Fig 7.11). Mudslides occur in most hilly areas developed on clay and are especially common on the coast. They move by sliding on a polished and grooved ('slickensided') shear surface, but when very wet they are almost like a spilt bowl of porridge and flow in sticky, wet streams across the surface. Normally they creep slowly along pushing boulders, trees and rubbish toward their margins, but sometimes they surge quickly forward, as they regularly do on the north Antrim coast road. Black Ven[4] (Plate 7.4), Fairlight[5], Bredon Hill[6], Petit Tor Cove at Torquay[7] and countless

other examples can be found. Recognition signs include an arcuate bowl at the head in which material accumulates; a long straight track through which material moves on its way downslope; very sharp margins defined by clear fissures (tension cracks), rather like knife cuts, where the shear plane comes to the surface; a heavily cracked or creased surface; a bulbous toe or lobe at the foot with overlapping lobes of mud and, if in the sea, an eroded margin of large boulders which mark how far out to sea the mudslide reached.

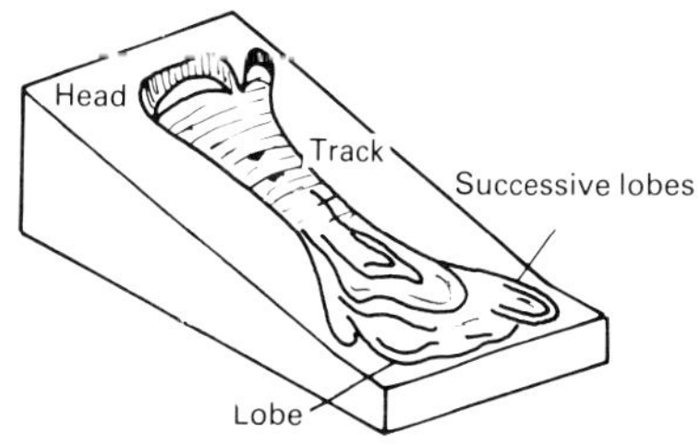


## THE ANATOMY OF LANDSLIDES

Although there are many diverse types of landslide there is nevertheless [illegible] material is sometimes confined within its *flanks* and moves on a *surface of rupture* or *shear surface*, which is often highly polished. The surface of

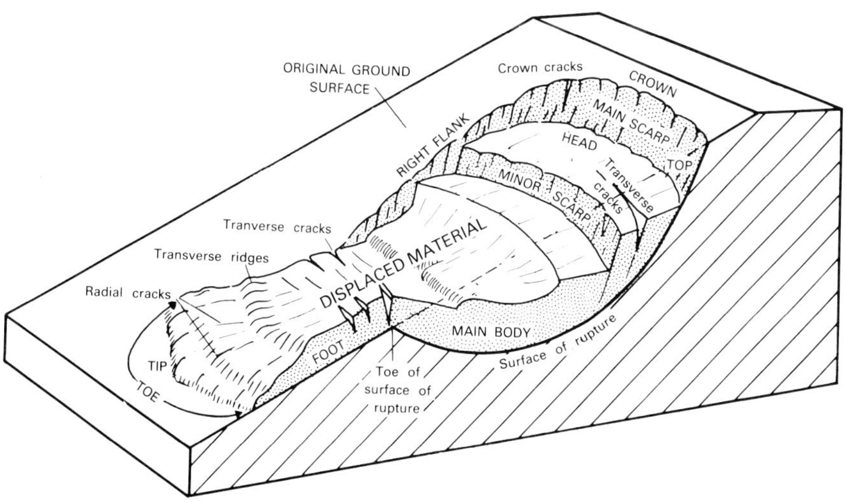


*FIG 7.12 The main features of a landslide.*

the material itself will be broken by cracks, which are *transverse* (along the slope), *longitudinal* (down the slope) or *radial* in exactly the same manner as the crevasses on a glacier.

The professional landslide expert uses these features to identify, describe and map landslides. This is very important for planning the wise use of land and for the guidance of engineering investigations into a landslide problem.

## CAN WE PREVENT LANDSLIDES?

Landslides can be prevented and controlled providing there is sufficient money available. There are four main methods: avoidance, control of groundwater, excavation and restraint.

*PLATE 7.11 The huge concrete sea-defence installations protect the failed undercliff at Folkestone Warren from further attack by the sea. The Folkestone to Dover railway line runs across the slipped mass, the undercliff, that has fallen away from the rock face behind.*

Avoidance is always the best method because it is easier to work with nature than to attempt to bludgeon her into submission. Where possible, engineers locating, say, a new roadline or designing the bridges will always choose to avoid unstable terrain. To do this they need to know where the landslides are, the causes of these landslides, and the likelihood of new movements developing. This can be achieved by careful mapping (Fig 7.2) and description using terms and recognition figures such as those shown in this chapter. Once a good map of the distribution of actual or potentially unstable slopes has been produced, it is often possible to relocate a proposed development or at least to minimise the hazard.

Where a hazard exists but cannot be avoided, it is essential to reduce the risk by removing surface water, preventing the infiltration of more water into the slope, sealing cracks and removing subsurface water using deep [illegible]

Excavation of the slope means the deliberate, but careful, modification of the shape of a slope in order to reduce the forces that are trying to push the slope-forming material downhill. Sometimes a landslide is removed completely and the hole filled with more stable materials such as coarse gravel (eg on the M20 east of Maidstone[1]). Arcuate patches of gravel on road cuttings always betray this form of stabilisation. Other techniques are to remove the top of the slope, to reduce the angle of the hillsides or to cut benches. In the right circumstances all are known to be effective.

Lastly, the stability of a slope can often be improved by placing a heavy weight of rock fill, earth or concrete on the toe of the moving mass in order to prevent it from moving forward. This is often effective on rotational landslides. A very well-engineered example of this is the sea wall at Folkestone Warren[2] (Plate 7.11). Buttresses of rock, stone walls, cribs, bulkheads, sheet piles, and stone-filled wire baskets (gabions), are all used by engineers to fortify hillslopes and many a road, railway and house in Britain depends on them for support. If the slope is made of hard, jointed rock, it is even possible to hold the whole lot together using steel bolts (rock bolts), anchors, grouting of joints or chain mesh. It all depends on the importance of the site and the amount of money available.

## CONCLUSION

There is a temptation when faced with the massive structure of a hillslope or a mountain to readily believe in the notion of 'the everlasting hills'. The reality is much more subtle. The Earth's surface is not fixed, immutable, unchanging, but a magic carpet moving ever downward toward the sea – sometimes smooth, sometimes ruckled up, torn open by rills and gullies, ripped by slides, hammered by falling rock. Yes indeed, the ground can and does move, but at greatly varying rates; fast in some places, slow in others and also stationary where it is perfectly flat. The rate of movement also varies with time in response to vertical movements of the earth (tectonic), changes in climate and the impact of human activities. It is perhaps useful to close with the words of Argand written in 1924: '. . .the structures that compose a tectonic edifice are not all there is to it: *there is movement that has vitalised them* and that still does so, because history continues and we live. . .at an arbitrary moment in this grand affair.'

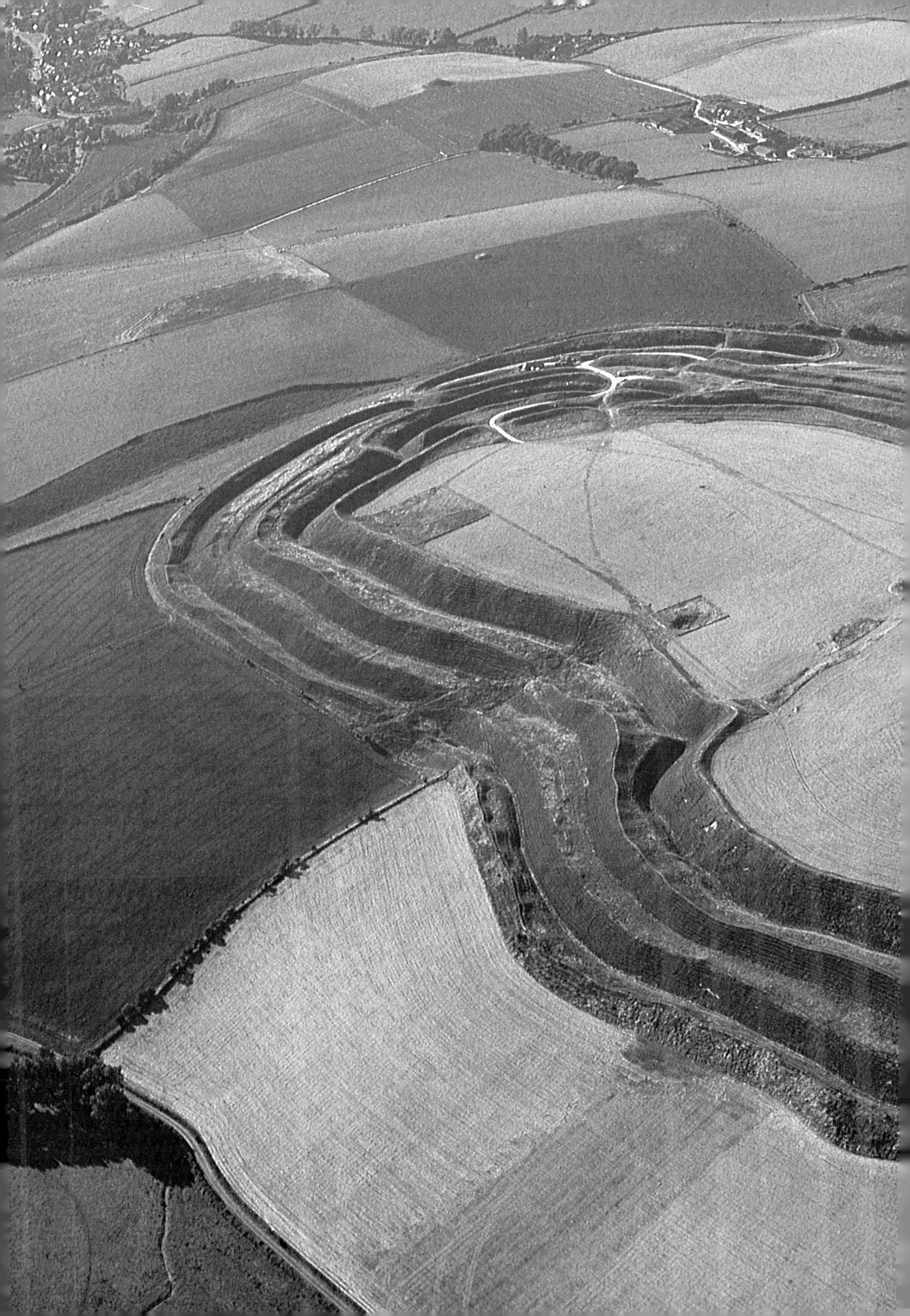

8

# THE HAND OF HUMANS

Andrew Goudie

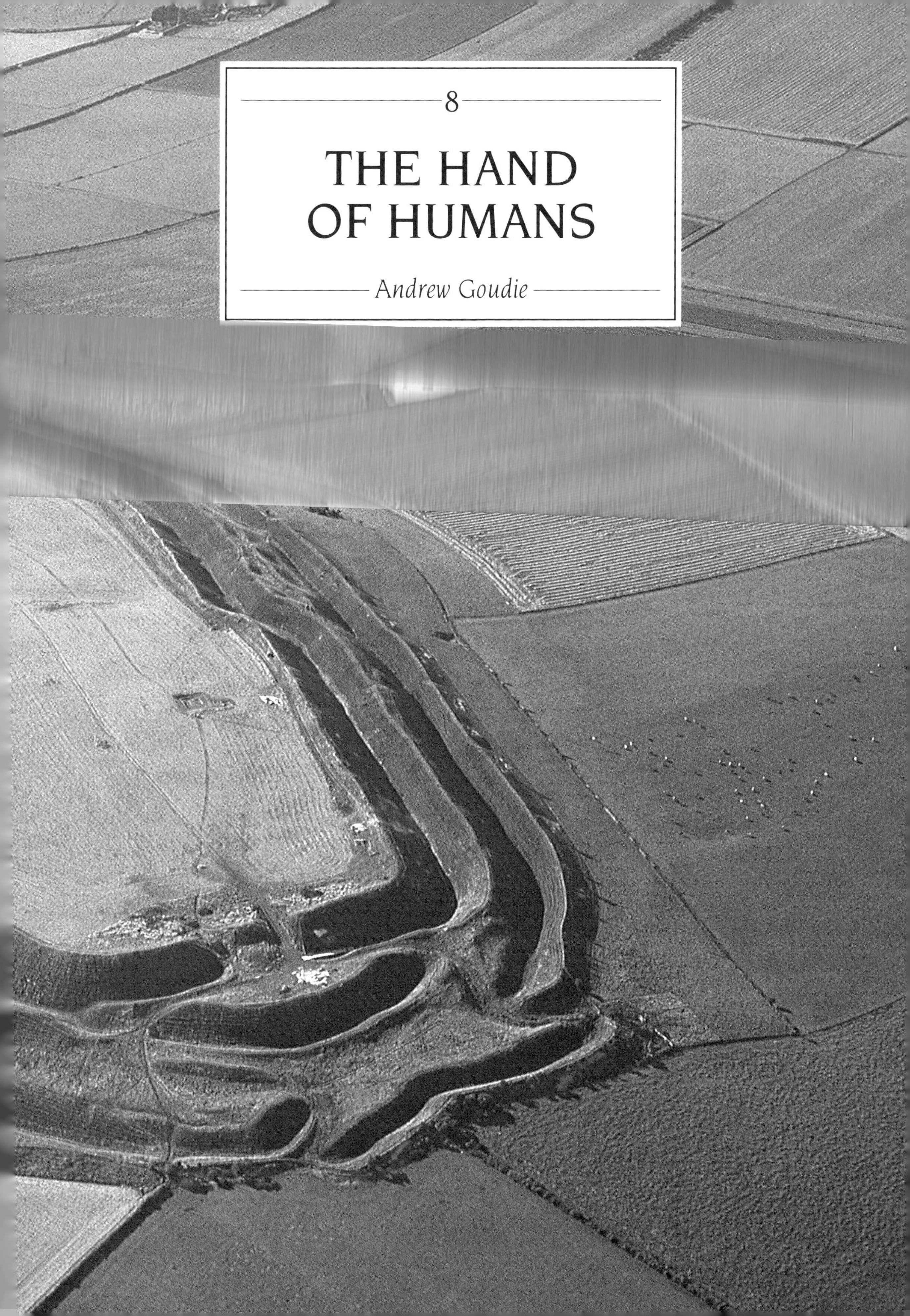

# THE HAND OF HUMANS

We all appreciate the ability of humans to reshape the land. The pyramids of ancient Egypt, the paddy terraces of Asia, the polders of Holland, huge holes torn in the ground by machines to win the raw materials essential for industry; all are clear testimony to the role of humans in changing the face of the Earth. But can these notions be applied to the landscape of the British Isles? Most readers would undoubtedly agree that they can, but mainly in regard to the industrial landscapes that are pimpled and pock-marked with heaps and holes. Thus commuters driving into Sheffield, or travellers to the City on the 7.32 from Sevenoaks probably acknowledge the ground remodelling activities of humans because they see the evidence on their daily journeys to work. But do they recognise the existence of the same influences when they go on holiday to the Lake District or climb the hill to Haytor on Dartmoor? Possibly not, because the scale and character of the changes by human influences are different.

Humans have inhabitated the Earth for perhaps 3 million years, a fraction of geological time. They have inhabitated the British Isles for an even shorter period – around 300,000 years. In spite of this short tenure of the globe, humans are capable of devastation in the landscape on a scale never seen before, and their impact is increasing all the time. This is partly because population levels have expanded so hugely. At the start of the Victorian era the world population total passed 1,000 million. In the 1980s it passed 5,000 million. Combined with this dramatic growth in population are the major technical advances, many of which are the result of industrialisation and urbanisation of the last couple of centuries. Thus humans have acquired enormous physical power to change the surface of the Earth because of a combination of sheer numbers and the progressive harnessing of new sources of energy. Bulldozers, trucks, explosives and the like ensure that the hand of humans is increasingly evident in the landscape.

It is scarcely credible to think that the Norfolk Broads[1] are medieval peat diggings but that indeed is what they are. Yet, impressive and beautiful manifestations though they may be of the power of unsophisticated workers to change the land with spade and cart, they pale into insignificance compared with what can be achieved today. For example, at present in Britain about 5 tonnes of building aggregate is excavated every year for every man, woman and child in the country, fourteen times the figure at the turn of the century.

There are very few human activities that do not change the landscape. Some of these changes are created deliberately and knowingly, such as by building, by excavation, by farming or by the management of rivers and coasts to prevent floods. Other changes, often more threatening, are caused by accidents or are the unanticipated by-products of human activity.

Look around the landscapes of Britain and Ireland, and you do not have to seek long before the scale of human digging activity becomes apparent. On the one hand there are all the mining activities: brickpits, railway ballast quarries, open-cast and underground coal mines, gravel pits, the peat diggings of the Irish bogs[2], the old iron-ore mines of Northamptonshire[3], the salt mines of Cheshire[4], cement works, and the stone quarries which provided the material for many of our finest buildings. On the other hand there are all the gashes produced by civil engineering projects both great and small: the Channel Tunnel, the London underground system, railway and motorway cuttings, canals and harbours, and innumerable pipelines for oil, gas, water and sewage.

Excavation in one place inevitably lead to deposition in another. It has, for example, been calculated that there are at least 2,000 million tonnes (tons) of shale waste lying in pit heaps in the coalfields of Britain. Less obvious is the fact that cities grow on top of their own waste. As towns grow older so the surface level tends to rise: buildings decay or burn and are rebuilt; litter, house and trade waste accumulate; cesspits become filled and bodies are buried. It has been calculated that, on average, cities dump about 0.3m (1ft) of debris per century. The City of London rests on an average of 3-5m (10-16ft) of debris.

The cutting down of trees is one of the most important ways in which humans modify the face of the Earth. If humans had not cleared so much of the woodland in Britain and Ireland, the natural landscape would be totally dominated by forests. There would be some treeless areas on high mountains and in the far north, and on coastal dunes and salt marshes, but overall a variety of different woodland types would exist. Pine would be dominant in the eastern Scottish Highlands, and some mountains in England and Ireland. Birch would dominate over large tracts of the western Scottish Highlands. Oak and hazel woodlands would carpet southern Scotland, highland England, most of Wales and parts of Ireland. Hazel [illegible]

[illegible] rainfall and breathes out much moisture (see Chapter [illegible]). [illegible] during a rainstorm less water reaches the ground than in an unvegetated area. In addition to their role as umbrellas, the trees bind the soil with their roots, and provide dead leaf debris to feed the soil fauna of worms and other small creatures. These play a key role in maintaining a good soil structure, which in turn aids the natural drainage of the soil. For all these reasons the amount of water running off the surface of the ground, and hence the amount of erosion, should be less beneath a forest than under any other type of land use.

The unanticipated soil erosion that often follows a major change in land use has led to very rapid accumulation of the eroded materials in areas like lakes and valley floodplains. But this is not only a recent phenomenon. Studies of cores of sediment recovered from lake floors in the Brecon Beacons[1], for example, have indicated that the rate of sediment dumping in the lake increased thirteen-fold about 5,000 years ago. This was due to the arrival of early Neolithic farmers, who cleared the forested land for the first time. Today soil erosion is enhanced by the ploughing up of ancient pasture, and of upland areas for afforestation, and the removal of hedgerows. Much of the soil erosion is achieved by water, but there are certain parts of Britain where wind is the culprit. This is particularly true of areas of light sandy or peaty soils, as in the Breckland[2], the Fens[3], east Yorkshire[4] and Lincolnshire[5].

Another unwelcome consequence of human activity is ground subsidence. Subsidence resulting from coal mining led to court cases in England as early as the fifteenth century. Besides causing damage to houses, it can produce depressions which disrupt surface drainage and cause flooding to give permanent lakes. The amount of subsidence can be appreciable. For example, there are reports of as much as 12m (40ft) in parts of Staffordshire[6]. Extreme examples of subsidence have also been associated with the exploitation of salt deposits, especially in Cheshire[7]. The mining of salt, which often relies on dissolving it and pumping out the brine, has sometimes led to subsidence of large areas. The Cheshire 'flashes' are lakes formed in the subsided areas. Salt mining also caused the LMS railway line between Crewe and Manchester to subside nearly 5m (16ft) between 1892 and 1956.

Other important examples of ground lowering are those associated with the artificial draining of areas of peaty, organic-rich soils. The drainage

lowers the water table, leaving the dry peat above susceptible to oxidation (a form of chemical decay) and to wind erosion. These processes destroy and remove the peat at the surface, and the land lowers. The classic example of this is provided by the Fens[1] in East Anglia, where around 4m (13ft) of lowering has occurred since 1848. Only about one-quarter of the natural area of peat now remains.

Not content with quarrying, draining and chopping down forests, humans also interfere with hillslopes. Humans can bring about landslides by altering the shape of the slope or the weight on the slope, or by decreasing the strength of the materials of which the slopes are made. The piling up of waste, soil and rock into unstable configuations is a common problem. In 1966, at Aberfan[2] in south Wales, a major and disastrous failure took place when part of a 180m (590ft) high coal-waste tip slid and flowed downhill. The tip had not only been constructed with a steep, potentially unstable slope, but it had also been located where water naturally seeped out of the ground. Saturation of the lower parts of the waste lowered its strength and increased the probability of failure.

Some of the most severe examples of slope instability, worsened by the actions of humans, occur on coasts. A classic example is the landslides at Folkestone Warren[3] (Plate 7.11) in Kent, where white Chalk overlies a slippery, impermeable clay. The Warren lies to the east of Folkestone. Originally the cliffs were protected by a beach that was fed with shingle and sand carried along the coast by waves and currents from the west. But the construction of large harbour works at Folkestone in the nineteenth century blocked the eastward movement of coastal shingle and the Warren area became depleted in beach material. Without a good protective beach the cliffs were more susceptible to undercutting by the waves. This oversteepened the cliffs and a series of failures occurred. In 1915 a particularly spectacular failure disrupted the main railway line from Folkestone to Dover, which was, and still is, routed across the failed landmasses. The area has now been stabilised by massive and costly sea-defence works.

The coast is an especially unstable environment in the face of human interference. Engineering works, including groynes, piers and breakwaters, can interrupt longshore sediment movement, causing accumulation at one point but erosion in the area starved of its sand supply further along the coast. For example, Seaford[1] in Sussex suffers from the construction of the Newhaven breakwater, and Lowestoft[2] suffers from the building of the pier at Gorleston. The recreational use of the coast creates problems too, as in the erosion and reactivation of sand dunes.

Engineering works are not restricted to slopes and coastlines. Rivers also have their share of human interference, usually for water supply, navigation, flood protection or agricultural purposes. Rivers are diverted, straightened, encased in concrete conduits, and their banks are carefully protected. The canalisation of rivers for navigation purposes, the embankment of estuaries like the Thames[3], and the excavation of artificial drainage lines in the Fens[4], are examples of deliberate and purposeful change. Rather less obvious, but no less important, are the various indirect effects of human interference on rivers. Channels downstream from dammed reservoirs tend to be smaller than their natural predecessors, because they are not subjected to the same size of peak flood flows.

Conversely, channels are often enlarged as a result of urbanisation. In urban areas there is often a dramatic increase in the peak flood flows in a river. This is partly because of the presence of impermeable surfaces of tile, tarmac and concrete, which rapidly shed rainfall, and partly because of the installation of sewers and storm drains which are designed for the speedy evacuation of fluids from the roads and gutters. So, very little water is trapped and much of it is transferred at high speed into the rivers. This increases the number of times the river experiences high flows, and increases the actual volume of the peak flows. Given that stream-channel shape and size depend on the flows they have to accommodate, banks will be eroded, where possible, to enlarge the channel.

Mining activity may also modify stream channels. The introduction of large amounts of coarse mining waste, be it from nineteenth-century lead and zinc mines in mid-Wales, or the china-clay mines of Cornwall, can silt up rivers and their estuaries. The ploughing up of land can have a similar silting effect, but generally on a smaller scale.

At the very smallest scale, humans even seem to affect the disintegration of rocks. In the last few decades, because of the accelerated burning of fossil fuels (coal, oil and gas), the rainfall has become markedly more acidic and corrosive. There are records of acid rain having acidity values [illegible] of less than 3, whereas unpolluted rain has an acidity value of just [illegible] in the atmosphere is [illegible]

short term profits will accrue as a result [illegible] however, the drainage may cause the soils to decay and be blown away, so that the nutrients on which the long-term fertility of the soil depends gradually disappear. Furthermore, the ground surface is lowered, so that the risk of flooding may become greater. Likewise, we may protect a piece of coastline by building a groyne, which traps sediment, but by doing so we starve another area of its replenishing shingle and thereby cause rapid erosion further along the coast. That area may then have to be protected, and if the same method is adopted, the problem will be shifted yet again. The costs of such actions may be huge.

[illegible]

LANDSCAPES OF DEFENCE

It is a sad commentary on the human condition that a high proportion of the visible antiquities of Britain and Ireland are military works. Of these, some of the most impressive, even though they are some of the earliest, are the great hillforts of the Iron Age, with their huge ditches and ramparts. It needs to be said at the start, however, that not all such forts occur on hills and that they are not universal in their distribution. There are, for example, very few in eastern England, whereas in certain districts, notably Dorset, they can be extremely common. Contour hillforts were built to exploit the natural shape of a hilltop and to capitalise upon the advantage of elevation. In some cases they are relatively simple affairs with only one set of ramparts, but in others they have multiple ditches and ramparts. Notable amongst these are some of the Dorset hillforts[1], Eggardon, Badbury Rings and Maiden Castle (Plate 8.1). The last was likened by Thomas Hardy, the Wessex novelist, to 'an enormous many-limbed organism of an antediluvian time'.

Another widespread type of fort is the promontory fort, where a spur of a hill is cut off by a rampart and ditch across the neck, as for example on Crickley Hill[2] in Gloucestershire and on Bredon Hill[3] in Worcestershire. Some forts are effectively 'cliff castles', embracing coastal headlands rather than ordinary spurs, for example Trevelgue Head[4] in Cornwall, or, perhaps most spectacularly of all, Dun Aongusa on the Isle of Aran[5], off Galway in western Ireland.

The Romans introduced further types of defensive features, their fortifications ranging from large forts to smaller signal stations and watch-towers. Hadrian's Wall[6] (Plate 2.4) and some town walls can still be seen in the landscape. Of Saxon fortifications relatively little remains, though there

are earthworks dating to this period, such as Offa's Dyke[1] in the Welsh Marches and the Devil's Dyke of Cambridgeshire[2]. However, the impact of the Normans is frequently dramatic. The Norman invasion led to the rapid building of earth castles (mottes) especially along the Welsh border. Subsequently, in the late thirteenth and fourteenth centuries, monumental and elaborate castles were constructed of stone, including those of Caernarvon[3], Beaumaris[4], and Harlech[5] in north Wales. The most spectacular castle in southern England, because of the way in which it is perched on a residual mass of Chalk, is Corfe Castle[6] in Dorset.

Even more widespread than Norman castles are moated settlements. These were normally manor houses or farms owned by the smaller landowners, and over 5,500 have been identified, many of which were constructed between 1200 and 1325. The moats probably had a variety of uses besides defence: they were a source of water, they may have given protection against wild animals, and they may have conferred prestige on the owner. They are specially common in the clay lowlands in Wales, the North and in the South West Peninsula. There are also around 750 moats known in Ireland, most of them in the south.

ANCIENT PEAT DIGGING: THE NORFOLK BROADS

We have seen in Chapters 4 and 6 that during glacial times sea-levels were lower than today, and as a consequence rivers deepened their valleys. As the sea-level rose, when the ice-sheets melted, the valleys were flooded. Subsequently the flooded inlets have been partially filled by sediments dumped by the rivers and the sea. In the process the remains of plants accumulated in certain areas, giving rise to peats.

The East Anglian rivers, the Bure, Yare and Waveney are unusual in that they have many lakes in their floodplains – the Norfolk Broads[1] (Plate 8.2). For a long time these were thought to be small natural lakes created by partial and uneven filling of the valleys with sediments. But recent studies have shown that, far from being natural, the Broads are Britain's biggest manmade landscape. They illustrate the great power that humans had to change the landscape even centuries ago. They were excavated, for the most part in medieval times, by peat cutters who dug up the peats that had accumulated in the valley bottoms. They were required as a source of fuel. Using spades and carts, they succeeded in cutting peat to a depth of around 3m (10ft) and in all it is estimated that they removed more than 25 million $m^3$ (approximately 33 million cu yd) of material.

What is the evidence that leads to this remarkable conclusion? First, the study of old documents showed that local names have changed through time, from turbary (a turf cutting area) to open water and then to marsh. Moreover, there is an absence of references to the Broads in place-names or in manuscripts until later medieval times. Also, the appearance in local records of references to valuable fisheries, where previously there had been none, gives further historical evidence for the artificial origin of the Broads. Secondly, careful investigation of the Broads confirmed this conclusion. Boreholes put down into the Broads revealed sudden changes, from the freshwater muds that are being deposited today on the floor of the lakes, to the vertical walls of peat or peat and clay that form the margins of the Broads. It is difficult to envisage a natural process that could account for this sharp break. Within the Broads there are also some curious ridges and islands of peat. These are bounded by vertical sides, they have a geometrical shape, and are often clearly aligned. These islands probably represent banks of uncut peat which were left between adjacent diggings. Sometimes their alignment follows parish boundaries.

Humans are continuing to change the Broads. Concern is being expressed that because of increasing recreational pressures their intrinsic character and beauty are being changed. The rapid development of the boating-holiday industry means that the banks of the Broads are being

*PLATE 8.2 The Norfolk Broads are a medieval manmade landscape, created by the demand for fuel. Even today they are probably Britain's largest artificial landscape.*

subjected to increasing erosion by the wash set up by powered boats, and increasing amounts of sewage effluents are entering the lakes. Pollution from agricultural fertilisers is yet another problem. Pollution changes the chemistry of the Broads and the nature of the plants that can grow along their banks.

MODERN PEAT EROSION

Anybody who walks across Dartmoor[1], the Brecon Beacons[2], the Peak District[3], the Dumfriesshire Hills[4] or central Ireland[5] will appreciate, as they squelch and stumble and sink, that peat covers large parts of the British Isles. In the moist western parts of the country, and in moist upland areas the cool, wet conditions encourage the accumulation of organic remains of plants like *Sphagnum moss*, and it is these that in turn create the peat. The peat has been accumulating for 5,000 or more years, particularly since the natural forest cover was removed by our early ancestors.

The peat provides not only an important source of fuel to rural communities, and in the case of Ireland to power stations, but also controls the stream flow from many of our important highland areas. It is capable of absorbing a lot of water, and thus helps to prevent floods, and it also protects the material beneath from erosion. However, all is not well with our peats. Many of them are being eroded, leaving bare, unstable and unvegetated surfaces separated by deep gullies (Plate 8.3). For example, three-quarters of the blanket of peat in the Peak National Park[3] is affected by erosion which is especially rife above 550m (1,804ft) altitude. The eroded peat particles and organic acids discolour rivers that drain the peats – formerly clear water acquires a murky brown hue. The following description by Dr J.H. Tallis summarises the problem:

*PLATE 8.3 Erosion is destroying many of the peatlands of Britain and Ireland. Here, in the Pennines, the cover of vegetation is being destroyed and gullies are eating into the peats.*

> Finely-divided peat, washed downslope, accumulates against objects in its path, such as walls and wire fences; even clumps of bilberry may be partly buried by the peat wash; and residual patches of snow, persisting after snow-melting in spring, quickly acquire a superficial layer of peat particles. In areas of scour, established individual plants come to be raised up on peat pedestals several centimetres high, as the surrounding peat surface is gradually lowered. After heavy rain and during snow melt, turbid water rushes down the drainage gullies, carrying away peat in suspension and solution. In dry weather the superficial layers of peat shrink and crack, and may blow away as dust, while the cracks extend downwards.

Some of the peat erosion may be a natural process, for the high water content of blanket peats, and their low cohesion, makes them inherently unstable. This instability normally becomes more pronounced with time, as peat continues to accumulate, and it eventually leads to disruption of the peats in bog slides and bog bursts. The sites of former slides or bursts are often exploited by gullies which then eat back into the peat mass itself. However, the tempo of peat erosion seems to have quickened in the last two to three centuries, and this is where the role of humans becomes crucial. These naturally fragile areas of peat have been subjected to more and more pressure: heavy sheep grazing; regular burning; peat cutting; the digging of boundary ditches; the incision of pack-horse tracks; military manoeuvres during World War I, and the recreational tramping of people. A particularly sinister, unseen influence is atmospheric pollution from the industries of northern England. This kills some of the plants which enable the peat to develop.

Sometimes, peat is deliberately eroded, as when deep ditches are scored across peat surfaces to drain the ground so that forest plantations can be established. This is presently happening over large areas in Caithness[1]. This practice can also have unexpected and unwelcome consequences. The ditching breaks up the protective sod and peat, and exposes the underlying materials – often debris dumped by ice sheets – to the force of water running off the land. Studies suggest such forestry drainage operations can locally quadruple the amount of sediment that is delivered to rivers.

The clearest case of the deliberate erosion of peat comes from the peatiest area in the British Isles, the plains of Ireland. Although, as in other parts of Britain, hand-won peat or 'turf' has long formed the traditional fuel of a large part of the population, there has in recent decades been a completely new development that has transformed the scale and speed of peat destruction. The state-directed Turf Development Board and the Bord Na Mona set about producing peat for use in electricity generating stations, factories and homes. Suitable bogs were thus drained, and mechanised [illegible] half of this century the deeper raised [illegible]

[illegible]

reached our shores for the first time. [illegible] technology were the first farmers. They cleared forest with polished flint axes, they kept herds of animals and, most important of all, we know from the imprints of grains on their pottery that they cultivated cereal crops – wheat and barley. They used a simple plough, and its furrows have been found preserved beneath a barrow near Avebury[6] in Wiltshire.

Lynchets provide more widespread and more impressive remains of early ploughing (Plate 8.4). These are like small terraces, and they form because plouging on a slope causes slow movement of the soil downhill (fig 8.1). When a field is tilled, the plough cuts a sharp line on the uphill side of the field. Soil disturbed by the ploughing will tend to move downhill, thereby leaving a well-marked little scarp along the edge of the ploughing. On the other, downhill side of the field where the ploughing stops, the soil accumulates, producing another break of slope. The lynchets thus appear as strips of land, often relatively flat, that stand out distinctively from the slopes above and below. The difference in height between the lynchet and the hillslope, or the next lynchet below, can vary from a few centimetres to more than 8m (26ft)!

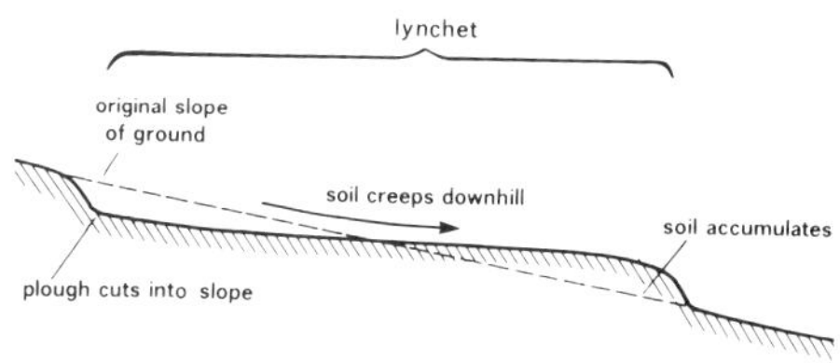


*FIG 8.1 The formation of a lynchet by soil creep results from ploughing. Walls were sometimes built on the downslope end to retain the soil.*

*PLATE 8.4 Swarms of parallel lynchets, near Mere in Wiltshire, stand out boldly in the landscape like a set of terraces.*

*PLATE 8.5 These beautiful and intricate ridge and furrow strips are the legacy of the early days of farming when the land was tilled with a heavy plough pulled by oxen. These patterns are near Padbury in Berkshire.*

Lynchets may occur as swarms of parallel strips, especially on steep slopes in southern and south-eastern England. Such swarms are probably of medieval age and are the result of the extension of the normal medieval open fields onto steep ground. Medieval lynchets tend to be longer than their prehistoric forebears, sometimes as long as 200m (650ft), and where whole flights lie together on a hillside they are often linked by ramps which provide access between them. Where the lynchets occur on very steep and exposed slopes, as at Worth Matravers[1] in Dorset, they show that there were severe population pressures on the land.

Another major impact of farming on our landshapes is the creation of striking ridge and furrow patterns (Plate 8.5). Large areas of the Midlands are striped by long, narrow ridges of soil, lying parallel to each other and usually arranged in blocks of approximately rectangular shape. They were formed by ploughing with heavy ploughs, probably pulled by teams of oxen. Such ploughing must have been practised over a long period in strip fields. The plough turned the ploughed slices of soil to the right.

There would have been no point in simply ploughing up and down the field, from one side to the other, for each up and down would have left the two turned slices side by side and covering an area of unploughed land. The way round this was to start in the middle of the field and work outwards. This meant that every slice was turned in towards the centre, from both sides, every time the plough went down one side and up the other. To work from the centre outwards over a whole field would have been very time consuming. Instead it made much more sense to divide the field into strips and to plough each of these from the centre outwards. As the slices, year after year, were turned in towards the centre on each strip, so the strip developed into a small ridge. The boundary between adjacent [illegible] at the centre of the furrow and marked the point where slices [illegible] ridges (Fig 8.2). [illegible] demarcate ownership of strips.

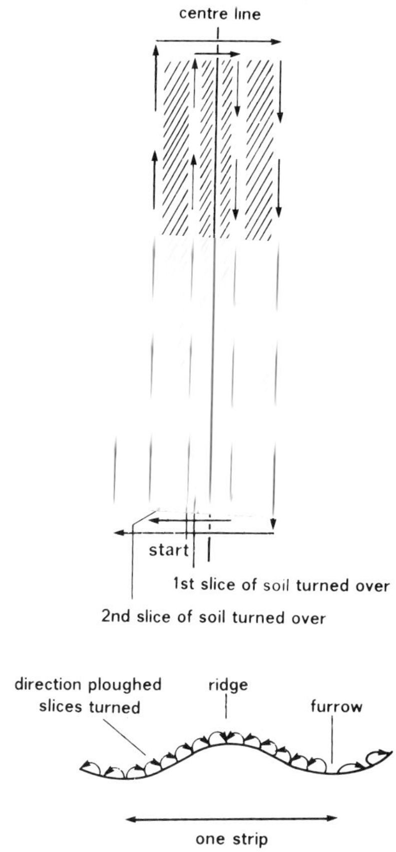


*FIG 8.2 The pattern of ploughing that is thought to give rise to ridge and furrow landshapes.*

AGRICULTURE AND SOIL EROSION

When mention is made of sand storms, dust storms and encroaching sand dunes, the mind turns to the world's great deserts rather than to the lowlands of England. However, in 1668 the village of Santon Downham[1] in the Breckland of East Anglia was overwhelmed by sand (Chapter 4). In the 1720s the 'horrid and frightful' Bagshot Heath[2] was little better, according to Daniel Defoe:

> Much of it is a sandy desert, and one may frequently be put in mind here of Arabia Deserta, where the winds raise the sands, so as to overwhelm whole caravans of travellers, cattle and people together; for in passing this heath on a windy day, I was so far in danger of smothering with the clouds of sand, which were raised by the storm, that I could neither keep it out of my mouth, nose or eyes; and when the wind was over, the sand appeared spread over the adjacent field...so that it ruins the very soil.

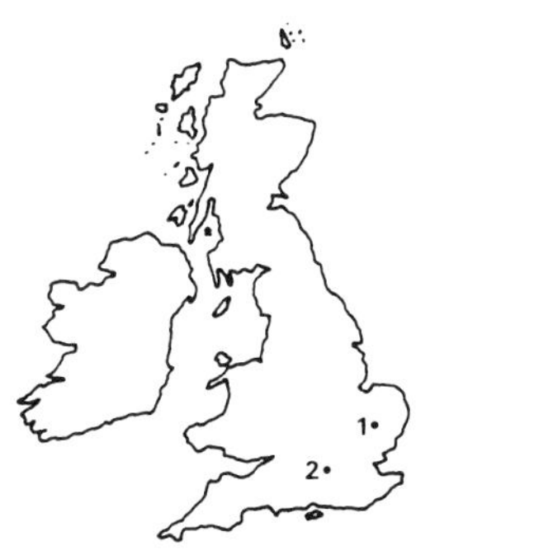


If badly tended, there are certain types of soil – the sandy soils – that are very susceptible to wind erosion. They are especially vulnerable if they have no cover of vegetation at those times of year, such as early summer, when they can dry out. Those areas most easily affected are the sandy heathlands, some of which are developed on sandy materials washed out of ice-sheets, or dumped by the wind in the Ice Age (see Chapters 3 and 4); others, such as Bagshot Heath, are formed on older sands originally laid down in the sea. The drained organic peats in areas like the Fenlands are also very vulnerable.

There is some evidence that in recent years sand and dust storms have increased. Since the 1920s, dust storms, locally often called 'soil blows' have been an all too common experience in the eastern, drier parts of England. Not only do they remove the fertile top soil and its enriching organic matter, but they also remove the expensive fertiliser that has been applied. If this is not enough, when the material is dumped it often blocks drains. The increasing incidence of soil blows results from changing agricultural practices, including the substitution of artificial fertilisers for farmyard manure, the removal of hedgerows to facilitate the use of bigger farm machinery and, perhaps most important, the increased cultivation of sugar beet. This crop requires a fine tilth and also tends to leave the soil

*PLATE 8.6 This sinuous ridge of silts in the English Fenlands marks the course of one of the meandering creeks that extended deep into the Fens before they were drained. The intensively cultivated, and eroded, peaty soils now lie at a lower level than the former creeks.*

relatively bare in early summer, a time when there can be long spells of dry, windy weather.

In earlier days, the blowing sand of areas like the Breckland may have been caused by the intensive grazing of rabbits, a species that was introduced to these islands in medieval times. The rabbit was able to exploit areas of land that were of little use for agriculture because they were too acidic, too stony or too sandy; moreover, rabbits provided a valuable source of meat for human consumption. However, their burrowing and nibbling activities could be disastrous on sandy soils, and it was to counter this threat that one of the most characteristic and evocative features of the Breckland[1] landscape was introduced in the nineteenth century – the gaunt windbreaks of pine trees.

One feature of the East Anglian Fenlands[2] which owes much to the removal of Fenland peats is the roddens – sinuous ridges of light-coloured material that snake across the flat Fens (Plate 8.6). Originally they were the silty tracks of creeks, bounded by raised banks, which extended from the main river estuaries far inland into the peat country. The remains of large marine animals, including whales, are sometimes found as fossils within the silts. With the drainage of the Fens and the reduction in level of the peats because of chemical changes and wind erosion, the peaty areas have been lowered much more than the silt areas. This is why the roddens now form ridges rising above the darker peat soils, and because of their elevation they have become favoured sites for roads and settlements.

MINING AND THE LANDSCAPE

Mining has a long history in the British Isles, and the landscape shows the imprint of this activity over extensive areas. The first mining was undertaken in Neolithic times, when holes were dug into the Chalk of southern England to get at seams of tough, unshattered flints. Among [illegible] make polished axes with which the [illegible] Langdale[5] district of the Lake [illegible] Antrim[6], Northern Ireland.

With the coming of the Bronze Age, copper mining was practised in Ireland and Scotland, and this was continued later by the Romans in Wales. Tin was mined in Cornwall and the spoil heaps of Roman workings can still be seen in the Bodmin Moor[7] area. Lead was a major British product in the Roman era and was mined in the Mendips[8], Yorkshire and in Shropshire. Lead mining was also a major industry in northern England in the seventeenth and eighteenth centuries and the spoil heaps, adits, old galleries and leets for ore-washing and drainage can still be detected in the landscape.

PLATE 8.7 *This pitted landscape is the result of Stone Age flint mining, near Thetford in Norfolk.*

*PLATE 8.8 Dramatic subsidence in the 1930s around Hodbarrow coal mine, near Millom in Cumbria.*

Iron working dates back to pre-Roman times, when various ores were used: bog iron in Ireland and Shetland, carstone in West Sussex and Surrey, haematite in Weardale and Glamorgan. The ores were got by grubbing and pitting, and the furnaces were shallow pits. The Romans worked sites in many parts of Britain, including the Weald[1] and the Forest of Dean[2]. The Wealden mines flourished and were still being exploited in the eighteenth century; they gave rise to perhaps the finest landscape relicts of this stage of our industrial history – the famous Wealden hammerponds. The ponds were created when the narrow valleys of the Weald were dammed with clay banks, and they provided water to work the iron mills. Water powered the hammers that crushed the ores, and worked the bellows for the blast furnaces. It is also possible to find cinders and slag, the lanes along which the products of the mines were taken away, and the depressions of the bellpits from which the ore was mined.

With the coming of the Industrial Revolution, the whole scale of mining changed, and so did its impact on the landscape. In Anglesey[3], exploitation of the huge copper deposits of Parys Mountain transformed the area into a desolate lunar landscape. Even today, a hundred or more years after most of the mining activity ceased, the poisoned landscape still persists as a stark reminder of the undesirable ecological effects of metal mining. In Devon and Cornwall[4] the great pits and spoil heaps associated with the winning of china clay are no less significant to the landscape, and the same applies to the great brickworks of Peterborough[5] and Bedfordshire[6]. Huge quarries have been dug to provide ballast for the railways, limestone for the iron furnaces, and building stones for the great cities. Above all, who could dispute the impact of coal mining on the scenery of areas like south Wales, the Potteries and County Durham, whether it be spoil tips (many of them now carefully landscaped), the great scars of open-cast mines, or the areas of subsidence from underground mining (Plate 8.8)?

## COASTAL EROSION AND HUMAN INTERFERENCE

All around the British coast, many landscapes are fashioned in shingle, and in many locations the shingle is extracted for use in the construction industry. Looking at the size of structures like Chesil Beach[7] in Dorset or Dungeness[8] in Sussex and Kent, one would think that there was an almost limitless supply of easily won shingle material. And listening to the waves moving the shingle in a storm, one would think that any shingle removed by human activity would be speedily replenished by nature. However, even shingle beaches are delicate structures and in many cases the shingle removed by humans is not very readily replenished. The reason for this is that a great deal of the shingle we find on our beaches is of some antiquity, and to appreciate this we need to consider the history of sea-level change.

During cold glacial phases, because so much water was stored up at the ice-caps, world sea-levels fell, exposing much of the continental shelves as dry land (see Chapter 4). Rivers, laden with debris washed out of the ice-sheets, dumped their load on these exposed surfaces such as the floor of the North Sea and the floor of most of the English Channel. When the [illegible] melted, the sea rose, and it combed up sand and shingle from [illegible]

[illegible] century it was a fishing settlement, sited on a small platform [illegible] and cliff at the southern end of Start Bay. The village was fortunate to possess a good shingle beach, which served to protect the village by acting as a great baffle that absorbed the force of storm waves. Today, however, the site is more or less deserted; the protecting beach has largely disappeared, the platform has been partly eroded, and the few remaining cottages are mostly in ruins (Plate 8.9). It is the disappearance of the beach which accounts for the ruining and desertion of the village. The former was severely depleted at the turn of the century to help build extensions to the naval dockyard at Devonport[10]. A contractor, Sir John Jackson, was licensed by the Board of Trade in 1887 to remove shingle by dredging and succeeded in removing over half a million tons, lowering the beach by 5m (16ft) in places. Thus it was that in 1917, when a severe easterly storm brought large waves across Start Bay and with no beach to offer protection, the village was ravaged by the sea.

The protective role of sand and shingle can be reduced in other ways (Fig 8.3). For example, at West Bay in Dorset the building of a breakwater at the western extremity of Chesil Beach has stopped the westerly movement of fine shingle by longshore drift (see Plate 6.4). Shingle has accumulated on the east side of the breakwater at the expense of shingle on the west. As a consequence erosion has become a problem on the west side, and expensive measures, including the provision of a sea wall and great boulders of Portland Stone, have had to be instituted to protect parts of the town and its cliffs.

But sea walls are not the placid, immutable features they appear to be. When the waves beat against the wall, very little of wave energy is absorbed, unlike on a beach. The waves tend to bounce back off the wall and in doing so to scour away sand and shingle at the base of the wall. Eventually, the wall may be undermined and then collapse (Fig 8.3).

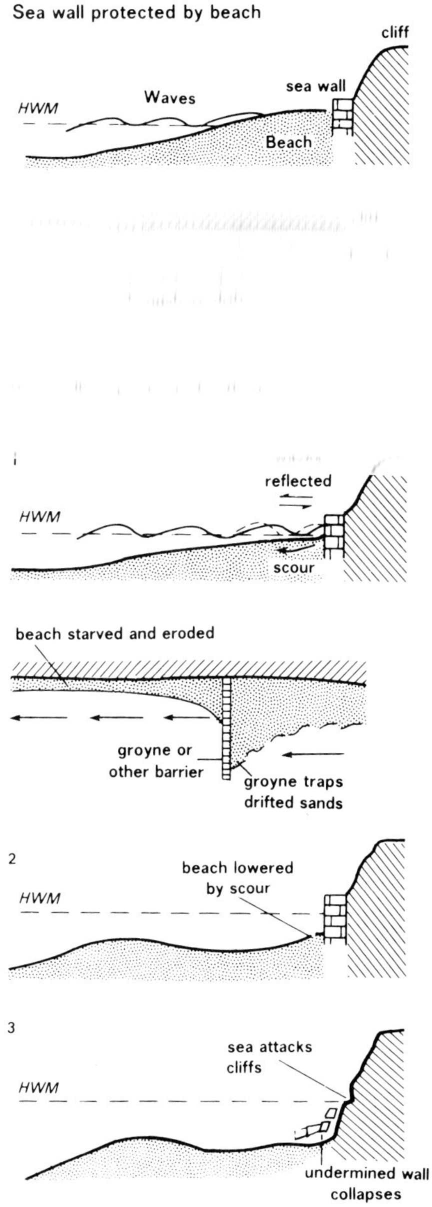


*FIG 8.3 The process by which a sea wall is undermined, and the effect of a barrier interrupting longshore drift on a beach.*

## DESTRUCTION AND PROTECTION OF COASTAL DUNES

Sand dunes are a common coastal feature in Great Britain. Recent surveys suggest that they cover something like 56,000 ha (138,500 acres) of land. Dunes are important because they are a major habitat for wildlife, because they are intrinsically beautiful, and because they are a major barrier against the sea's attack.

*PLATE 8.9 The coastal platform at Hallsands that once housed a fishing village is now virtually deserted, and all because humans interfered with the coast without understanding how it worked.*

*PLATE 8.10 The dunes at Culbin Sands have been stabilised by extensive conifer plantations.*

Very few of the dunes are actively growing today. There are some notable exceptions, such as Tentsmuir Point[1] in Fife, Morfa Dyffryn[2] and Morfa Harlech[3] in north Wales, and Towyn Point[4] in south Wales, but the great bulk of dunefields are actively eroding. Possibly the most spectacular area of erosion is on the Sefton coast of Merseyside, where there is an especially rapid loss of dunes northwards from Formby Point[5]. The most frequent cause of dune erosion is the trampling of human feet and the rutting effects of motor vehicles. Long-continued passage from holiday accommodation to a beach across a dune kills the vegetation which is so crucial for binding the sand. The death of the vegetation enables the wind to scour the sand and erode a great hollow in the dune.

There are many methods being adopted around the British coast to reverse the effects of undesirable erosion, though it has to be said that many of them are unsightly. This stricture applies particularly to wood and wire fences, areas of nylon netting, and certain trackways. While such mechanical means may be necessary in particular places, they are not the only effective ways to manage dunes. Car parks and access routes need to be carefully planned to cause minimum disruption; vegetation needs to be protected by controlling the grazing of it; and sand-trapping plants such as marram grass needs to be encouraged, planted or protected. The depredations of rabbits have sometimes been a problem, and they need to be controlled. Erosion control, however, is not always compatible with the requirements of nature conservationists. Some plants have proved to be so effective at colonising sand that they have invaded and crowded out ecologically valuable species in the moister hollows between dunes. A major culprit here is the sea buckthorn, *Hippophae rhamnoides*, which has frequently been introduced to control sand movement, but has then become rampant, necessitating control by herbicides and other methods.

Possibly the most spectacular, long-lived and large-scale attempt to control troublesome, mobile coastal dunes in the British Isles is that in the Culbin Sands[6] of north-east Scotland. The Culbin Estate appears to have been a prosperous one, but late in 1694 or early 1695, under storm conditions, it suffered a final inundation under blowing sand. Culbin House had to be abandoned, along with its farming implements, as it was covered by a large dune. The area became the largest area of moving sand in the country, and was the nearest approach to a desert landscape in the British Isles. However, in 1921 the Forestry Commission acquired much of the area, and the great sand hills have now been largely conquered (Plate 8.10). Marram grass was planted, the sand surface was thatched with branches of birch and broom, and then conifers were planted, notably Corsican pine, Scots pine and the Lodge Pole pine.

## CONCLUSION

The landshape of Britain and Ireland has been made both by natural processes and by human activities, interacting with each other over millennia. While it is true that we see in these landscapes the imprint of natural processes acting on areas of distinctive geological structure and rock type, it is also true that we can see the long-continued impact of humans. Mesolithic pastoralists and hunters began the process just after the Ice Age, and the subsequent generations of farmers have profoundly changed the surface of the countryside. Our power to transform has vastly accelerated as we have progressively expanded our numbers and harnessed more and more sources of energy. Our power will continue to grow in the generations to come, but just as we now see the need to protect rare plants, rare animals and patches of their habitat, we must also seek to protect some of the landshapes described in this book. The countryside would be the poorer if we used our power to remove some of its more delicate features, whether they be dewponds or drumlins, roddens or rias, or moats or moraines.

# ACKNOWLEDGEMENTS AND BIBLIOGRAPHY

The authors owe thanks to many people for their assistance and support in the preparation of this book in such a short period of time. In particular we would like to mention the Drawing Office and Map Room at King's [illegible] photograph); D. Brunsden (Plates [illegible] (Plate 8.3); Cambridge University Committee for Aerial Photography (Plates 1.2, 2.4, 3.2, 3.4, 3.8, 3.9, 4.4, 4.7, 5.1, 5.7, 6.10, 6.11, 7.1, 7.8, 7.9, 7.11, 8.5, 8.6); S. Cobbin (Plates 1.1, 2.1, rear jacket photograph (top right)); C. Embleton (Plate 3.1); T. Fell (Plates 1.3, 1.7, 1.11, 2.3, 2.9, 2.11, 3.5, 3.11, 4.1, 4.3, 5.4–5.6, 5.8, 6.3–6.6, 6.9, 6.12, 7.4, 7.7, 7.10, 8.1, 8.2, 8.7, 8.9, rear jacket photographs (top and bottom left)); R. Gardner (Plates 3.3, 3.6, 3.7, 4.2, 4.5, 4.8, 4.10, 5.3, 6.2); D. K. C. Jones (Plates 1.4, 1.6, 1.8, 1.9, 1.12, rear jacket photograph (bottom right)); Science Photo Library (Plate 2.2); Studio Jon (Plate 6.8).

Grateful acknowledgements are given for permission to reproduce line drawings and tables: Heinemann (Fig 2.2); Unwin Hyman, R. Gardner and A. Goudie (Figs 4.4 and 4.5); British Geological Survey (Fig 2.8); Methuen and D. K. C. Jones (Fig 5.6); Wiley and J. Lewin (Table 5.1); Geomorphological Services Limited (Figs 7.4–7.11).

There is no single text that adequately covers the material contained in this book. Readers interested in the relationships between rocks and scenery should begin with the trilogy of 'geology and scenery' books published by Penguin: A. E. Trueman, *Geology and Scenery in England and Wales*, 2nd Edit. Penguin, 1971; J. B. Whittow, *Geology and Scenery in Ireland*, (Penguin, 1974); and J. B. Whittow, *Geology and Scenery in Scotland*, (Penguin, 1977) and the *Geology Explained* series produced by David and Charles.

Unfortunately, the two most readable books on the general geological evolution of the British Isles: L. D. Stamp's, *Britain's Structure and Scenery*, (Collins/Fontana, 1960); and Jacquetta Hawkes', *A Land*, [illegible] are both badly dated, but the more [illegible] (Cambridge Univ. Press, 1985).

Readable discussions of the nature and evolution of coastal scenery are to be found in J. A. Steers, *The English Coast*, (Collins/Fontana, 1966); J. A. Steers, *The Sea Coast*, (Collins, 1962) and J. A. Steers, *The Coastline of England and Wales*, (Cambridge, 1964).

Problems will be experienced in gaining an insight into the evolution of inland landforms. Numerous descriptions exist regarding the land forms and evolution of small tracts of country (eg Dartmoor) or of notable landforms within a region (eg the 'Classic Landforms' Series produced by the Geographical Association). More general syntheses are rare and tend to be rather academic and couched in technical language (eg the *Geomorphology of the British Isles* series published by Methuen. Arguably the best attempt to produce a systematic discussion of notable landform features (eg Cheddar Gorge, Malham Cove, etc) is R. A. M. Gardner and A. Goudie, *Discovering Landscapes in England and Wales*, (Allen and Unwin, 1985), while D. K. C. Jones 'The Geomorphological Background' in R. S. J. Woodell, *The English Landscape: Past, Present and Future*, (Oxford Univesity Press, 1985) presents a reasonable attempt at a coherent picture of landform evolution.

Numerous texts exist on the subject of geomorphological processes. Why not try M. J. Selby *Earth's Changing Surface*, (Oxford University Press, 1985).

# INDEX

Page numbers in *italic* indicate illustrations